SYMPOSIA OF THE FARADAY SOCIETY
NO. 7   1973

Fogs and Smokes

THE FARADAY DIVISION
CHEMICAL SOCIETY
LONDON

ISBN: 0 85186 828 2
Library of Congress Catalog Card No. 73–92913

A SYMPOSIUM

ON

Fogs and Smokes

28th, 29th, 30th March, 1973

A SYMPOSIUM on Fogs and Smokes was held at the Applied Science Buildings, University of Swansea on the 28th, 29th and 30th March, 1973.

This Symposium was sponsored by the Faraday Division and formed part of the second Annual Chemical Congress of the Chemical Society and the Royal Institute of Chemistry. The President of the Faraday Division, Sir George Porter, F.R.S. was in the chair at the opening session. The present volume, Faraday Symposia of the Chemical Society, no. 7, contains all the papers and discussion thereon.

CONTENTS

5

Nucleation, Growth, Ripening and Coagulation in Aerosol Formation

By W. J. Dunning

School of Chemistry, University of Bristol, Bristol BS8 1TS

Received 4th December, 1972

The atmosphere may be regarded as a carrier gas (the permanent gases) containing water vapour, CO_2 and trace substances. The latter comprise gaseous compounds of nitrogen, sulphur, chlorine, carbon and oxygen, together with an aerosol of fine particles.

The sources of these particles are diverse; winds lift many from the earth; smoke from forest fires contributes inorganic ash and carbon compounds; the bursting of bubbles in the sea surface provides salt particles; some come from volcanic eruptions and meteorites and yet others are of biological origin. Nor must we forget radioactive fallout.

Each year domestic and industrial activities introduce hundreds of millions of tons of pollutants, gaseous and particulate, into the atmosphere. Much of this discharge is invisible but fogs and smokes may often be seen when readily condensible vapours ranging from water vapour and partly burnt fuels to metallic oxides are emitted from cooling towers, chimneys and exhausts to undergo cooling by turbulent diffusive mixing with the atmosphere. Fumes from smelting contain volatile metallic salts which condense as fine particles. Sulphuric mist and alkali mist are other undesirable aerosols. When fired, heavy guns often produce smoke composed of water droplets and metallic particles. On the other hand, signal smokes serve a useful purpose and the manufacture of carbon black, of titanium dioxide and silica involves the production of very fine particles. The knowledge gained by atmospheric scientists is very relevant to the technology of such processes.

SIZE DISTRIBUTION OF THE ATMOSPHERIC AEROSOL

When the relative humidity is below saturation, the particles in the atmosphere may be grouped according to size [1] as follows; " small ions " (radius $r \sim 10^{-3}$ μm) which consist generally of a singly charged molecule with a cluster of a few neutral molecules; Aitken particles (5×10^{-3} μm $< r < 10^{-1}$ μm); " large particles " (10^{-1} μm $< r < 1$ μm) and " giant particles " (1 μm $< r < 20$ μm).

For the size range 0.1 μm $< r < 10$ μm, Junge [2] found that the size distribution measured at Frankfurt and on the Zugspitze could be expressed by

$$n(r) = A/r^4 \tag{1}$$

where $n(r)dr$ is the number of particles with sizes between r and $r + dr$; $A = 0.05\phi$ (ref. (3)) with ϕ the volume fraction of the disperse phase. This remarkable law has been confirmed for " country " and " industrial " atmospheres.[3-6] The size distribution for salt particles in marine air deviates from Junge's law.[7, 8] Eqn (1) has been found to describe the size distributions in certain artificial aerosols.[9]

BASIC PROCESSES

The following basic processes must be considered: prenucleation kinetics, nucleation growth, ripening and coagulation, sedimentation, impaction and dispersal.

PRENUCLEATION KINETICS

In the atmosphere chemical and photo-chemical reactions may take place in the gas phase, in water droplets or on the surface of particles and as a result new particles may be nucleated or changes in preformed particles result.[10] Hydrogen sulphide and SO_2 are oxidized to form sulphuric acid and sulphates, in particular $(NH_4)_2SO_4$. The photolysis of NO_2 gives atomic oxygen which reacts with unsaturated and aromatic hydrocarbons to form aldehydes, ketones, peroxyacyl nitrates and ozone. Salt particles react with nitrogen oxides and sulphuric acid droplets to give hydrogen chloride, nitrates and sulphates.[11]

In industrial processes the mechanism by which supersaturation is generated may be relatively simple, for example, the admixture of a cool gas or it may involve a complex sequence of elementary reactions as in the production of TiO_2.

NUCLEATION

Condensation may take place on surfaces,[12] on insoluble[13] and soluble particles,[14] on positive and negative ions[15] and even on other molecules in the gas phase.[16] In the atmosphere, condensation occurs at supersaturations ranging from a few tenths of one per cent to a few tens per cent.[17] Heterogeneous nucleation on " foreign " particles is also common in industrial processes. Attrition may produce particles of the product, which then act as centres for further growth.

In the absence of foreign nuclei, condensation of a vapour make take place by homogeneous nucleation, but this requires much larger supersaturations. There are technical processes in which homogeneous nucleation is predominant and the theories of homogeneous nucleation, ripening and coagulation are, in any case, branches of a single comprehensive theory.

Chance collisions of single vapour molecules A form dimers A_2 which in turn form trimers A_3 and so on. The sequence of reactions may be represented by

$$\ldots A_{i-1} \underset{-A}{\overset{+A}{\rightleftharpoons}} A_i \underset{-A}{\overset{+A}{\rightleftharpoons}} A_{i+1} \ldots (i \geqslant 2) \tag{2}$$

implying the assumption that only single molecules and not clusters are gained or lost. The rate of formation of the cluster A_i is given by

$$dn_i(t)/dt = \beta_{i-1}n_{i-1}(t) - \alpha_i n_i(t) - \beta_i n_i(t) + \alpha_{i+1}n_{i+1}(t) \tag{3}$$

where $n_i(t)$ is the concentration of A_i and β_i and α_i are respectively the frequencies of capture and escape from an i-mer.

Clusters which are not too small are considered to be very similar to small droplets containing the same number of molecules. There is a critical size of cluster-droplet containing $i = K$ molecules, the vapour pressure of which is just equal to the partial pressure p_I of the supersaturated vapour and

$$p_I = p_\infty \exp(2\sigma v_{II}/kT r_K) \tag{4}$$

where $p_{I\infty}$ is the vapour pressure over a plane liquid surface ($r \to \infty$), σ is the surface tension, v_{II} the liquid molecular volume and r_K the radius of the critical nucleus.

Droplets smaller than this tends to evaporate, those larger to grow. The steady state rate at which critical nuclei are formed and become free growing is given by

$$J = Z\beta_K n_K \tag{5}$$

where Z is the Zeldovich [18] factor, and classical theory [19] gives

$$n_K = n_I \exp\{-16\pi\sigma^3 v_{II}^2/[3k^3 T^3 \log^2(p_I/p_{I\infty})]\}. \tag{6}$$

Thus J is a very strong function of the supersaturation ratio $p_I/p_{I\infty}$; there is a critical supersaturation ratio below which J is negligibly small.

How closely clusters resemble droplets endowed with macroscopic properties is questionable. A " revision " of the theory by Lothe and Pound [20] predicts that the nucleation rate should be higher by a factor of 10^{17} than that resulting from classical theory. Dunning [21] approached the problem in a different manner and predicted a factor of about 10^4 instead of 10^{17}. Further studies by Reiss [22] support the view that the classical expression is effectively valid.

REVIEW OF EXPERIMENTAL METHODS AND RESULTS

The experimental techniques available for testing the theory are piston cloud chambers, diffusion cloud chambers, supersonic nozzles and shock tubes.

CLOUD CHAMBER EXPERIMENTS

Successive expansions of the piston cloud chamber to increasing volumes leads to the appearance of condensation. The results of Wilson [23] and of Powell [24] show a straight line dependence [25] between $\log(p_I/p_{I\infty})_{crit}$ and $T^{-\frac{3}{2}}$ as predicted by classical theory. Lothe and Pound [26] consider that the data of Wilson,[23] of Powell [24] and of Volmer and Flood [27] are in agreement with classical theory if $\sigma = \sigma_\infty$.

In the diffusion cloud chamber,[28] vapour and an inert gas lie between the surface of the liquid and a cooler horizontal plate. At a certain height within the gas the upwardly diffusing vapour condenses and drops descend into the pool. The supersaturation at the condensation level may be calculated. Katz and Ostermeier [22] have found remarkably good agreement with classical theory and state that the Lothe-Pound revision does not fit their results at all.

NOZZLE EXPERIMENTS

When a vapour, flowing through a convergent–divergent nozzle, reaches supersonic speeds, it expands adiabatically and its temperature falls. At a critical supersaturation, condensation occurs and the heat released causes the pressure to increase above the value it would have had in the absence of condensation. Oswatitsch [30] showed how gas dynamics and the kinetics of nucleation and growth may be combined to furnish a detailed description of the pressure changes during the whole course of condensation.

Experiments by Wegener and Pouring,[31] Stein,[32] Barschdorff [33] and Jaeger et al.[34] show that the experimental nucleation rates for water vapour in air agree roughly with classical theory. Similar agreement has been found for CO_2 in air,[35] for benzene in air [36] and for C_2H_5OH in air.[37] On the other hand, measurements on NH_3,[34] $CHCl_3$ [38] and CCl_3F [34, 38] agree with the Lothe–Pound revision. For steam [39] (i.e., pure water vapour without a carrier gas) condensation occurs at a rate slower (by a factor of about 10^{-2}) than classical theory predicts, and about 10^{-18} times more slowly than that predicted by Lothe and Pound. Wegener et al.[39] point out that

in the steam case all effects which may be due to heterogeneous nuclei can be categoric-
ally ruled out.   Barschdorff *et al.*[40] have shown that data [41] for the condensation of
pure steam is in accord with classical theory modified to include the effect of non-
isothermal nucleation.   Pure nitrogen shows the same effect.[42]

SHOCK TUBE EXPERIMENTS

In a shock tube (fig. 1), a thin diaphragm divides a long tube into two sections.
In the " driver " section the gas is at a higher pressure than in the other section.   On
bursting the diaphragm a shock wave propagates into the low pressure section while
an expansion wave passes into the high pressure section.   The use of the shock wave

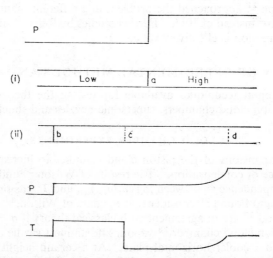

FIG. 1.—(i) Shock tube before bursting diaphragm *a*.   Pressure in tube shown above.   (ii) Shock tube
a short time after bursting diaphragm ; *b* shock wave, *c* contact surface, *d* limit of expansion wave.
Pressure and temperature in tube shown below.

for observing relaxation effects and reaction rates is familiar to chemists.   Less
well known is the technique of Wegener and Lundquist [43] in which the expansion
is used to study condensation phenomena.   This technique allows a wide range of
cooling rates to be investigated in the same experiment [44] and the closed system has
advantages.   Some preliminary results of such experiments, carried out at Yale, have
been reported.[33]

DIRECT INVESTIGATIONS ON CLUSTERS

Stein and Wegener [45] have measured the relative intensity of Rayleigh scattered
light from a free jet placed in the cavity of an argon laser and found, for example, in
one experiment, that there were 10^{12} particles cm^{-3} and that their average size was
about 45 Å.   These figures are in agreement with classical theory.

When a supersonic jet of vapour emerges from a nozzle and is collimated by a
skimmer and a slit, the resulting molecular beam may be examined.   Bentley [46] and
also Henkes [47] passed the beam into the source of a mass spectrometer and measured
the ion currents for the various cluster masses.[48, 49]   High energy electron diffraction
patterns have been obtained from clusters by Anderson and Stein.[50]

NUCLEATION TIME-LAG

When a system suddenly becomes supersaturated, clusters must be built up to critical size.[51, 52]   During this time lag, the rate of nucleation $J(t)$ is given approximately by [53]

$$J(t) = J \exp(-\tau/t) \tag{7}$$

where J is the steady-state rate (eqn (5)) and $\tau = K^2/\beta_K$ where β_K is the frequency of monomer capture by the critical nucleus of size K.   In cloud chamber and supersonic nozzle experiments, τ for water vapour is appreciably less than the " time of observation " during which the supersaturation persists and the steady state approximation is valid.[54]

When the growth process of the embryos is not simple but, say, the result of chemical reactions at the surface of the embryos, the possibility that the nucleation rate is non-steady must be considered.

GROWTH, OSTWALD RIPENING AND SMOLUCHOWSKI COAGULATION

Fig. 2 illustrates schematically the change in the size distribution $n(r)$ with time. The initial cluster distribution ab relaxes to the steady state distribution cd during the build up period ($\sim 10\tau$).   The strip ec corresponds to $n(r_K)dr$ and to the number of critical nuclei.   In the next interval of time these nuclei are born and become free-growing.   In the second-next interval, the first-born grow and another lot of nuclei are born.   In the third-next interval the first-born continue growing, the second-born grow and a third batch of nuclei appear, and so on until the distribution is that of A.

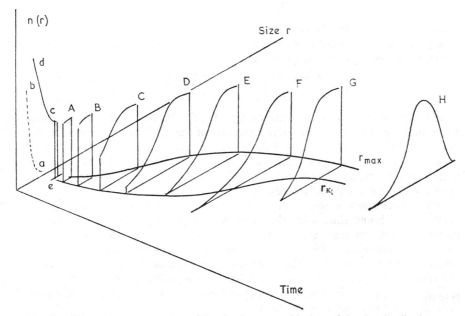

FIG. 2.—Schematic representation of the development with time of the size distribution.

As a result of growth the supersaturation decreases with time, hence the rate of nucleation is greatest at $t \sim 10\tau$ and decreases to become negligible at the metastable limit ; beyond this limit the continued decrease in the supersaturation is solely the result of growth.   Clearly the first born are the most numerous class and the largest in size.   The foot of the leading edge of the distribution, tracing the curve r_{max} in the (r, t) plane shows the growth of the first-born.

The number of nuclei being born at any time is related to the height of the ordinate at the trailing edge of the distribution, the foot of which *initially* follows the curve r_K. When the supersaturation reaches the metastable limit the height of the trailing edge is negligible (curve E).   The supersaturation continues to decrease and in consequence r_K continues to increase since r_K and supersaturation are related by the Gibbs–Thomson relation (eqn (4)); r_K overtakes the size of the smallest drops and then Ostwald ripening occurs (curves F, G).   Droplets larger than r_K continue to grow but those which have become smaller than r_K begin to evaporate and there is a flux of droplets in the direction $r = 0$.   The distribution now begins to spread out on both sides of r_K which is itself changing with time.   At all times r_K must remain smaller than r_{max}, otherwise the whole precipitate would evaporate contrary to thermodynamic principles.

OSTWALD RIPENING

The sequence of reactions in eqn (2) and the corresponding rate, eqn (3), apply not only to subcritical clusters but also to the drops of condensate, so long as the assumption remains valid that only single molecules are gained or lost and that reactions between droplets (i.e., coagulation) may be neglected.   When we change from discrete distributions n_i with integral i to continuous distributions $n(r)dr$, eqn (3) becomes the equation of continuity

$$\frac{\partial n(r,t)}{\partial t} + \frac{\partial [\dot{r}n(r,t)]}{\partial r} = 0 \tag{8}$$

where $\dot{r} = dr/dt$ is the rate of growth.

Gyarmathy [55] has derived an expression for $\dot{r}$, the rate of growth of a droplet from a supersaturated vapour in a carrier gas

$$\dot{r} = \frac{(1 - r_K/r)}{\rho(r + 1.59l)} \left[\frac{L^2}{\bar{\lambda}R_v T^2} + \frac{R_v T p_g}{DP p_{I\infty}} \right]^{-1} \log \frac{p_I}{p_{I\infty}}. \tag{9}$$

Here L is the latent heat of condensation per kg, R_v the gas constant per kg of vapour, P the total pressure and p_g the partial pressure of the carrier gas far from the droplet; D is the diffusion coefficient and l the mean free path, $\bar{\lambda}$ the thermal conductivity of the medium, ρ the density of the liquid and r_K is given by eqn (4).   Size distributions during nucleation and growth (e.g., A, B, C, D, E in fig. 2) may be computed from the expressions for $\dot{r}$ and J and the equation for continuity.

When nucleation ceases, this source of particles is replaced by a sink for particles near $r = 0$.   Some time after this, still assuming that coagulation is absent, net growth from the vapour becomes unimportant and the supersaturation changes only very slowly with time; this is the stage of secular ripening.   Lifshitz and Slezov [56] obtained an " asymptotic " solution of the ripening eqns (4), (8) and (9).   Wagner [57] extended their results and Dunning [58] further simplified the procedure.   If we use Gyarmathy's eqn (9) for growth ($r > r_K$) and evaporation ($r < r_K$), the size distribution during secular ripening is of the form

$$n(r, t) = g(t) \cdot h(\rho) \cdot \rho \tag{10}$$

in which $g(t)$ depends only on the time and $h(\rho)$ only on the relative size ρ ($\rho = r/r_K$). Further

$$g(t) = g(t_0) \cdot [1 + (t - t_0)/\tau_R]^{-2} \tag{11}$$

where the ripening time constant τ_R is given by

$$\tau_R = [(L^2/\lambda R_v T) + (R_v T p_g/PD p_{I\infty})]1.5 l R_v T \rho^3 r_{K0}^2/\sigma \qquad (12)$$

and $g(t_0)$ and r_{K0} are the values of $g(t)$ and r_K at a " start " time t_0 within the period of secular ripening and $t > t_0$.

The expression for $h(\rho) \cdot \rho$ is

$$h(\rho) \cdot \rho = \rho[2/(2-\rho)]^5 \exp[3\rho/(2-\rho)] \quad \text{for} \quad \rho \leqslant 2 \qquad (13)$$
$$= 0 \quad \text{for} \quad \rho \geqslant 2.$$

The total number of particles $N(0, t)$ present during secular ripening varies with time as

$$N(0, t) = N(0, t_0)[1 + (t - t_0)/\tau_R]^{-\frac{3}{2}} \qquad (14)$$

where $N(0, t_0)$ is the number present at the start time.

The quasi-stationary size distribution is independent of the original size distribution. Its form depends upon the growth-evaporation law.

SMOLUCHOWSKI COAGULATION

When in addition to the gain and loss of single molecules, reactions between all size classes are taken into consideration, e.g.,

$$A_{i-j} + A_j \rightleftharpoons A_i$$
$$A_i + A_l \rightleftharpoons A_{i+l} \qquad (15)$$

the problem becomes more complex. It may be simplified by assuming that Smoluchowski coagulation occurs for which only the forward reactions in 15 take place. We then have for this process

$$\frac{dn_i(t)}{dt} = \frac{1}{2} \sum_{j=1}^{j=i-1} \beta(v_j, v_{i-j}) n_j n_{i-j} - \sum_{l=1}^{l=\infty} \beta(v_i, v_l) n_i n_l \qquad (16)$$

where $\beta(v_i, v_l)$ is the coefficient of coagulation for particles of volumes v_i and v_l and n is the concentration (time dependent) of particles in the volume size class v_i.

On passing from a discrete to a continuous distribution, eqn (16) becomes [59, 60]

$$\frac{\partial n(v,t)}{\partial t} + \frac{\partial}{\partial v}[\dot{v} n(v,t)] = \frac{1}{2} \int_0^v \beta(\tilde{v}, v - \tilde{v}) n(\tilde{v}, t) \, n(v - \tilde{v}, t) d\tilde{v} - \int_0^\infty \beta(\tilde{v}, v) n(\tilde{v}, t) n(v, t) d\tilde{v}. \qquad (17)$$

The left hand side of this equation, with $\dot{v} = dv/dt$, corresponds to the terms in eqn (8) and the right hand side to Smoluchowski coagulation. Friedlander and his collaborators [60-62] have sought a solution to this equation of the form

$$n(v, t) = g(t) \cdot \psi(\eta) \qquad (18)$$

in which $g(t)$ is a function only of the time and ψ a function only of η. The dimensionless number η is equal to v/v^*, where the mean particle volume $v^* = V(0, t)/N(0, t)$ and $V(0, t)$, $N(0, t)$ are respectively the total volume and total number of all the particles.

Friedlander and Wang [60] have shown that, in the case when β is assumed constant, an " asymptotic " solution is obtained with

$$g(t) = [N(0, t)]^2/V(0, t) \qquad (19)$$

and for $\psi(\eta)$, analytical expressions [62] have been obtained for the lower and upper ends of the distribution. Numerical solutions over the whole distribution have been obtained by Hidy [63] and by Pich, Friedlander and Lai.[62] These results suggest strongly that a quasi-stationary distribution of size is obtained after a prolonged time but a general proof is not available.

A size distribution for the hypothetical steady state resulting from coagulation is shown schematically as curve *H* in fig. 2.

CONCLUSION

Although, with the possible exception of prenucleation kinetics, the basic processes are aspects of a single conceptual scheme, it is still necessary to treat them as separate stages in the development of an aerosol.

In the simplest production systems, these processes develop and follow each other in sequence. For example, when gases flow into a tube, diffusive mixing or chemical reactions generate an increasing supersaturation as the gases move downstream. Further downstream, nucleation or growth on foreign nuclei takes place and these are followed by the other processes in overlapping sequence. Should the mixture emerge and mix with the atmosphere, a simple first approach would be to suppose that the concentration fields of the components depend only on location and not on time. A steady state is conceived in which a cloud is centred on the source of partly reacted gases and partly condensed products and within it all concentrations and process rates depend only on position. When realistic factors such as turbulence, wind, convection, topography and climate are introduced the complexity of the problem becomes great.

Another conceptually simple system would be an analogy with the continuous stirred tank reactor into which reactants enter at a steady rate and the contents are removed at a rate to balance the input. The contents of the tank reach a steady state for which all concentrations, rates of reaction, nucleation, and growth etc. everywhere in the tank become steady and the size distribution becomes steady.[64] This bears a faint resemblance to the atmosphere but again the introduction of realism complicates the problem.

[1] C. E. Junge in *Adv. Geophys.*, ed. H. E. Landsberg and J. van Mieghem (Academic Press, New York, 1958), vol. 4, p. 1.

[2] C. E. Junge, *J. Meteorol.*, 1955, **12**, 13 ; *Tellus*, 1953, **5**, 1.

[3] W. E. Clark and K. T. Whitby, *J. Atmos. Sci.*, 1967, **24**, 677.

[4] J. Cartwright, G. Nagelschmidt and J. W. Skidmore, *Quart. J. Roy. Met. Soc.*, 1956, **82**, 82.

[5] S. Twomey and G. T. Severynse, *J. Atmos. Sci.*, 1963, **20**, 392.

[6] S. K. Friedlander and R. E. Pasceri, *J. Atmos. Sci.*, 1965, **22**, 571.

[7] A. H. Woodcock, *J. Meteorol.*, 1953, **10**, 362.

[8] D. J. Moore and B. J. Mason, *Quart. J. Roy. Met. Soc.*, 1954, **80**, 583.

[9] B. Y. Liu, also R. Husar and K. T. Whitby, see S. K. Friedlander, *Aerosol Sci.*, 1970, **1**, 295.

[10] R. D. Cadle and R. C. Robbins, *Discuss. Faraday Soc.*, 1961, **30**, 155.

[11] R. D. Cadle, in *An International Workshop on Nucleation and its Applications*, ed. C. S. Kiang and V. A. Mohnen (Clark College, Atlanta, 1972), p. 156 ; P. A. Leighton, *Photochemistry of Air Pollution* (Academic Press, N.Y. 1961) ; M. D. Carabine, *Chem. Soc. Rev.*, 1972, **1**, 411.

[12] M. Volmer, *Kinetik der Phasenbildung* (Steinkopff, Dresden, 1939), p. 100.

[13] N. H. Fletcher, *J. Chem. Phys.*, 1958, **29**, 572 ; 1959, **31**, 1136.

[14] H. Köhler, *Medd. Met. Hydr. Anst.*, (Stockholm), 1926, **3**, No. 8.

[15] G. Tohmfor and M. Volmer, *Ann. Phys.*, 1938, **33**, 109 ; N. H. Fletcher, *Physics of Rainclouds* (Cambridge, London, 1962), p. 48.

[16] L. B. Allen and J. L. Kassner, *J. Colloid Interf. Sci.*, 1969, **30**, 81.

[17] N. H. Fletcher, *loc. cit.* ref. (15), p. 32.

[18] J. B. Zeldovich, *J. Exp. Theor. Phys.*, 1942, **12**, 525 ; *Acta Phys. Chem. URSS*, 1943, **18**, 1.

[19] M. Volmer and A. Weber, *Z. phys. Chem.*, 1926, **A119**, 277 ; R. Becker and W. Döring, *Ann. Phys.*, 1935, **24**, 719 ; R. Becker, *Theorie der Wärme* (Springer, Berlin, 1955); F. Kuhrt, *Z. Phys.*, 1952, **131**, 205.

20 J. Lothe and G. M. Pound, *J. Chem. Phys.*, 1962, **36**, 2080; J. Feder, K. C. Russell, J. Lothe and G. M. Pound, *Adv. Phys.*, 1966, **15**, 111; J. Lothe and G. M. Pound, *J. Chem. Phys.*, 1968, **48**, 1849; J. Lothe and G. M. Pound, in *Nucleation*, ed. A. C. Zettlemoyer (Marcel Dekker, N.Y., 1969); K. Nishioka, G. M. Pound and F. F. Abraham, *Phys. Rev. A*, 1970, **1**, 1522.

21 W. J. Dunning, in *Colloques Internationaux du Centre National de la Recherche Scientifique*, No. 152 (CNRS Paris, 1965), p. 369; in *Nucleation*, ed. A. C. Zettlemoyer (Marcel Dekker, N.Y., 1969).

22 H. Reiss and J. L. Katz, *J. Chem. Phys.*, 1967, **46**, 2496; H. Reiss, J. L. Katz and E. R. Cohen, *J. Chem. Phys.*, 1968, **48**, 5553; H. Reiss, *J. Statistical Phys.*, 1970, **2**, 84; R. Kikuchi, *J. Statistical Phys.*, 1969, **1**, 351.

23 C. T. R. Wilson, *Phil. Mag.* 1897, **A189**, 265; 1900, **193**, 289.

24 C. F. Powell, *Proc. Roy. Soc. A*, 1928, **119**, 553.

25 W. J. Dunning, *Disc. Faraday Soc.*, 1960, **30**, 9; P. Wegener and J. Y. Parlange, *Naturwiss.*, 1970, **57**, 525.

26 J. Lothe and G. M. Pound in *Nucleation*, ed. A. C. Zettlemoyer (Marcel Dekker, N.Y., 1969).

27 M. Volmer and H. Flood, *Z. phys. Chem.*, 1934, **A170**, 273.

28 A. Langsdorff, *Rev. Sci. Instr.*, 1939, **10**, 91; J. P. Franck and H. G. Hertz, *Z. Phys.*, 1956, **143**, 559.

29 J. L. Katz and B. J. Ostermeier, *J. Chem. Phys.*, 1967, **47**, 478; J. L. Katz, *J. Chem. Phys.*, 1970, **52**, 4733; *loc. cit.* ref. (11) (*An International Workshop* etc.), p. 128.

30 K. Oswatitsch, *Z. angew. Math. Mechanik*, 1942, **22**, 1; *Gasdynamik* (Springer, Wien, 1952); P. Wegener and L. M. Mack in *Adv. Appl. Mech.*, ed. Dryden and Karman (Academic Press, New York, 1958), p. 307; P. P. Wegener, *Non-Equilibrium Flow* in *Gas Dynamics*, ed. P. P. Wegener (Marcel Dekker, New York, 1969), vol. I, part I; P. P. Wegener and J. Y. Parlange, *loc. cit.* ref. (25); W. J. Dunning, *Discuss. Faraday Soc.*, 1960, **30**, 9.

31 P. P. Wegener and A. A. Pouring, *Phys. Fluids*, 1964, **7**, 352.

32 G. D. Stein, *Thesis* (Yale University, 1967).

33 D. Barschdorff, *loc. cit.* ref. (11) (*An International Workshop*, etc.), p. 124.

34 H. L. Jaeger, E. J. Willson, P. G. Hill and K. C. Russell, *J. Chem. Phys.*, 1969, **51**, 5380.

35 K. M. Duff and P. G. Hill in *Proceedings of the 1966 Heat Transfer and Fluid Mechanics Institute*, ed. M. A. Saad and J. A. Miller (Stanford U.P., Stanford, 1966), p. 268.

36 B. J. Wu, *loc. cit.* ref. (11) (*An International Workshop*, etc.), p. 121.

37 J. A. Clumpner, *Thesis*, (Yale University, 1970); P. P. Wegener, J. A. Clumpner and B. J. C. Wu, *Phys. Fluids*, 1972, **15**, 1869.

38 D. B. Dawson, E. J. Willson, P. G. Hill and K. C. Russell, *J. Chem. Phys.*, 1969, **51**, 5389.

39 P. P. Wegener, B. J. C. Wu and D. Barschdorff, *loc. cit.* ref. (11) (*An International Workshop*, etc.), p. 120.

40 D. Barschdorff, W. J. Dunning, B. J. C. Wu and P. P. Wegener, *Nature* (*Phys. Sci.*), 1972, **240**, 166.

41 A. M. Binnie and J. R. Green, *Proc. Roy. Soc. A*, 1943, **181**, 134; M. E. Deych, V. F. Stepanchuk and G. A. Saltanov, *Energetika i Transport*, 1968, **2**, 34; D. Barschdorff, *Forschung. Ing.-Wes.*, 1971, **37**, 146; G. Gyarmathy and E. Meyer, *VDI-Forschungsheft* 508 (VDI Verlag, Düsseldorf, 1965.

42 P. D. Arthur, *Thesis* (Calif. Inst. Technol, 1952).

43 P. P. Wegener and G. Lundquist, *J. Appl. Phys.*, 1959, **22**, 233, for nucleation studies utilizing the Shock Wave, see R. T. V. Kung and S. H. Bauer, *Proc. 8th Internat. Shock Tube Symp.*, London, July 1971, paper No. 61; J. R. Homer, I. R. Hurle and P. J. Swain, *Nature*, 1971, **229**, 251.

44 P. P. Wegener and J. Y. Parlange, *loc. cit.* ref. (25).

45 G. D. Stein and P. P. Wegener, *J. Chem. Phys.*, 1967, **46**, 3685; *Twelfth Symposium* (*International*) *on Combustion* (Combustion Institute, Pittsburgh, 1969), p. 1183; G. D. Stein, *LASER und angewandte Strahltechnik*, No. 3, 1970; J. A. Clumpner, *J. Chem. Phys.*, 1971, **55**, 5042.

46 P. G. Bentley, *Nature*, 1961, **190**, 432.

47 W. Henkes, *Z. Naturforsch*, 1961, **16a**, 842.

48 R. F. Leckenby, E. J. Robbins and P. A. Trevalion, *Proc. Roy. Soc. A*, 1964, **280**, 409; R. F. Leckenby and E. J. Robbins, *Proc. Roy. Soc. A*, 1966, **291**, 389.

49 F. T. Greene and T. A. Milne, *J. Chem. Phys.*, 1963, **39**, 3150; T. A. Milne and F. T. Green *J. Chem. Phys.*, 1967, **47**, 4095.

50 J. A. Anderson and G. D. Stein, *loc. cit.* ref. (11) (*An International Workshop* etc.), p. 149.

51 J. Frenkel, *J. Chem. Phys.*, 1939, **7**, 200, 538.

52 J. C. Fisher, J. H. Hollomon and D. Turnbull, *J. Appl. Phys.*, 1948, **19**, 775.

53 A. Kantrowitz, *J. Chem. Phys.*, 1951, **19**, 1097; see also R. Probstein, *J. Chem. Phys.*, 1951,

19, 619 ; B. K. Chakraverty, *Colloques. Intern. Centre Nat. Rech. Sci.*, No. 152, p. 375 (1965)
W. G. Courtney, *J. Chem. Phys.*, 1962, **36**, 2009.

[54] P. P. Wegener and J. Y. Parlange, *loc. cit.* ref. (25).

[55] G. Gyarmathy, *Z. angew. Math. Phys.*, 1963, **14**, 280 ; see also P. P. Wegener, J. A. Clumpner and B. J. C. Wu, *Phys. Fluids*, 1972, **15**, 1869 ; J. C. Carstens and J. T. Zung, *J. Colloid Interf. Sci.*, 1970, **33**, 299 ; J. C. Carstens and J. L. Kassner, *J. Recherch. Atmos.*, 1968, **3**, 33 ; N. A. Fuchs, *Evaporation and Droplet Growth* (Pergamon, London, 1957).

[56] M. Lifshitz and V. V. Slezov, *Soviet Phys. J.E.T.P.*, 1958, **35**, 331 ; see also O. M. Todes *J. Phys. Chem. URSS*, 1946, **20**, 630 ; O. M. Todes and W. W. Kruschev, *J. Phys. Chem. URSS*, 1947, **21**, 301.

[57] C. Wagner, *Z. Elektrochem.*, 1961, **65**, 581.

[58] W. J. Dunning, in *Particle Growth in Suspensions* (ed. A. L. Smith), Soc. Chem. Ind. Monograph no. 28, (Academic Press, London, 1973).

[59] M. V. Smoluchowski, *Phys. Z.*, 1916, **17**, 385 ; *Z. phys. Chem.*, 1917, **92**, 120.

[60] S. K. Friedlander and C. S. Wang, *J. Colloid Interf. Sci.*, 1966, **22**, 126.

[61] S. K. Friedlander, *J. Meteorol.*, 1960, **17**, 375, 478 ; *J. Meteorol.*, 1961, **18**, 753.

[62] J. Pich, C. S. Friedlander and F. S. Lai, *Aerosol Sci.*, 1970, **1**, 115.

[63] G. M. Hidy, *J. Colloid Sci.*, 1965, **20**, 123.

[64] S. H. Bransom, W. J. Dunning and B. Millard, *Disc. Faraday Soc.*, 1949, **5**, 83.

Kinetic Processes in the Condensation and Evaporation of Aerosols

By E. R. Buckle

Department of Metallurgy, The University, Sheffield S1 3JD

Received 15th December, 1972

The stable and metastable states of a vapour are considered in relation to the process of condensation. By modelling these states on a gaseous system of growing and evaporating molecular clusters, kinetically balanced, and by consideration of the requirements of the thermodynamic limit, two important properties may be defined ; a number J, dependent on temperature and pressure, which is a parameter of the cluster populations, and an interfacial free energy ζ, which varies with temperature and cluster size but not with pressure. Expressions for J and ζ, and for the critical cluster size in metastable states, are derived for simple models of cluster reactions. The rates of these reactions are considered for particles in the form of large clusters, and coefficients of evaporation and growth obtained which tend to zero with increase in particle size. It is concluded that particles of visible size are not formed by spontaneous condensation under uniform conditions of temperature and pressure.

This paper gives further consideration to certain results of a kinetic theory of gaseous clusters.[1] The system treated is a homogeneous, isothermal assembly of particles formed as a suspension in the vapour by condensation. By a *homogeneous* assembly is meant one of spacial uniformity in the distribution of particles of the various sizes. The term spontaneous, rather than homogeneous, is used to describe the *process* of condensation when this occurs on natural centres and not on impurities or foreign substrates. Application of the cluster theory to the kinetic properties of aerosols will be preceded by some general considerations on the condition of stability of cluster assemblies. This is helpful in clarifying the behaviour of volatile particles in an aerosol under conditions of change.

1. PROPERTIES OF A KINETICALLY BALANCED ASSEMBLY

In this section the consequences of the kinetic models are deduced for uniform, balanced states representative of stable and metastable equilibrium. The Kelvin equation for the radius of an isolated droplet in supersaturated vapour represents a system in unstable equilibrium. By contrast, the thermodynamic states of a system in which the condensed phase is considered to be the macroscopic equivalent of a cluster in the vapour are stable states in which clusters of all sizes are in equilibrium with single molecules, or monomers. We use the results of the previous paper [1] as the starting point for a fuller discussion of the equilibrium issues.

In cluster reactions involving one-atom growth or decay,

$$A_{g-1} + A_1 = A_g,$$

the number densities (m^{-3}) at detailed balance are interrelated by the equilibrium quotients,

$$\omega_g = c_g/c_1 c_{g-1}, \tag{1.1}$$

17

from which

$$c_g = c_1^g \prod_{i=2}^{g} \omega_i. \tag{1.2}$$

This may be formally written as

$$c_g = c_1 \exp\{(g-1)J - \zeta_g/kT\} \tag{1.3}$$

by defining the functions

$$J = \ln c_1 \omega_\infty, \tag{1.4}$$

$$\omega_\infty = \underset{g \to \infty}{\mathrm{Lt}}\ \omega_g, \tag{1.5}$$

$$\zeta_g = -kT \sum_{i=2}^{g} \ln(\omega_i/\omega_\infty); \qquad \zeta_1 = 0. \tag{1.6}$$

It will be noted that ζ_g is size-dependent but J is not.

The distributions of (1.3) are kinetically balanced (as distinct from being merely stationary but with a net flow of molecules through the sizes) for all values of J. They should therefore represent characteristic macroscopic states of the vapour of A.

Let $N_1 = \Sigma g c_g$ be the total number of A atoms in all states of combination in the system volume V. In order that g may be unrestricted in size, we proceed to the thermodynamic limit, i.e., we let $N_1, V \to \infty$ while keeping a finite value for the number density $N_1/V = \rho$. The physical significance of J and ζ is arrived at as follows.

From (1.5),

$$\underset{g \to \infty}{\mathrm{Lt}}\ \Delta\zeta_g/\Delta g = 0, \tag{1.7}$$

so from (1.3),

$$\underset{g \to \infty}{\mathrm{Lt}}\ \Delta(\ln c_g)/\Delta g = J. \tag{1.8}$$

The distribution of c_g over g therefore ultimately rises, falls, or levels off, according as the value of J is positive, negative or zero (fig. 1). States with $J > 0$ do not represent true equilibrium because they violate the requirement of finite density, but for $J = 0$ an equilibrium distribution is possible if ζ_g tends to positive values with increasing g because the concentrations then tail off (eqn (1.8)). For $J < 0$ the fall-off of c_g is steeper and continuous, $\Delta c_g/\Delta g$ being negative in the limit as $g \to \infty$.

The above results were obtained without specifying any details about the clusters other than the existence of certain limiting properties. It has been found by calculations on simple models for argon [1] and water clusters [2] that, except under conditions of high pressure and high temperature to which the theory has not been extended, the value of ζ_g is positive at all g and decreases as the temperature is raised.

Assuming that clusters behave as ideal gas molecules the total pressure is

$$p = \sum_{g>0} p_g = kT \sum_{g>0} c_g, \tag{1.9}$$

and from (1.3) the partial pressures are

$$p_g = p_1 \exp\{(g-1)J - \zeta_g/kT\}, \tag{1.10}$$

where $p_1 = kT c_1$.

By (1.4), J is determined for a given temperature if c_1 is determined. Putting (1.10) into (1.9) and eliminating J by (1.4) we obtain

$$p = kT \sum_{g>0} c_1^g \omega_\infty^{g-1} \exp(-\zeta_g/kT). \tag{1.11}$$

J and c_1 are therefore determined by p and T. Reversion of (1.11) would enable c_1, J, and therefore the distribution function c_g to be computed directly for any p, T. In default of this, c_1 may be roughly obtained from $p = c_1 kT$ and the value then refined by employing successive approximations to satisfy (1.11).

We define

$$p_g^\circ = p_g(J = 0) = p_1 \exp(-\zeta_g/kT). \tag{1.12}$$

Now by fig. 1, $J = 0$ is the condition for the greatest value of p_g consistent with thermodynamic stability. Also, by (1.1) and (1.4), $J = 0$ represents a vapour state in which the cluster concentrations depend only on ζ_g and become independent of size in the limit $g \to \infty$. Therefore p_g° is the partial pressure of g-clusters in saturated vapour and ζ_g is the surface free enthalpy per g-cluster.

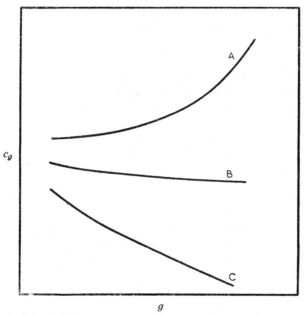

FIG. 1.—Terminal behaviour (diagrammatic) of kinetically balanced cluster distributions. A, $J>0$; B, $J = 0$; C, $J<0$.

Putting $J = 0$ in (1.4),

$$\omega_\infty = 1/c_1^\circ, \tag{1.13}$$

giving, with (1.4),

$$p_1/p_1^\circ = \exp J. \tag{1.14}$$

$$p_1^\circ = kT/\omega_\infty. \tag{1.15}$$

Thus, c_1° is the monomeric concentration in saturated vapour, p_1° is the corresponding partial pressure and (1.14) gives the monomeric saturation ratio. The last two results enable (1.12) to be written as

$$p_g^\circ = (kT/\omega_\infty) \exp(-\zeta_g/kT). \tag{1.16}$$

Finally, by combining (1.10) with (1.16), we obtain for the saturation ratio of g-clusters,

$$p_g/p_g^\circ = (p_1 \omega_\infty/kT) \exp(g-1)J. \tag{1.17}$$

In the Volmer theory [3,4] the kinetics of nucleus formation is deduced from the rate of a critical size fluctuation in a distribution of clusters supposedly stationary and close to equilibrium.   This distribution is expressed by

$$c_g = c_1 \exp\left(-W_g/kT\right), \tag{1.18}$$

where W_g is the reversible isothermal work of formation of a single g-cluster by the process,

$$gA_1 = A_g, \tag{1.19}$$

which occurs in $g-1$ of the steps,

$$A_1 + A_{i-1} = A_i. \tag{1.20}$$

W_g consists of two terms,

$$W_g = W_g' + W_g''. \tag{1.21}$$

W_g' is the work of formation of the cluster surface, taken as positive.   Under conditions of T, p favourable to condensation, W_g'' is negative, and is equal to the value of W_g for the process in which the g molecules of the gas A are incorporated into the bulk of the macroscopic liquid phase.

Comparison of (1.18) with the stationary distributions (1.3) of the present treatment gives $W_g' = \zeta_g$, $-W_g'' = (g-1)J\,kT$, with $J > 0$ in Volmer's case.   In Volmer's formula, W_g' is taken as proportional to the macroscopic surface tension γ, regardless of the value of g, and $-W_g''/kT$ is equated with $(g-1)\ln(p/p^\circ)$.   Equivalent assumptions are made in the derivation of Kelvin's formula for the critical droplet radius.

The first assumption has often been criticized as an oversimplification.   Calculations of ζ_g for the very simple cluster models of the previous paper [1] suggest that use of the macroscopic value of the surface tension over-estimates ζ_g, and its use in the theory of condensation consequently under-estimates the numbers of clusters, particularly at very small sizes.   Volmer's formula, for example, gives for equilibrium in the vapour :

$$c_g^\circ/c_1^\circ = \exp\left(-\gamma O_g/kT\right), \tag{1.22}$$

where O_g is the surface area.   As the temperature is lowered the fractions of small clusters increase (ref. (1), fig. 4) and the error on using (1.22) will therefore be larger.

The assumption that $-W_g'' = (g-1)kT\ln(p/p^\circ)$ is equivalent to writing $p/p^\circ = \exp J$ in contrast to (1.14).   Volmer's approximation is therefore equivalent to $p = p_1$, and is appropriate only for *stable* states of the vapour because in these c_g falls monotonically and steeply with g at low enough temperatures (fig. 1).   Eqn (1.17) shows that in a *metastable* state the concentrations must rise eventually relative to stable concentrations.   This was known but disregarded by Volmer in his formulation of W_g in (1.18).   The observability of metastable states is due to time-lag in the evolution of c_g for sizes exceeding the critical size.[1]

APPROXIMATE FORMULAE

Accurate computations of ζ_g and properties of the critical cluster are lengthy but some insight into their roles in the formation of aerosols is obtainable from the present theory with the aid of certain approximations.   Both ζ and J are functions of the reciprocal reduced temperature $\theta = u_{11}^\circ/kT$, where u_{11}° is equal to the depth of the A_1–A_1 potential well.

Beginning with ζ_g, a property of the g-cluster and not of the whole assembly, the results of §8, ref. (1) for ω_i and ω_∞ give* when substituted into (1.6):

$$\zeta_g = -kT \sum_{i=4}^{g} \ln \left\{ \frac{L_i[\exp(\theta[\lambda_i-1])-\exp(-\theta[\lambda_i-\lambda_{i-1}-1])](1+\lambda_\infty\theta+\lambda_\infty^2\theta^2/2)}{L_\infty[\exp(\theta[\lambda_\infty-1])-\exp\theta](1+\lambda_i\theta+\lambda_i^2\theta^2/2)} \right\}$$

$$-kT \ln \left\{ \frac{2L_3(\exp\theta-1)(1+\lambda_\infty\theta+\lambda_\infty^2\theta^2/2)}{L_\infty[\exp(\theta[\lambda_\infty-1])-\exp\theta](1+2\theta)} \right\}$$

$$-kT \ln \left\{ \frac{L_2(1+\lambda_\infty\theta+\lambda_\infty^2\theta^2/2)}{L_\infty[\exp(\theta[\lambda_\infty-1])-\exp\theta]} \right\} \tag{1.23}$$

For $\lambda_i\theta\gg 1\gg \lambda_i-\lambda_{i-1}$,

$$\zeta_g = -kT \sum_{i=2}^{g} \{\ln (L_i/L_\infty)-\theta(\lambda_\infty-\lambda_i)\}, \tag{1.24}$$

where we have put $\lambda_2 = 1$, $\lambda_3 = 2$ for the co-ordination numbers of atoms A in dimers and trimers, respectively. The first term in brackets tends to zero faster than the second, so that $\zeta_g>0$ for large clusters. To the same approximation:

$$\Delta\zeta_g = u_{11}^\circ(\lambda_\infty-\lambda_g). \tag{1.25}$$

To determine the critical cluster size g^* in a metastable vapour we minimize $\ln c_g$ with respect to g by a finite difference procedure. By (1.3),

$$(\Delta/\Delta g) \ln c_g = \ln (c_g/c_{g-1}) = J-\Delta\zeta_g/kT. \tag{1.26}$$

By (1.6),

$$\Delta\zeta_g = \zeta_g-\zeta_{g-1} = -kT \sum_{i=2}^{g} \ln (\omega_i/\omega_\infty)+kT \sum_{i=2}^{g-1} \ln (\omega_i/\omega_\infty),$$

$$= -kT \ln (\omega_g/\omega_\infty). \tag{1.27}$$

The condition for the minimum, at which $\omega_g = \omega_{g^*}$, now gives

$$\omega_{g^*} = \omega_\infty \exp(-J), \tag{1.28}$$

and from (1.4),

$$c_1\omega_{g^*} = 1. \tag{1.29}$$

The minimum in c_g lies at $g = \infty$ when $J = 0$ and moves in as J increases. We now obtain g^* by solution of (1.28) for $\lambda_g\theta\gg 1\gg \lambda_g-\lambda_{g-1}$, and introducing an approximate formula for λ_g. Since λ_g rises slowly from unity at $g = 2$ to $\lambda_\infty \leqslant 10$, say, in a macroscopic cluster, we may write

$$\lambda_{g>10} = \lambda_{10}+(g-10)\Delta\lambda, \tag{1.30}$$

where the size $g = 10$ has been arbitrarily taken as the point after which λ increases by a fixed amount $\Delta\lambda$ in each growth step. A uniform increment is probably a reasonable approximation at very large sizes. Then (1.28) reduces in a similar way to $\exp(-\zeta_g/kT)$ in (1.23) to give

$$J = \theta(\lambda_\infty-\lambda_{g^*})-\ln (L_{g^*}/L_\infty). \tag{1.31}$$

Again ignoring the logarithm, and substituting (1.30), one finds

$$g^*-10 = (\lambda_\infty-\lambda_{10}-J/\theta)/\Delta\lambda. \tag{1.32}$$

* Dr. A. A. Pouring has kindly pointed out that eqn (8.5) and (8.8) of ref. (1) should read, respectively: $\kappa_g = (\sigma_{1,g}/r_1^2)/(\mu_{1,g}/m_1)^{\frac{1}{2}}$; $G(3, \theta) = 2(\exp\theta-1)/(1+2\theta)$. Eqn (8.9) should read: $G(g>3, \theta) = [\exp(\theta[\lambda_g-1])-\exp(-\theta[\lambda_g-\lambda_{g-1}-1])]/(1+\lambda_g\theta+\lambda_g^2\theta^2/2)$.

This shows qualitatively how sensitive is the position of the Volmer minimum to the value of J; the smaller is $\Delta\lambda$ the more rapidly g^* decreases when J is increased.

The response of a vapour of clusters to changes in pressure is a considerable problem involving extensive calculation. In view of the general hazard of heterogeneous condensation, it has been necessary to devise experiments using rapid adiabatic flow to isolate foreign nuclei. This greatly complicates the theoretical analysis.

2. KINETIC PROCESSES IN UNBALANCED ASSEMBLIES

There are special problems in relating the kinetic laws of growth and evaporation of large particles to those of clusters in a condensation aerosol. The results that follow are derived from the general formulae for reaction rates of clusters with $g > 4$. The results for $g = 2, 3, 4$ were given previously.[1]

UNIMOLECULAR REACTIONS

For the process of unimolecular decay, or evaporation,

$$A_g = A_{g-1} + A_1, \tag{2.1}$$

the rate equation is

$$R_{gu}^- = \bar{v} f_g Y_{gu}, \quad \mathrm{m}^{-3}\,\mathrm{s}^{-1}, \tag{2.2}$$

in which the probability of process (2.1) occurring as the result of one of the random re-distributions $(\bar{v}/s)$ of internal energy in A_g is given for $g > 4$ by

$$Y_{gu} = \left\{ \alpha_g \exp\left(-\lambda_g\theta\right) \Big/ \binom{\chi_g-1}{n_g-1} \right\} \sum_{i=1}^{n_g} (\lambda_g\theta)^{n_g-i} / (n_g-i)!. \tag{2.3}$$

This holds for

$$\exp \lambda_g\theta \ll \exp(\chi_g+\xi_g)\theta,$$

where $\chi_g+\xi_g$ equals the number of activated internal degrees of freedom, of which χ_g are vibrational. The number of vibrational modes associated with surface atoms is written $\alpha_g\chi_g$, which defines α_g.

Absolute Evaporation Coefficient

This coefficient may be defined as the fraction of potential unimolecular evaporation events in a cluster that in the absence of any other size-changing process succeed in inducing process (2.1). The coefficient is therefore given by Y_{gu} and depends in general on the temperature. Since $n_g = 3$, $g > 4$, (2.3) becomes

$$Y_{gu} = \{2\alpha_g \exp\left(-\lambda_g\theta\right)/(\chi_g-1)(\chi_g-2)\}(1+\lambda_g\theta+\lambda_g^2\theta^2/2). \tag{2.4}$$

Our present interest is in the approach to macroscopic dimensions $(g \to \infty)$. Then, $\chi_g = 3g-6 \sim 3g$, and for a spherical particle $\alpha_g \sim (36\pi/g)^{\frac{1}{3}}$ and (2.4) becomes

$$Y_{gu} = (36\pi/g)^{\frac{1}{3}}(2/9g^2) \exp\left(-\lambda_g\theta\right)(1+\lambda_g\theta+\lambda_g^2\theta^2/2). \tag{2.5}$$

The lifetime of a g-cluster under these conditions therefore increases with size more rapidly than as $g^{\frac{1}{3}}$.

Unimolecular Fission

This process we represent by

$$A_g = A_{g-k} + A_k, \quad g > 2k > 2, \tag{2.6}$$

where A_k is the fission fragment and A_{g-k} the remnant. Let n_k be the number of specified vibrational modes lost by A_g on escape of A_k. Also, now that $k>1$, let λ_{gk} be the number of nearest neighbours of the fragment A_k about to be expelled. The case has previously been given brief consideration,[5] and is complicated because λ_{gk} may vary for fixed g, k on account of the shape of A_k. The decay group of n_k vibrations will then involve various combinations of both surface and bulk interactions, affecting the term α_{gk}.

A simple case is $\chi_g > n_k \gg 1$, when (2.3) gives for the fission probability,

$$Y_{gu} = (n_k/3g)^{n_k} \qquad (2.7)$$

on the rather strong assumption that for such large particles any differences in the relative contributions of surface and bulk interactions do not affect the probabilities of the various critical energy distributions that lead to fission. The result is that the probability of fission will depend only on the random circulation of internal energy and not on the value of λ_{gk} or the temperature.

It is difficult to assess the size at which this assumption becomes permissible but it appears reasonable to regard the considerations under which (2.3) reduces first to (2.5) and then to (2.7) as establishing that, not only is the fission probability greatly reduced but the level of temperature loses its significance as the cluster and its fragment become larger.

BIMOLECULAR REACTIONS

Coalescence

The reverse of (2.6) represents bimolecular coalescence. This will be distinguished from coagulation, by which is meant the mutual adhesion after collision of particles which do not fuse to form a particle of uniform λ_g. It is assumed that coalescence is a property that depends on high volatility and is therefore characteristic of clusters that are embryonic droplets. The concept is somewhat rudimentary in terms of the present cluster models which are regarded as solid-like,[1] and a quantitative theory has yet to be worked out. It is evident that those cases of coalescence that are the inverse of slow fission will either have low intrinsic probability or depend upon species in short supply at equilibrium. In view of this and a later conclusion about the time scales for the growth of large particles, it is permissible to ignore fission and coalescence as factors contributing to the breakdown of supersaturation.

Condensation Coefficient

Of frequent use in conventional treatments of the later stages of particle growth is the concept of the condensation coefficient. A theoretical coefficient a^{VS} for the condensation of vapour V on substrate S may be defined as the fraction of molecular collisions on S that in the absence of re-evaporation result in capture. The present theory assumes thermal equilibrium, and a^{VS} is therefore unaffected by considerations of thermal accommodation. We obtain a^{VS} for the inverse of process (2.1) by dividing the rate R^+ by the collision number Z.

The rate of $A_g + A_1 = A_{g+1}$ when $g>4$ is

$$R_{g+1}^+ = Z_{1,g}(1 - Y_{gb}') \Big/ \binom{\chi_g}{n_g}, \qquad (2.8)$$

giving

$$a_g^{VS} = \{1 - \exp(-\lambda_g \theta)\} \Big/ \binom{\chi_g}{n_g}, \qquad (2.9)$$

where $n_g = 3$. In this case, S is the surface of the cluster A_g. For only the smallest clusters is the numerator on the right of (2.9) appreciably different from unity. Under thermal equilibrium conditions, therefore, the temperature level loses its influence over a^{VS} quite early in the growth of A_g. For $g \gg 1$ the denominator becomes $(\chi_g/n_g)^{n_g}$, or substituting $n_g = 3$, $\chi_g = 3g$,

$$a_g^{VS} = 1/g^3. \tag{2.10}$$

Net Condensation Coefficient

The experimental quantity analogous to a^{VS} is a, the net condensation coefficient. This is usually defined in terms of the net condensation flux $F(m^{-2} \, s^{-1})$ from the vapour to the macroscopic surface $(g \to \infty)$ and the ideal-gas equations for the separate fluxes to (F^{VS}) and from (F^{SV}) the surface:

$$F = a(F^{VS} - F^{SV}), \tag{2.11}$$

where

$$F^{VS} = p/(2\pi m \, kT)^{\frac{1}{2}}, \tag{2.12}$$

$$F^{SV} = p^\circ/(2\pi m \, kT)^{\frac{1}{2}}. \tag{2.13}$$

Eqn (2.13) follows from (2.12) by the equilibrium requirement of balance of macroscopic fluxes. The pressures are assumed to be those of monomeric gas, so that $m = m(A_1) = m_1$, $p = p_1$, $p^\circ = p_1^\circ$ in the present context. Fission and coalescence are not considered in the simple derivation of (2.12) and (2.13) and experimentally a is obtained from the measured flux F and the total pressures p and p°.

The net condensation coefficient of a cluster in a condensing aerosol is obtained as follows. The net forward rate of the growth step is

$$R_{g+1}^+ - R_{g+1}^- = Z_{1,g} a_g^{VS} - \bar{v} f_{g+1} Y_{g+1,u}, \tag{2.14}$$

it being assumed that the forward and reverse processes on a single cluster occur independently. This requires moderate or low pressures $(p \lesssim 1 \text{ bar})$. Equating (2.14) to zero at equilibrium, the second term on the right becomes

$$Z_{1,g}'' c_1^\circ c_g^\circ a_g^{VS} f_{g+1}/c_{g+1}^\circ,$$

where the c° are saturated concentrations at a temperature equal to that of the condensing vapour and $Z_{1,g}'' = Z_{1,g}/f_1 f_g$. This gives for the net flux on the particle,

$$F_g = (R_{g+1}^+ - R_{g+1}^-)/f_g O_g = (Z_{1,g}'' a_g^{VS}/O_g kT)\{p_1 - p_1^\circ(f_{g+1}/f_g) \exp(\Delta \zeta_{g+1}/kT)\}, \tag{2.15}$$

where (1.3) was used to eliminate c_g°/c_{g+1}° from the evaporation term.

Eqn (2.15) applies to net growth or evaporation. F_g is not expressible in a simple form dependent on total pressure and in which a becomes independent of g as $g \to \infty$. In this size limit,

$$Z_{1,g}''/O_g kT = 1/(2\pi m_1 kT)^{\frac{1}{2}}, \tag{2.16}$$

but the coefficient of p_1° is unity only for a $J = 0$ state, when F_g vanishes at all g. That it should do so is a fundamental requirement of vapour stability.

3. OBSERVATION OF PARTICLES IN CONDENSATION AEROSOLS

Experiments to determine a in (2.11) involve control over pressure, temperature and particle size. The relaxation times of processes affecting pressure and temperature must therefore substantially exceed the observation time for visible growth on S. An approximate analysis for low temperatures $(f_1 \sim p)$ and supersaturations $(0 \sim J < 1)$

shows [1] that the evolution of f_g depends on $(1+g/2)(g-1)$ time-dependent terms and involves the $g-1$ relaxation times $\tau_s = f_s/(R_s^- + R_{s+1}^+)$ of the successive growth steps $A_1 + A_{s-1} = A_s$. For $s \gg 1$,

$$\tau_s = g^{7/3}(2\pi m_1 kT)^{1/2}/O_1\{p_1 + p_1^\circ \exp (\Delta\zeta_g/kT)\}. \qquad (3.1)$$

Growth of even 1 μm particles would be infinitely slow in the final stages according to (3.1), and the conclusion is that the time scales are against the observation of particles of visible size produced in uniform suspension by spontaneous condensation. This appears to be confirmed experimentally in the type of experiment where spontaneous and uniform condensation is reliably observed.[6-8] In such experiments the particles are too small to be distinguished individually. What is observed is a change in pressure or scattering of light resulting from the combined effect of a large number of particles distributed over size. It may be concluded that the coefficient a is without experimental or theoretical significance for the condensation of aerosols.

The theory of this paper is restricted to situations in which thermal relaxation maintains equipartition in the cluster reactions. In the condensation of substances, like water, that are sufficiently volatile at ordinary temperatures, latent heat is dissipated relatively slowly by collisions, and an excess of the inert diluent gas B is required by the theory. The aerosol particles will remain volatile for a long time and may re-evaporate if the system is not kept cold.

The internal energy of clusters condensing at high temperatures will be affected by the wall temperature, and radiative heat transfer may occur homogeneously at low enough pressure. In systems where the high temperature is achieved locally in a flowing gas by exothermic chemical reaction, as in the wake of a shock wave [9] or by combustion of fuel gas in a jet, both the reaction and the condensation of products may be facilitated by rapid heat transfer. If the condensing product is involatile, a homogeneous particle size distribution will be frozen-in and, assuming spontaneous condensation of atoms or molecules, the smoke so formed will contain only ultra-fine particles in large numbers. Further growth would depend on properties not considered in this paper, such as ionization or field-induced effects, capable of promoting the non-random motion and coagulation of such small particles.

[1] E. R. Buckle, *Trans. Faraday Soc.*, 1969, **65**, 1267.
[2] E. R. Buckle and A. A. Pouring, unpublished.
[3] M. Volmer and A. Weber, *Z. phys. Chem.*, 1926, **119**, 277.
[4] M. Volmer, *Kinetik der Phasenbildung* (Theodor Steinkopff, Dresden, 1939).
[5] E. R. Buckle, *Discuss. Faraday Soc.*, 1967, **44**, 287.
[6] P. P. Wegener and A. A. Pouring, *Phys. Fluids*, 1964, **7**, 352.
[7] E. R. Buckle and A. A. Pouring, *Nature*, 1965, **208**, 367.
[8] G. D. Stein and P. P. Wegener, *J. Chem. Phys.*, 1967, **46**, 3685.
[9] J. B. Homer and I. R. Hurle, *Proc. Roy. Soc. A*, 1972, **327**, 61.

Chemical Nucleation Theory for Various Humidities and Pollutants

By C. S. Kiang and D. Stauffer

Physics Department, Clark College, Atlanta, Georgia 30314, U.S.A.

Received 28th November, 1972

The Flood–Neumann–Döring–Reiss–Doyle theory gives a strong dependence of the nucleation rate on the humidity (for r.h. < 100 %) and shows that under atmospheric condition H_2SO_4, but not HNO_3, SO_2, or NH_3, contributes directly to the aerosol nucleation without pre-existing nuclei. Typically, 10^9 H_2SO_4 molecules per cm^3 are enough to form droplets of aqueous sulphuric acid solutions.

One possible mechanism for the formation of atmospheric aerosols is the formation of small droplets consisting of a liquid mixture of water and a pollutant, e.g., H_2SO_4. Even around pre-existing nuclei, pure water can form droplets that grow to infinite size only if the relative humidity of the atmosphere is greater than 100 %; and a pure pollutant like H_2SO_4 can form large droplets only if its partial gas pressure is greater than the equilibrium vapour pressure over liquid H_2SO_4, i.e., only if its "activity" is greater than one. But droplets consisting of an aqueous solution of the pollutant can grow even for activities smaller than one and humidities smaller than 100 %, since the partial pressures of both components over a liquid mixture can be much smaller than over the pure materials.

If a small mixture droplet is formed out of the gas phase with at least two components (e.g., H_2SO_4 and H_2O), then we call this process "chemical nucleation" to distinguish it from other nucleation processes. This paper applies the theory of chemical nucleation to various materials as a function of the relative atmospheric humidity. Our calculations are based on the work of Flood,[1] Neumann and Döring,[2] Reiss,[3] and Doyle.[4] Our main results and the connection with experiments were reported earlier.[5]

REVIEW OF CHEMICAL NUCLEATION THEORY

The nucleation process is determined mainly by the free energy $\Delta G = \Delta(E - TS - \mu N)$ necessary to form a droplet. We write for the formation energy of a droplet consisting of n_A water and n_B pollutant molecules:

$$\Delta G = (\mu_{cA} - \mu_A)n_A + (\mu_{cB} - \mu_B)n_B + S(n_A, n_B)\gamma(x), \qquad (1)$$

where the μ_c are the chemical potentials of the two materials (A = H_2O, B = pollutant, e.g., H_2SO_4) if gas and liquid are in equilibrium over a flat mixture surface. The μ are the actual chemical potentials in the supersaturated atmosphere; S is the surface area of the droplet and depends on n_A and n_B; γ is the concentration-dependent surface tension of the liquid mixture;

$$x = n_B/(n_A + n_B) \qquad (2)$$

is the mol fraction of the pollutant in the droplet. We assume the volume of a droplet

26

to be given by $V_A n_A + V_B n_B = 4\pi r^3/3$, where r is the droplet radius, and V_A and V_B are the volumes per molecule of pure water and pure pollutant. Thus, $S = 4\pi r^2$.

Large mixture droplets can be formed from a gas only if both chemical potentials μ_A and μ_B are greater than their values μ_{cA} and μ_{cB} on the coexistence curve; that means supersaturation with respect to both vapours is required. In this case, the first two terms of the right-hand side of (1) are negative; the last term is positive and dominates for small droplets. Thus, due to the surface tension, the droplets have to overcome an energy maximum before they can grow further. For a binary mixture, the free energy ΔG depends on n_A and n_B and thus can be represented by a surface ("mountain") in three dimensions. In order to grow, the droplets have to overcome the lowest free energy maximum (saddle point). In the growth process, most droplets approach this saddle point along the deepest valley leading to this mountain pass.[2]

This saddle point condition yields two equations:

$$(\partial G/\partial n_A)_{n_B} = 0 \quad \text{and} \quad (\partial G/\partial n_B)_{n_A} = 0.$$

In the evaluation of these two derivatives, the changes of the μ_c with the mol fraction x (eqn (2)) cancel out because of the Gibbs–Duhem–Margule equation,[2, 6]

$$n_A d\mu_{cA} + n_B d\mu_{cB} = 0, \tag{3}$$

(or $(1-x)d\mu_{cA}/dx = -x\,d\mu_{cB}/dx$). Then the saddle point condition gives for the composition x^* and the droplet radius r^* at the saddle point[4]:

$$\Delta\mu_A^* \equiv \mu_A - \mu_{cA}^* = (2\gamma V_A/r^*)/(1 - a^* x^*) > 0, \tag{4a}$$

$$\Delta\mu_B^* \equiv \mu_B - \mu_{cB}^* = (2\gamma V_B/r^*)/(1 + a^*(1-x^*)) > 0, \tag{4b}$$

or, equivalently,

$$\Delta\mu_A^*/\Delta\mu_B^* = (V_A/V_B)(1 + a^*(1-x^*))/(1 - a^* x^*), \tag{4c}$$

$$r^* = 2\gamma V_A/((1 - a^* x^*)\Delta\mu_A^*), \tag{4d}$$

with

$$a = 1.5(1 - x + V_B/V_A)(d\gamma/dx)/\gamma. \tag{4e}$$

(The star * denotes values at the saddle point.) On insertion of (4) into (1), the a^*-corrections cancel out:

$$\Delta G^* = (4\pi/3)\gamma^* r^{*2} \tag{5}$$

The equilibrium number of droplets of critical size r^* and critical composition x^* is proportional to $\exp(-\Delta G^*/kT)$; the factor of proportionality is assumed by Reiss[3] and Doyle[4] to be the total number $N_A + N_B$ of gaseous water and pollutant molecules.

Under usual atmospheric conditions, there exists much less pollutant than water, $N_A \gg N_B$. Droplets at the saddle point grow by incorporation of single molecules such that the composition x remains roughly unchanged (at least for the examples used in this paper). Therefore, the growth rate at the saddle point is determined by the pollutant concentrations N_B whereas the proportionality factor for the droplet numbers is given by N_A for $N_A \gg N_B$. (Most of the water molecules impinging on the critical size droplets will evaporate again; only if additional H_2SO_4 molecules have been incorporated into the droplet, then also more water molecules can remain with the droplet and keep its composition near x^*.)

Thus, the rate at which new molecules are incorporated into the droplets is given roughly by the product of surface area $4\pi r^{*2}$ and pollutant impinging rate

$$\beta_B = N_B\,kT/(2\pi m_B\,kT)^{\frac{1}{2}},$$

where m_B is the mass of a pollutant molecule. The nucleation rate J is the rate at which droplets grow over the saddle point (per cm^3 per s) and thus can be approximated as

$$J = 4\pi r^{*2}\beta_B N_A \exp{(-\Delta G^*/kT)}. \tag{6}$$

The $\Delta\mu$ appearing in (4) can easily be evaluated since in the atmosphere the gas densities are very low and therefore application of the ideal gas law gives

$$\Delta\mu_A(x) = kT \ln{(P_A/P_{\infty A}(x))}; \quad \Delta\mu_B(x) = kT \ln{(P_B/P_{\infty B}(x))}, \tag{7}$$

where P_A and P_B are the actual partial pressures of the water and the pollutant, whereas $P_{\infty A}(x)$ and $P_{\infty B}(x)$ are the equilibrium partial pressures over a large solution with composition x (mol fraction).

Historically, this theory of " chemical nucleation " was developped by Flood [1] who applied it to water+alcohol mixtures. Neumann and Döring [2] introduced the saddle point picture and took into account the possible enrichment of one phase near the droplet surface. (This effect is neglected by us; for the $H_2O+H_2SO_4$ nucleation we found its influence on J to be negligible if calculated as in the theory of ref. (2)). In ref. (1) and ref. (2), the pre-exponential factor for the nucleation rate was simply chosen to be the same as that of pure water, which would be too high an estimate for $H_2O+H_2SO_4$ nucleation. Reiss [3] derived in detail the pre-exponential factor but used only special limiting cases in the evaluation of the exponential term (e.g., dilute solutions in the liquid droplet). In ref. (1)-(3), the a^*-corrections in (4) were neglected. They were introduced by Doyle [4] who applied this theory to $H_2O+H_2SO_4$ mixtures at 50 % relative humidity. Bricard et al.[7] recently evaluated J also for 30 % and 70 % relative humidity. In the next section Doyle's formulae are applied to different materials and humidities in order to give a more complete picture than known to us before.

NUMERICAL RESULTS

Our figures show the main results from a numerical solution of (4c) and (7) (iteration on an IBM 1130 computer) and the application of (4d) and (6) for the nucleation rate J. The $H_2O+H_2SO_4$ nucleation rate is evaluated at 25°C, the H_2O+HNO_3 nucleation at 20°C; data is taken from ref. (6).

Fig. 1 shows some cuts through a free energy surface. Fig. 2 gives some nucleation rates J for chemical nucleation of $H_2O+H_2SO_4$ and H_2O+HNO_3 mixtures. The " activity " in the figures is simply the actual pollutant partial pressure in units of the pressure of a pure pollutant (10^{-6} Torr for H_2SO_4 from ref. (4); 45 Torr for HNO_3 from ref. (6)). Thus, the activity is for the pollutant what the relative humidity is for water.

For atmospheric applications, it seems to be useful to know the characteristic time τ during which the atmospheric content of gaseous pollutant is reduced appreciably due to chemical nucleation rates. Fig. 3 gives this time as estimated from

$$\tau = N_B/x^*J \sim N_B/J.$$

Fig. 4 shows the activities necessary to achieve a fixed J = one droplet per cm^3/s or a fixed τ = one second or one month. Critical composition x^* and number of molecules in a critical size droplet are given by fig. 5.

All these results describe homogeneous chemical nucleation without preexisting nuclei. Nucleation of a mixture can also occur as heterogeneous chemical nucleation on pre-existing nuclei [8] like flat surfaces, insoluble particles, soluble particles [9] or ions. But also for such heterogeneous nucleation, the actual partial pressures of

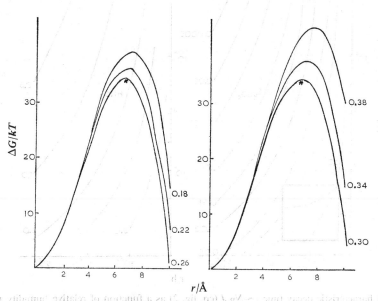

Fig. 1.—Droplet formation energy ΔG as a function of droplet radius r ($H_2O + H_2SO_4$ at 50 % relative humidity; activity = 0.005). The numbers on the curves give the mol fraction x of H_2SO_4 in the droplet; the star indicates the saddle point.

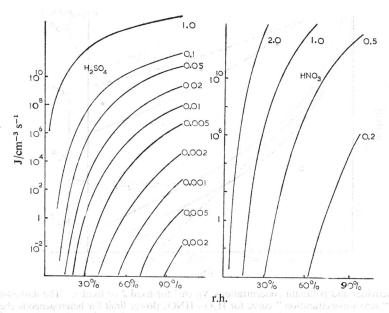

Fig. 2.—Nucleation rate J as a function of relative humidity r.h. for $H_2O + H_2SO_4$ (left) and $H_2O +$ HNO_3 (right). The numbers on the curves give the activity (= partial pollutant gas pressure in units of 10^{-6} Torr for H_2SO_4 (25°C) and of 45 Torr for HNO_3 (20°C)).

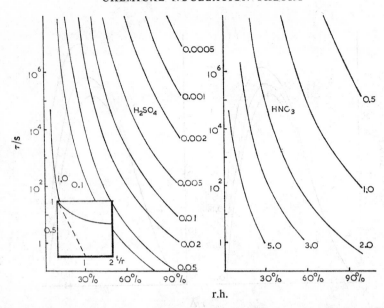

FIG. 3.—Characteristic decay time $\tau \sim N_B/J$ (cp. fig. 2) as a function of relative humidity r.h.; the numbers on the curves give the activity. The insert shows the gaseous pollutant concentration $N_B(t)/N_B(t=0)$ as a function of time t/τ (solid line) and the tangent to this curve at $t=0$ (dashed line). Initial activity 0.005, r.h. $= 80\%$, $\tau \sim 1$h.

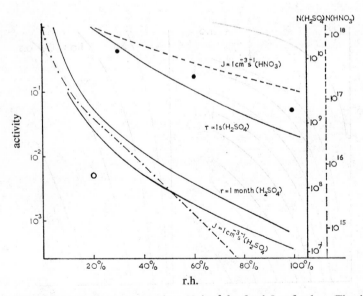

FIG. 4.—Activities and pollutant concentrations N_B/cm^3 for fixed J or fixed τ. The dashed-dotted line is the " zero supersaturation " curve for $H_2O + HNO_3$ (lower limit for heterogeneous chemical nucleation). Heterogeneous nucleation on ions or wetted particles with 8 Å radius is indicated by full ($H_2O + HNO_3$) and open ($H_2O + H_2SO_4$) circles. ($J = 1$ droplet per second and ion or particle for HNO_3, $10^{-3}/s$ for H_2SO_4.)

water and pollutant cannot be smaller than those over a flat surface of a liquid mixture in equilibrium with its vapours. This condition (actual partial pressures = equilibrium partial pressures) determines the " zero supersaturation curve " of fig. 4.

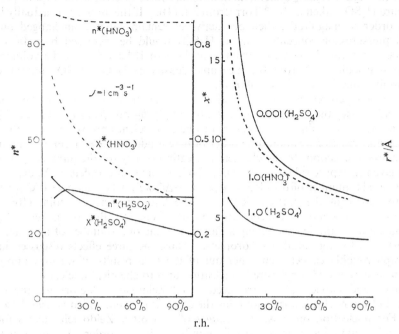

FIG. 5.—Number of molecules n^* (left scale), composition x^* (centre scale), and radius r^* (right scale) of " critical " saddle point droplets for fixed J (left) or fixed activity (right; as given by the numbers on the curves). Roughly, r^* is the minimum radius of wetted particles which can produce heterogeneous chemical nucleation for the given activity and humidity.

Nucleation, whether heterogeneous or homogeneous, does not occur for activities smaller than the activity on the zero supersaturation curve. (For $H_2O + H_2SO_4$, activity $= 10^{-5}$ at 20 % relative humidity, activity $= 10^{-9.5}$ at 80 % relative humidity.) Heterogeneous chemical nucleation processes may be important for activities between the one on the zero supersaturation curve and the higher ones shown in fig. 4 for homogeneous chemical nucleation. Using the same models as in ref. (10) we find for nucleation on ions or on " dust " particles of 8 Å radius the activities indicated by the circles in fig. 4. (For $H_2O + H_2SO_4$, the pre-exponential factor for J_{ion}/N_{ion} is smaller than 1 s^{-1}; thus, J_{ion}/N_{ion} cannot be greater than 1 s^{-1} for the activities for which nucleation theory is valid $(\Delta G^* \gg kT)$. The same holds for "dust" nucleation.)

DISCUSSION

This theory shares with others the disadvantage of applying macroscopic concepts to small droplets. Recent indirect evidence [11] indicates that this is a much better approximation than usually assumed; the results of ref. (11) leave little space for a correction factor like 10^{17} for the droplet concentrations. But it may be necessary to employ a " microscopic surface tension " for the free energy of the droplet. For pure water near 0°C, this microscopic surface tension was found in ref. (12) to agree with the measured bulk surface tension. However, the activities of H_2SO_4 or HNO_3

predicted in our theory might well be wrong by one order of magnitude. (The " zero supersaturation curve " of fig. 4 should be more accurate since no surface tension enters there.) Hydration effects could produce additional complications.

For the $H_2O + H_2SO_4$ system, an additional source of error is the vapour pressure over pure H_2SO_4 taken as 10^{-6} Torr (from ref. (4)). If this pressure is actually larger by an order of magnitude, then our activities remain roughly unchanged but the partial pressures or concentrations of H_2SO_4 would be increased by a factor 10. The nucleation rate is increased from $1 \, cm^{-3} \, s^{-1}$ to $10^3 \, cm^{-3} \, s^{-1}$ if the volume of a droplet is calculated [14] from the measured density of $H_2O + H_2SO_4$ mixtures and not simply from $V_A n_A + V_B n_B = 4\pi r^3/3$.

Some other corrections were found to be rather unimportant. In the work of Reiss and Doyle, the impinging rate is not simply β_B but $\beta_A \beta_B (1 + \tan^2 \phi)/(\beta_B + \beta_A \tan^2 \phi)$. We found $\tan \phi = x^*/(1 - x^*)$ to be a sufficient approximation; then this correction increases J by about one order of magnitude near $J = 1 \, cm^{-3} \, s^{-1}$. In ref. (12) we used corrections to the classical nucleation theory for the number of droplets with a given size (pure substances); instead of: number of droplets $= N_1 \exp(-\Delta G/kT)$, we used: number of droplets $= q_0 \exp(-\Delta G/kT)$, where q_0 near $0°C$ for water is of the order of the particle density at the liquid-gas critical point ($10^{22} \, cm^{-3}$ instead of $N_1 =$ monomer concentration $= 10^{17.5} \, cm^{-3}$). But ΔG, in ref. (12), also contained a logarithmic term giving an additional factor: (number of molecules in a droplet)$^{-2.23}$, for the number of droplets. Thus, the three effects discussed in this paragraph roughly cancel each other out of the final results, if we may apply our previous experience [12] for " pure " nucleation also to chemical nucleation.

Reiss [3] and Doyle [4] also introduced two " Zeldovich " factors for the saddle point; but the nucleation rate contains the *quotient* of them which is near 1 (see ref. (4)). For nucleation on ions, the *product* of two other Zeldovich factors for the energy minimum appears in the droplet numbers; it is of order 10^{-1} and was taken into account in fig. 4.

We conclude that our results may be inaccurate but should give the correct trends for the dependence on humidities, activities, ions etc. This could be confirmed by experiment.[1, 5] Our fig. 4 shows that for different materials the activities are roughly the same; only the transformation from activity to partial pressure or concentration differed by many orders of magnitude for H_2SO_4 and HNO_3. Thus, under usual atmospheric conditions on earth, where impurities are measured in parts per million or less, the high concentration of HNO_3 necessary for chemical nucleation cannot be reached. Similarly, SO_2, C_2H_5OH, or NH_3 cannot form directly liquid aqueous solution droplets in the atmosphere because of their high pressure, whereas H_2SO_4 forms very easily a mixture droplet. The typical partial pressure of the pollutant vapour over a pollutant + water mixture thus indicates directly whether this pollutant can form droplets with water by (homogeneous) chemical nucleation. On the other hand, the vapour pressure of NaCl is so small at room temperature (10^{-29} Torr from an extrapolation of the results of ref. (13)) that the atmosphere should practically not contain gaseous neutral NaCl molecules. Then again chemical nucleation does not occur. Only for intermediate vapour pressures, e.g., near the 10^{-6} Torr of H_2SO_4, is this chemical nucleation process of direct importance in the atmosphere.

Indirectly, both SO_2 and NaCl can contribute to aerosol formation by chemical nucleation. As discussed in ref. (4), (15), concentrations of SO_2 in the parts per million range are sufficient to produce $H_2O + H_2SO_4$ aerosols via photoxidation of SO_2 to H_2SO_4. And solid NaCl particles in the atmosphere can serve as soluble condensation nuclei for heterogeneous nucleation of pure water [8, 9] (for relative humidities > 100 %) or solution droplets (humidities < 100 %).   For relative humidities less than 100 % and activities less than 1, our chemical nucleation theory describes the only mechanism for the formation of large aerosols from the gas phase.   For relative humidities greater than 100 %, this chemical nucleation mechanism can be regarded as the initial stage of other aerosol formation processes (e.g., heterogeneous water nucleation on soluble particles [8, 9]).   We hope to discuss this second nucleation process in a later paper.[15]

We thank Prof. V. A. Mohnen for drawing our attention to this problem and for encouraging discussions, and the National Center for Atmospheric Research, Boulder, for its hospitality.   This investigation is partially supported by NSF Grant GA-33422, Atmospheric Science section, and by NIH Grant RR 8006, from the General Research Support Branch, Division of General Resources, National Institute of Health.

[1] H. Flood, Z. phys. Chem. A, 1934, 170, 286.
[2] K. Neumann and W. Döring, Z. phys. Chem. A, 1940, 186, 203.
[3] H. Ress, J. Chem. Phys., 1950, 18, 840.
[4] G. J. Doyle, J. Chem. Phys., 1961, 35, 795.
[5] C. S. Kiang, D. Stauffer, V. A. Mohnen, J. Bricard and D. Vigla, submitted to Atmospheric Environment.
[6] W. R. Forsythe and W. F. Giauque, J. Amer. Chem. Soc., 1941, 64, 48 ; W. F. Giauque, E. W. Hornung, J. E. Kunzler and T. R. Rubin, ibid., 1960, 82, 62 ; Int. Critical Tables, vol. IV (E. W. Washburn et al., ed.) (McGraw Hill Book Company, New York and London, 1928), Landolt-Börnstein, Zahlenwerte und Funktionen, vol. II 2a (K. Schäfer and E. Lax, ed.) (Springer Verlag, Berlin, 1960).
Private communication of J. Bricard, September 1972.
[7] B. J. Mason, The Physics of Clouds (Clarendon Press, Oxford, 1957).
[8] K. G. Vohra and P. V. N. Nair, J. Atm. Sci., 1971, 28, 280.
[9] Clark College Research Group, Phys. Rev. B, 1972, 6, 2780.
[10] C. S. Kiang, Phys. Rev. Letters, 1970, 24, 47 ; K. Binder et al., J. Stat. Phys., 1972, 6, 49 ; and
[11] Phys. Rev. B, 1972, 6, 2777 ; C. Carlier and H. L. Frisch, J. Chem. Phys., 1972, to be published.
[12] Clark College Research Group, J. Atm. Sci., 1971, 28, 1222.
[13] B. H. Zimm and J. E. Mayer, J. Chem. Phys., 1944, 12, 362.
[14] We thank Mr. L. Roland for help on this calculation.
[15] D. Stauffer, V. A. Mohnen, C. S. Kiang, to be submitted to J. Aerosol Sc.

Notes added in proof:

1: The calculation of τ in fig. 3 overestimates the time after which the gaseous pollutant is consumed, since it neglects condensation on already nucleated droplets.[15]

2: At the third Chemist-Meteorologist Workshop (Ft. Lauderdale, Florida, Jan. 1973) the name " heteromolecular nucleation " was proposed for what we called here " chemical nucleation."

Evaporation of Fine Atmospheric Particles

By C. N. Davies

Dept of Chemistry, University of Essex, Wivenhoe Park, Colchester, Essex

Received 6th December, 1972

The decrease in size of aerosol particles due to evaporation is calculated for two situations. In the first, the air is saturated with vapour so that evaporation is due to the Kelvin effect and proceeds at the minimal rate; in the second, the air is free from vapour and the rate of evaporation is maximal. The calculations are based upon an interpolation formula covering the transition with decreasing particle size from diffusion control to free molecular flow.

---

1. INTRODUCTION

The rate of evaporation of a pure substance in the form of a spherical particle of radius a, when subject to diffusion control in a gas at rest, is equal to

$$\phi_0 = -\mathrm{d}m/\mathrm{d}t = 4\pi a \nabla (n_s - n_\infty) \tag{1.1}$$

where n_s is the concentration of vapour in equilibrium with the surface of the particle, n_∞ the vapour concentration at a distance from the surface and ∇, the coefficient of diffusion of vapour molecules through the surrounding gas. This equation is valid when the Knudsen number

$$\mathrm{Kn} = \lambda/a \tag{1.2}$$

λ being the mean free path of the gas molecules, is near to zero. Increase of the rate of evaporation due to the particles falling under gravity can be seen from the equation of Frössling [1] to be negligible for radii below 10 μm.

If the gas pressure is low or the particle is very small, so that Kn is very large, the rate of evaporation is

$$\phi_K = 4\pi a^2 \tfrac{1}{4}(n_s - n_\infty)\bar{c}\alpha \tag{1.3}$$

where $\bar{c}$ is the mean velocity of the evaporating molecules and the fraction α is the evaporation coefficient.

For intermediate values of Kn, the rate of evaporation has been calculated by Fuchs [2] on the assumption that free molecular flow of molecules of vapour, as in (1.3), proceeds from the surface of the particle outwards for a distance, Δ, and diffusive flow continues from radius $a+\Delta$ to infinity, as in eqn (1.1). Δ is a length near to the mean free path of the molecules of the surrounding gas. Suppose that the concentration of vapour at distance Δ from the surface is n_1 and that $n_\infty = 0$. The rates of transport across the zones inside and outside radius $a+\Delta$ must be the same, hence

$$\phi = 4\pi(a+\Delta)\nabla n_1 = \pi a^2 (n_s - n_1)\bar{c}\alpha \tag{1.4}$$

which gives, after eliminating n_1

$$\phi = \phi_0/(4\nabla/a\bar{c}\alpha + a/(a+\Delta)). \tag{1.5}$$

34

In the opinion of Wright,[3] his experiments indicate that the thickness of the free molecule region is

$$\Delta = 2\nabla/\bar{c} \qquad (1.6)$$

and, from the kinetic theory of gases, the coeffiicent of diffusion is given by

$$\nabla = \bar{c}\lambda/3. \qquad (1.7)$$

The coefficient of diffusion of the evaporating molecules can therefore be eliminated from eqn (1.5) which becomes

$$\phi = \phi_0/(4Kn/3\alpha + 1/(1 + 2Kn/3)). \qquad (1.8)$$

For small values of Kn this reduces to

$$\phi \simeq \phi_0/(1 + 2Kn(2/\alpha - 1)/3) \qquad (1.9)$$

which is considered by Fuchs and Sutugin [4] to be accurate for $Kn \ll 1$.

From eqn (1.1) and (1.2)

$$\phi_0 = \phi_K 4\nabla/a\bar{c}\alpha = \phi_K 4Kn/3\alpha \qquad (1.10)$$

so that (1.8) can be written for large values of Kn as

$$\phi = \phi_K/(1 + 9\alpha/8Kn^2). \qquad (1.11)$$

However, this equation involves Kn in a manner which Fuchs and Sutugin [4] show to be incompatible with current theory of free molecular flow. The Δ concept is thus invalid at high values of Kn. They have pointed out that a theoretical solution exists of a mathematically analogous problem which brings the value of ϕ to the correct limits as Kn tends to zero and to infinity. They have given an interpolation formula which fits the exact solution closely. This formula results in eqn (1.8) being replaced by the expression

$$\phi = \phi_0/(1 + Kn(1.333Kn + 0.71)/(Kn + 1)) \qquad (1.12)$$

which reduces to

$$\phi = \phi_0/(1 + 0.71Kn) \text{ for } Kn \ll 1 \qquad (1.13)$$

and to

$$\phi = (\phi_K/\alpha)/(1 + 0.283Kn^{-1}) \text{ for } Kn \gg 1. \qquad (1.14)$$

Eqn (1.13) is the same as (1.9) when $\alpha = 0.97$. For other values of α the difference between them decreases as Kn decreases and increases as α decreases. At $Kn = 0.25$, they agree better than 1 % for $\alpha = 1$ and eqn (1.13) is 18 % low at $\alpha = 0.6$. At $Kn = 0.1$, eqn (1.13) predicts a value of ϕ, low by 8.4 %. Eqn (1.14) is in reasonable agreement with free molecule theory.

As far as is known eqn (1.12) is satisfactory for calculating the rate of evaporation of aerosol particles, particularly so because for most substances α is probably equal to unity. Hitherto, this calculation has been tiresome because of the need for making exploratory determinations of the values of the terms in the denominator of eqn (1.5) or (1.8) as evaporation proceeds and their relative importance changes. This necessity can be avoided when eqn (1.12) is used, as explained below.

2. GENERAL FORMULAE FOR THE RATE OF EVAPORATION OF AEROSOL PARTICLES

From eqn (1.1) and (1.12)

$$dm/dt = -4\pi a\nabla(n_s - n_\infty)(Kn + 1)/(1 + 1.71Kn + 1.333Kn^2). \qquad (2.1)$$

Let

$$y = Kn^{-1} = a/\lambda \tag{2.2}$$

and the saturation ratio of vapour in equilibrium with the surface of the particle be

$$S = n_s/n_0 \tag{2.3}$$

where n_0 is the saturation vapour pressure of the evaporating substance in bulk. Then

$$\frac{dy}{dt} = \frac{-\nabla n_0(S - n_\infty/n_0)}{\rho\lambda^2} \frac{y+1}{y^2 + 1.71y + 1.333}. \tag{2.4}$$

The saturation ratio, S, is determined by Kelvin's equation which, for low values of $S-1$, approximates to

$$S - 1 \simeq 2\gamma M/RTa\rho \tag{2.5}$$

where γ is the surface tension of the evaporating substance, M is its molecular weight, R is the gas constant per gram molecule and ρ is the density of the particle; T is the absolute temperature, assumed to be the same throughout the particle and the surrounding gas. A water droplet evaporating in air cools to the wet bulb temperature, which considerably slows down the rate of evaporation; this is on account of the high latent heat of evaporation and high saturation vapour concentration. Substances of lower volatility, such as the others shown in table 2 below, cool only to a negligible extent, which can be calculated by the methods described by Fuchs.[5]

Two limiting cases arise which correspond to maximal and minimal rates of evaporation. The maximal rate occurs during evaporation into gas which is free from vapour, so that $n_\infty = 0$. The minimal rate is for evaporation into gas which is saturated with vapour so that $n_\infty = n_0$.

For evaporation into saturated vapour, eqn (2.4) and (2.5) give

$$\frac{dy}{dt} = -\frac{\nabla n_0}{\rho\lambda^2} \frac{2\gamma M}{RM\rho\lambda} \frac{y+1}{y(y^2 + 1.71y + 1.333)}$$

$$= -DK \frac{y+1}{y(y^2 + 1.71y + 1.333)} \tag{2.6}$$

where the diffusion factor $\quad D = \nabla n_0/\rho\lambda^2 \text{ s}^{-1}$ $\left.\vphantom{\begin{array}{c}a\\b\end{array}}\right\}$ (2.7)
and the Kelvin factor $\quad K = 2\gamma M/RT\rho\lambda$, dimensionless

Suppose that the particle size initially corresponds to $y = y_0$ and reduces to $y = y_1$ at $t = t_1$, then

$$[t]_0^{t_1} = \frac{1}{DK} \int_{y_1}^{y_0} \frac{y(y^2 + 1.71y + 1.333)\,dy}{y+1} \tag{2.8}$$

therefore

$$[t_1]_{sat} = \frac{1}{DK}\left\{0.333(y_0^3 - y_1^3) + 0.355(y_0^2 - y_1^2) + 0.623(y_0 - y_1) - 0.623\ln\frac{y_0+1}{y_1+1}\right\}. \tag{2.9}$$

When the particle is evaporating into vapour-free gas, $n_\infty = 0$ and in place of (2.6) eqn (2.4) and (2.5) give

$$\frac{dy}{dt} = -\frac{\nabla n_0}{\rho\lambda^2}\left(1 + \frac{2\gamma M}{RT\rho\lambda}\frac{1}{y}\right)\frac{y+1}{y^2 + 1.71y + 1.333}$$

$$= -D(1 + K/y)\frac{y+1}{y^2 + 1.71y + 1.333}, \tag{2.10}$$

whence

$$[t]_0^{t_1} = \frac{1}{D} \int_{y_1}^{y_0} \frac{y(y^2 + 1.71y + 1.333)\,dy}{(y+1)(y+K)},$$

so that

$$D[t]_0^{t_1} = \int_{y_1}^{y_0} \frac{y^2\,dy}{y+1} + \frac{0.377 - K}{1-K} \int_{y_1}^{y_0} \frac{y\,dy}{y+1} + \frac{1.333 - 1.71K + K^2}{1-K} \int_{y_1}^{y_0} \frac{y\,dy}{y+K}$$

and

$$[t_1]_{vf} = \frac{1}{D} \left\{ 0.5(y_0^2 - y_1^2) - \frac{0.623}{1-K}\left(y_0 - y_1 - \ln\frac{y_0+1}{y_1+1}\right) + \right.$$
$$\left. \frac{1.333 - 1.71K + K^2}{1-K}\left(y_0 - y_1 - K\ln\frac{y_0+K}{y_1+K}\right)\right\}. \qquad (2.11)$$

Owing to the approximation of the Kelvin vapour pressure formula, which was used for eqn (2.5), expressions (2.9) and (2.11) are only strictly valid for particles which are initially of a sufficiently large size, so that

$$\ln S \simeq S - 1. \qquad (2.12)$$

The times, t_1, should not be so long as to allow the particle to diminish to a size beyond which this is no longer true.

Table 1 compares values of $\ln S$ and $S-1$ for droplets of dibutylphthalate, a substance of moderate vapour pressure, in air at 20°C; Kelvin's equation gives the exact value of S as

$$\ln S = 2\gamma M / RTa\rho. \qquad (2.13)$$

It will be seen that the approximation used for formulae (2.9) and (2.11) predicts too low a value for S so that the actual size of the droplet after evaporating for a certain time will be smaller than the size calculated by the formulae.   The theoretical

TABLE 1

radius of droplet /μm	In S	S—1
1.0	0.00787	0.00787
0.5	0.0159	0.0157
0.1	0.0819	0.0787
0.05	0.1705	0.1574
0.01	1.197	0.787
0.005	3.826	1.574

lifetimes are thus too long.   However, this is not often of practical importance, even for quite small drops, because the rate of evaporation increases rapidly as the size diminishes; the error in the calculated lifetime of a drop which was initially greater than about 0.1 μm radius is not too great, especially when it is evaporating into a saturated atmosphere.

3. LIFETIMES OF AEROSOL PARTICLES

The lifetime of a particle is calculated by making $y_1 = 0$ in eqn (2.9) and (2.11), y_0 being the initial value, a_0/λ.

For particles in a saturated atmosphere, this gives the lifetime

$$[t_l]_{\text{sat}} = \frac{1}{DK}\left(0.333y_0^3 + 0.355y_0^2 + 0.623y_0 - 0.623\ln(y_0+1)\right) \tag{3.1}$$

and for particles in a vapour-free atmosphere,

$$[t_l]_{\text{vf}} = \frac{1}{D}\left[0.5y_0^2 - \left(\frac{0.623}{1-K}\right)(y_0 - \ln[y_0+1]) + \frac{1.333 - 1.71K + K^2}{1-K}\left(y_0 - K\ln\frac{y_0+K}{K}\right)\right] \tag{3.2}$$

where D and K, as defined by (2.7), depend on the substance of which the particle is composed and on the gas temperature and pressure. In eqn (2.9) and (3.1), it will be seen that if the time is measured in units of $(DK)^{-1}$ there is a relation between the dimensionless quantity, tDK, and the dimensionless quantity, y, which is the radius measured in units of the gas mean free path.

For evaporation into vapour free space, the situation is more complicated because tD, in eqn (2.11) and (3.2), is a function of both the dimensionless particle size, y, and the dimensionless Kelvin factor, K, the latter depending on the nature of the substance of the particle and also on the temperature and pressure of the gas. The progression of y with tD is therefore specific when evaporation takes place into a vapour-free atmosphere.

Values of D and K have been calculated for five pure substances and are shown, with the basic properties required, in table 2; the data are for pure air at one atmosphere and 20°C, the mean free path being taken as 6×10^{-6} cm.

TABLE 2

substance	γ/dyn cm^{-1}	M	ρ/g cm^{-3}	∇/cm^2 s^{-1}	sat. v.p./Torr	n_0/g cm^{-3}	vapour molecules/cm^3	D/s^{-1}	
sodium chloride	124	58.5	2.165	0.1	3×10^{-25}	9.6×10^{-31}	10^{-8}	1.21×10^{-21}	0.0459
diethylhexyl-sebacate	30	426	0.92	0.024	1.49×10^{-9}	3.5×10^{-14}	5×10^{7}	2.54×10^{-5}	0.19
dibutyl-phthalate	36	278	1.048	0.031	3×10^{-5}	4.6×10^{-10}	10^{12}	0.38	0.131
sulphuric acid	55	98	1.84	0.09	7.1×10^{-5}	3.8×10^{-10}	2.3×10^{12}	0.52	0.04
water	72	18	1.00	0.26	17.54	1.72×10^{-5}	5.7×10^{12}	1.24×10^{5}	0.0178

Fig. 1 shows the decrease in size of aerosol particles with time when evaporating into a saturated atmosphere, according to eqn (2.9) and (3.1). The curves are common to all substances and all gases. By dividing the values on the scale of abscissa by DK, times in seconds for specific conditions are obtained.

In fig. 2 similar curves of particle radius against the dimensionless time, Dt in this case, are shown for evaporation into vapour-free gas. It turns out that the curve for a particular initial radius is not very sensitive to the value of K and is, therefore, only slightly dependent on the specific circumstances. Curves for $a_0 = 0.24\ \mu\text{m}$ are shown for $K = 0.04$, 0.13 and 0.19, corresponding to sulphuric acid, dibutylphthalate and diethylhexylsebacate, respectively, evaporating into dry air at 20°C and 1 atm. pressure. There is not a lot of difference between these curves. The big difference in absolute time comes about when the dimensionless times are divided by the values of D appropriate to the systems. For example, dibutylphthalate evaporates 15 000 times more rapidly than does diethylhexylsebacate and this substance, in turn, goes 2.1×10^{16} times faster than sodium chloride. The figures assume $\alpha \simeq 1$ in all cases.

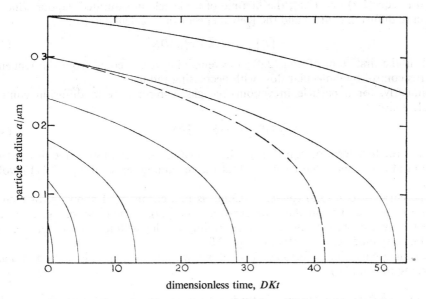

Fig. 1.—Evaporation of particles into vapour-saturated air at 20°C and 1 atm pressure. —, eqn (2.9) and (3.1); – – –, eqn (3.3) evaporation without allowance for free molecular flow. These curves are common to all substances.

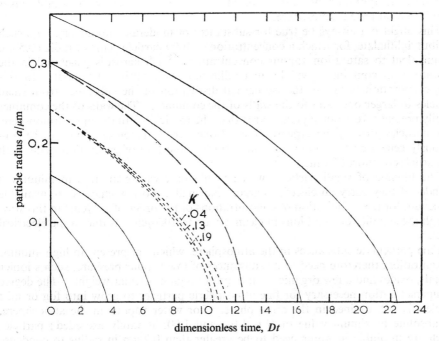

Fig. 2.—Evaporation of particles into vapour-free air at 20°C and 1 atm. pressure. —, eqn (2.11) and (3.2) $K = 0.1$; – - -, eqn (2.11) and (3.2) $K = 0.04, 0.13$ and 0.19; – – –, eqn (3.4) evaporation with diffusion control only.

From eqn (1.1) and (2.5), the lifetime of a particle in saturated vapour which is subject to diffusion control and the Kelvin effect can be calculated from

$$[t'_1]_{sat} = (y_0^3 - y_1^3)/3DK \tag{3.3}$$

which is the first term of eqn (2.9); the remaining terms come from the tendency towards control by molecular flow with decreasing radius.

Similarly, for a particle in vapour-free gas, subject only to diffusion control, eqn (1.1) gives

$$[t'_1]_{vf} = (y_0^2 - y_1^2)/2D \tag{3.4}$$

which is the first term of eqn (2.11). In this case, the Kelvin and free flow effects come in at about the same radius so that the remaining terms of eqn (2.11) involve both.

The curve of eqn (3.3) for $a_0 = 0.3 \, \mu m$ is plotted on fig. 1 showing, of course, a more rapid evaporation than the curve of eqn (2.9). The exact curve, using the correct Kelvin expression instead of expanding the logarithm, will lie between the two, but very much closer to that of eqn (2.9).

A similar curve for diffusion control alone, with $a_0 = 0.3 \, \mu m$, is plotted on fig. 2 according to eqn (3.4).

4. APPLICATION TO PARTICLES IN THE ATMOSPHERE

Saturation vapour concentration with substances such as diethylhexylsebacate, or sodium chloride, is equivalent to only a low concentration of small particles, $1000/cm^3$ of radius $0.03 \, \mu m$ for the former and $10^{-9}/cm^3$ of radius $0.0005 \, \mu m$ with the latter. Evaporation of aerosols of such substances, therefore, invariably takes place into a saturated atmosphere.

This might not always be true for substances of moderate vapour pressure, such as dibutylphthalate, for which a concentration of 1000 particles/cm^3 of radius $0.5 \, \mu m$ is equivalent to saturation vapour concentration. Such aerosols generated in the laboratory, in containers, will be in equilibrium with saturated vapour. In this case, evaporation results in the isothermal distillation of the substance from small particles to larger ones and to the walls of the container. The walls of the container usually present a very much greater area than the particles. In the open atmopshere, large particles grow at the expense of small ones which therefore require to be continuously generated to maintain a concentration, the rate of generation being high for particles of short lifetime.

The lifetime of small particles which would otherwise evaporate in minutes is extended if they carry an electric charge. Normally, too few charges are available to account for the stabilisation of concentrations of the order of $10^6/cm^3$ in this way, though the stability of small ions in clean air, up to $1000/cm^3$, is due to the electrical effect.

Fine particulate substances in the atmosphere, which are present in high anumbe concentration, therefore need to be substances of low vapour pressure, such s ionicr crystals, oxides and a few organic compounds of high molecular weight. The degree of supersaturation necessary for fine atmospheric particles to grow into fog or mist droplets is not attained in the atmosphere. For water vapour in the atmoshpere, the absolute maximum value of S is 1.01, and 1.003 is rarely exceeded; particles which are insoluble in water need to be greater than $0.2 \, \mu m$ in radius to condense growing water droplets and soluble particles must be greater than $0.06 \, \mu m$ radius. Electric charge is of no significance. The life-times of these particles in dry air can be calculated by the equations given above. The possible constituents of condensation nuclei are limited by the evaporating tendency.

[1] N. Frössling, *Gerlands Beitr. z. Geophys.*, 1938, **52**, 170.
[2] N. Fuchs, *Phys, Z. Sowjetunion*, 1934, **6** (3), 224.
[3] P. G. Wright, *Disc. Faraday Soc.*, 1960, **30**, 100.
[4] N. A. Fuchs and A. G. Sutugin, *Topics in Current Aerosol Research*, Ed. G. M. Hidy and J. R. Brock. (Pergamon Press, Oxford, 1971). See *High Dispersed Aerosols*, chap. 3.2, p. 31.
[5] N. A. Fuchs, *Evaporation and Droplet Growth in Gaseous Media* (Pergamon Press, Oxford, 1959), chap. 1.6, p. 11.

GENERAL DISCUSSION

Dr. E. R. Buckle (*University of Sheffield*) said: In introducing his paper Dunning compared the experimental nucleation rates J_{exp} for water condensation with those predicted by the so-called " classical " theory, J_{theor}, such that by and large $J_{exp}/J_{theor} \sim 10^3$. What confidence can be placed on the actual values given for J_{exp} by the various workers?

Dr. W. J. Dunning (*Bristol University*) said: Prof. J. Clumpner (now at the American University, Beirut) has considered all the possible errors (including the so-called " influence coefficients " of gas dynamics) which may affect the evaluation of J_{exp} from the Yale nozzle experiments. His conclusions have not yet been published, but I understand that for the best work, J_{exp} is known to within a factor of 10 and there is no problem in achieving a factor of 10^2. Clearly the precision is adequate to discriminate between theories which predict values of J which differ by factors of 10^{12}-10^{17}.

Dr. C. S. Kiang (*Clark College, Atlanta, Ga.*) said : Would Dunning comment on the present state of his eqn (6)?

Dr. W. J. Dunning (*Bristol University*) said: In reply to Kiang's question of the present status of my eqn (6), experimenters find it useful to compare their results with classical theory (my eqn (6)) by using a factor Γ_{exp} to match this theory with their experimental results

$$J_{exp} = \Gamma_{exp} \cdot J_{class}.$$

In the same way, it is useful to compare the rates of nucleation J_{theor} predicted by the different theories

$$J_{theor} = \Gamma_{theor} \cdot J_{class}.$$

For example, Lothe and Pound's [1] theory predicts $\Gamma_{L-P} \sim 10^{17}$, and my theory [2] predicts $\Gamma_D \sim 10^4$ for water vapour condensation.

The careful work of Wegener, Clumpner and Wu [3] on the nucleation and growth of ethanol drops in supersonic flow yielded values of Γ_{exp} at different stations x along the nozzle (fig. 1). Also illustrated in the figure are the corresponding values of Γ_{LP} and Γ_D; if the classical theory applied, Γ_{exp} would run along the x axis. The value of Γ_{LP} at the onset point is about 10^{17}, the value of Γ_D at this point is about 10^5, matching the experimental value of Γ_{exp} closely. Thus, the Lothe–Pound theory predicts nucleation rates which are far too high ; classical theory predicts rates which are rather low (10^{-5}). In these ethanol experiments the following conditions are favourable. The ethanol was carefully purified, the mass-fraction of water vapour in the air was less than 10^{-6}. The critical nuclei are comparitively large, containing 15-20 molecules. The condensation takes place above the triple point so that the nuclei are almost certain to be liquid.

In the presence of a carrier gas (e.g., air), the nuclei and droplets grow under

[1] Lothe and Pound, *J. Chem. Phys.*, 1962, **36**, 2080.
[2] Dunning, *Adsorption et Croissance Cristalline* (Coll. Int. C.N.R.S. no. 152, Paris), 1965.
[3] Wegener, Clumpner and Wu, *Phys. Fluids*, 1972, **15**, 1869.

isothermal conditions; for pure vapour (e.g., steam) the nuclei and droplets are at a higher temperature than the vapour and nucleation proceeds more slowly. In fig. 2,* the values, uniformly calculated, of Γ_{exp} for ethanol, water and benzene are shown plotted against the mass-fraction ω_0 of vapour. For the two latter substances, there is more uncertainty about the thermodynamic state of the nuclei and the results for both solid and liquid states are shown; in each case the lower of the pairs is to be preferred for kinetic reasons. Barschdorff, Dunning, Wu and Wegener have recalculated all experimental results for pure steam and these are all in the range of the hatching at log $\omega_0 = 0$. These results give $10^{-2} < \Gamma_{exp} < 10^6$ to be compared with $\Gamma = 1$ if the classical theory held, and with $\Gamma_{LP} \sim 10^{17}$ and $\Gamma_D \sim 10^4$.

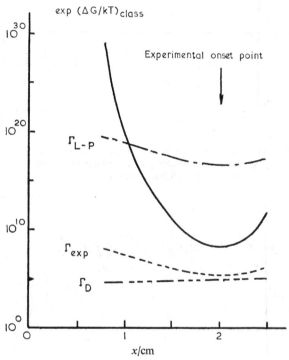

FIG. 1.—Nucleation of ethanol in air. Showing the dependence of Γ_{exp}, Γ_{LP}, Γ_D on x, the station, after Wegener, Clumpner and Wu, ref. (3)).

Using a shock tube, Barschdorff * (unpublished) has investigated the effect of various carrier gases at various mass-fractions on the nucleation rate for water vapour and his results are illustrated in fig. 3; here, $J_{exp}/J_{theor} \equiv \Gamma_{exp}$ is plotted against ω_0 and we find $10^{-2} < \Gamma_{exp} < 10^3$. Investigations on other materials have not been so intensive. Pure nitrogen gives $\Gamma_{exp} \sim 10^{-6}$. On the other hand, experiments on freon and chloroform have given results close to values predicted by the Lothe–Pound theory.

* I wish to thank Prof. Wegener and Dr. Barschdorff for allowing me to quote their unpublished results.

[4] Dawson, Wilson, Hill and Russell, *J. Chem. Phys.*, 1969, **51**, 5389.

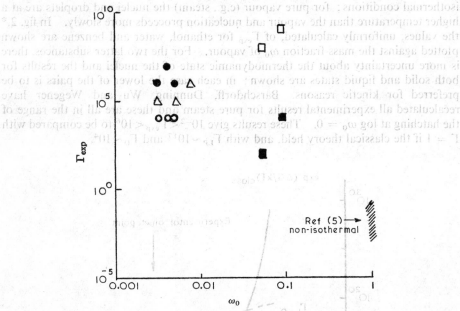

FIG. 2.—Nucleation of ethanol, water and benzene. Γ_{exp} as a function of the mass-fraction ω_0 of the substance in air (courtesy of Prof. P. Wegener). $\triangle$, Ethanol; $\bigcirc$, $\bullet$, H_2O; $\square$, $\blacksquare$, benzene; open symbols, liquid; solid symbols, crystal.

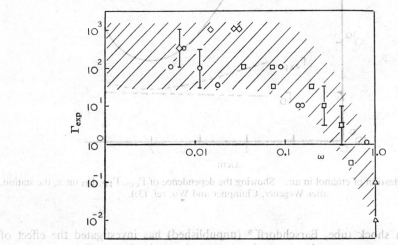

FIG. 3.—Nucleation of H_2O. Γ_{exp} as a function of ω_0 for various carrier gases. $\triangle$, Steam; $\bigcirc$, H_2O in argon; $\square$, H_2O in helium; $\diamondsuit$, moist air.

It must be remembered that " binary " and " hetero-molecular " nucleation theory as discussed by Kiang and Stauffer in this Discussion, indicates that impurities in the substance examined would, if they were effective always tend to increase the value of Γ_{exp}.

Prof. M. Kerker (*Clarkson Coll. Techn., Potsdam*) said: I would ask Dunning, what can be said about the form of the size distribution prior to the onset of coagulation? We have assumed that the aerosols, having a somewhat narrow size distribution, formed by condensation upon heterogeneous nuclei, could be represented by a logarithmic distribution.

Dr. W. J. Dunning (*Bristol University*) said: In reply to Kerker, the mathematical form of the classical nucleation rate equation seems to be accepted, although the values of some of the parameters have been subject to controversy. In a well-defined experiment, it is possible to calculate the rates of nucleation and the rates of growth and evaporation of all classes of particles at all stages of the collapse of the supersaturation. Thus the form of the size distribution is ascertainable under such conditions. It is necessary to check by calculation the progress of coagulation since, under certain circumstances, coagulation may become significant before growth is effectively complete.

I have no experience of the Kerker type of aerosol generator and I cannot judge how well defined the thermodynamic variables are. It may be possible to idealize it and calculate the aerosol size distribution to be expected. In this, one could assume that, Volmer's theory of heterogeneous nucleation was valid and that an appropriate rate of growth was applicable and at least determine the form of the size distribution thus predicted. Until such studies are made, it is not possible to assess whether the logarithmic distribution closely approximates the experimental distribution or not.

Dr. E. R. Buckle (*Sheffield University*) (*communicated*): The size distribution in a spontaneously condensed aerosol will adjust by growth and evaporation towards the stationary form of eqn (1.3) of my paper, which resembles Volmer's distribution (eqn (1.18)). If the conditions change, the system will approach a new distribution of similar form. The distribution will be cut off at a size in the region of the critical size in the early stages but eventually will extend to larger sizes as the result of coagulation. In seeded condensation it may happen that the growing centres are too large at the outset for them to qualify as labile gaseous species, and the distributions of my paper would not apply.

Prof. C. S. Kiang and **Dr. D. Stauffer** (*Clark College, Atlanta, Ga.*) said: Would Dunning give his opinion of the reason why some materials obey classical nucleation theory and some do not. Theoretically, the capillarity approximation using the bulk surface tension for small droplets may be inaccurate. Computer simulations of small droplets (" micro-crystalline calculations ") do not need such an approximation. Calculations of this type by Burton [1] explain from *one* model most of the observed deviations from and agreements with the classical nucleation theory. His comparison with classical theory depends on the temperature and the supersaturation, which are different for different experiments. (In another preprint, Burton proves convincingly the presence of a Lothe–Pound translation–rotation term in such microcrystalline calculations based on vibration frequencies and binding energies of the molecules. This does not yet solve the question whether the capillarity approximation requires, too, a Lothe–Pound correction since it might already be included in the effective surface tension.)

Another (simpler but so far less successful) approach is to make the capillarity approximation, to neglect the Lothe–Pound factor, but to use a microscopic droplet surface tension different from the measured bulk surface tension. The smaller the

---

[1] J. J. Burton, *Acta Met.*, to be published.

droplet surface tension is compared to the measured bulk surface tension, the higher should the nucleation rate be compared with classical theory. We determined this " microscopic " surface tension from the two methods,[1] (density)/(critical density) and from $1-PV/RT$. We found, for H_2O, CH_3OH, and C_2H_5OH, good agreement of these microscopic surface tensions with the bulk surface tension. (Experimentally, classical nucleation theory works here.) For NH_3, C_6H_6, $CHCl_3$, and $CFCl_3$, the microscopic surface tensions were much lower than the bulk surface tension (classical nucleation rates are too low here). But unfortunately, for hexane, heptane, octane, we also found lower microscopic surface tensions although classical theory works here.

Experimentally, the possibility cannot be excluded that the water impurities in NH_3 lowered the supersaturation necessary for nucleation.[2] Our paper on hetero-molecular nucleation indicates that such effects are quite strong for $H_2O + H_2SO_4$.

Dr. W. J. Dunning (*Bristol University*) said: In reply to the question of Kiang and Stauffer, all possibilities should be considered.

With regard to Stauffer's report on calculations by Burton, if we imagine a bulk crystal containing $n = km$ particles to be subdivided into m crystalline nuclei each containing k particles and if ε_k° is the specific surface energy and O_k the surface area of a nucleus, the replacement factor q_{rep} will be [3]

$$q_{rep} = (\varepsilon_k^\circ - \sigma_\infty)O_k + \sum_{j=1}^{3k-6} (\phi_j + \eta_j) - \frac{1}{m} \sum_{i=1}^{3n-6} (f_i + \varepsilon_i).$$

In this, σ_∞ is the surface tension of the bulk crystal, ε_i and η_i are the zero-point energies of the ith and jth normal modes of vibration in the nucleus and in the bulk crystal respectively, and f_i and ϕ_j are their free energies, given by

$$\phi_j = -kT \log \sum_{n_i \geqslant 0} \exp\left(-hu_j n_j/kT\right)$$

with a similar expression for f_i.

The calculation of q_{rep} thus requires a precise evaluation of ε_k° and the frequencies μ_j of the normal modes in the nucleus and in the bulk crystal.

Dr. E. R. Buckle (*University of Sheffield*) said: The contention in the original paper of Lothe and Pound (ref. (20) of Dunning's paper) was that the Volmer theory of nucleation is in error in taking no account of the natural chaotic motion of the growing nuclei in the parent phase. I know of no reason for supposing that it was in Volmer's mind that the embryonic particles were motionless, so that it is to be presumed that the particle distribution in his treatment (eqn (1.18) of my paper) was intended to be one of equilibrium involving all thermally accessible energy levels in the various degrees of freedom.

In the kinetic formulation of the problem given in ref. (1) of my paper, the terms W_g' and W_g'' of Volmer's theory are given their molecular interpretations for vapour condensation. The collision terms for the motion of the gaseous clusters appear in the quantity ζ_g, the interfacial free enthalpy. As stated in my paper, $\zeta_g = W_g'$, so that the same terms are contained in γO_g of Volmer's formula. The Brownian motion is therefore taken into the surface tension term, and the error in Volmer's formulation of the reversible work of nucleus formation will reside in the use of a single value of

[1] *J. Atm. Sci.*, 1972, **28**, 1222: Appendix B.

[2] see *J. Chem. Phys.*, 1972, **51**, 5380, in particular, p. 5387.

[3] W. J. Dunning in *Nucleation*, ed. A. C. Zettlemoyer (Marcel Dekker, New York, 1969), p. 35.

surface tension for all cluster sizes. As a likely source of error, this has long been appreciated, and the conclusion is that there is no additional source of error due to the omission of thermal motion terms. It is incorrect to add free enthalpy terms for this motion to W_g as given by Volmer.

Dr. W. J. Dunning (*Bristol University*) said : We all recognize the great achievements of Volmer, but we should not, with hindsight, attempt to read into his work more than is there. For example, on p. 97 of his book,[1] Volmer describes a method due to Gibbs for determining the work of formation of a nucleus of radius r_K. One step in this process involves some of the bulk liquid, confined in a cylinder by a piston, being extruded as a droplet through a small orific in the cylinder wall. The work done in forcing out the droplet is given as

$$\int_0^{r_K} (2\sigma/r)4\pi r^2 \, \mathrm{d}r = 4\pi r_K^2 \sigma.$$

This seems to imply that Volmer considered σ, the surface tension, to be independent of the radius which it would not be if the Brownian motion is taken into the surface tension term. It seems that both Volmer and Gibbs were tacitly assuming that the droplet stands still on the orifice. In fact, the still-attached droplet will be bobbing about on the orifice in Brownian motion and at some stage must be liberated to dance away into the vapour space.

The contributions of Kuhrt,[2] Lothe and Pound,[3] Dunning[4] and others analyze the consequences of this last stage of liberation. There is a large measure of common agreement, but where they differ is in their assessment of the magnitude of the so-called replacement factor.[5]

Prof. C. S. Kiang (*Clark College, Atlanta, Ga.*) said: Dunning mentioned various nucleation processes and their roles in his introductory remarks. From our recent studies, we believe that the heteromolecular nucleation (homogeneous or heterogeneous) process should be included as one of the most important nucleation processes for the fogs and smokes formation in the earth's atmosphere. For relative humidity less than 100 %, this nucleation process seems to be the only nucleation mechanism with water in the atmosphere. Most of the primary chemical constituents in the atmosphere do not have low vapour pressures and their atmospheric concentrations are measured in p.p.m. or p.p.b. and are not sufficient to allow nucleation in the gas phase. However, by chemical reactions or radiation or other energy input, secondary products with low volatility can be formed and these reactants may mix with water and undergo heteromolecular nucleation to form new aerosol. For example, at room temperature, SO_2 has vapour pressure around 4 atm. In the presence of oxidants (e.g., $NO_2 + h\nu \rightarrow NO + O$, $SO_2 + O \rightarrow SO_3$, $SO_3 + H_2O \rightarrow H_2SO_4$), H_2SO_4 can be formed. With only 10^{-6} Torr vapour pressure, $H_2SO_4 + H_2O$ will undergo the heteromolecular nucleation to form aqueous sulphuric acid aerosol. After reacting with NH_3, $(NH_4)_2SO_4$ may be formed as stated by Dunning.

[1] M. Volmer, *Kinetik der Phasenbildung* (Steinkopff, Dresden 1939).
[2] F. Kuhrt, *Z. Physik*, 1952, **131**, 185, 205.
[3] J. Lothe and G. M. Pound, *J. Chem. Phys.*, 1962, **36**, 2080.
[4] W. J. Dunning in *Chemistry of the Solid State*, ed. W. E. Garner (Butterworths, 1955), p. 159 ; *Adsorption et Croissance Cristalline* (Coll. Int. C.N.R.S., Paris, 1965), p. 369.
[5] see W. J. Dunning *Nucleation*, ed. A. C. Zettlemoyer (Marcel Dekker Inc., New York, 1969), pp. 37-47.

Dr. E. R. Buckle (*Sheffield University*) said: The purpose of my paper is to show that on simple kinetic grounds a particle in a volatile aerosol that is homogeneous and isothermal must grow or evaporate in a way that is dictated by the properties of the whole particulate system. The role of coagulation in particle growth is certainly paramount at low temperatures in very dense clouds of ultra-fine particles although for condensation aerosols the centres of coagulation are particles formed during the previous volatile stage.

The properties J, ζ that are characteristic of the particle size distribution are found in the growth and evaporation equations of a particle. For instance, in eqn (2.15), which gives the net rate of increase of material in a particle, the term $\Delta\zeta_{g+1}$ reflects the joint influence of all the particles because its value is related to the size distribution at equilibrium. Now although $\Delta\zeta_{g+1}$ tends to zero for very large clusters the ratio f_{g+1}/f_g is still dependent on J if the processes in the aerosol are occurring naturally. Theoretically, therefore, the communal effects of the particles are unavoidable.

Dr. W. J. Dunning (*Bristol University*) said: Referring to eqn (1)-(5) of Buckle's paper, is it possible to assert at this stage of his argument that there is a limiting value of ω_g as $g \rightarrow \infty$? If the clusters are bizarre in form, how the equilibrium between one such monster and another monster behaves as the monsters increase in size can, at present, only be conjectured. At the other extreme, if the clusters were perfect crystals, the equilibrium quotients would oscillate.

Dr. E. R. Buckle (*Sheffield University*) said: In reply to Dunning, if by " monsters " is meant thread-like or branching clusters, especially ones without a centre of symmetry, I would expect them to have little chance of formation by homogeneous processes under the moderate conditions assumed in my paper. They are therefore unlikely to contribute to the formation of stationary states. To prove this it would be necessary to extend the concepts of internal energy fluctuations to include such species. Gaseous ions might interfere in the condensation of heteropolar substances like water to produce elongated structures. For this to have a sensible effect on the condensation process there would have to be very many ions and the gas would be properly regarded as a mixture.

Very large clusters are without influence kinetically and I do not visualize the growth of clusters as ever involving the perfect crystalline state. The size at which a pure particle, with its inherent structural imperfections, is able to assume crystallinity is unknown but it could well be too great for it to have any importance as a rate-determining factor in condensation.

Such considerations are important because they bear on a well-known dilemma of " classical " nucleation theory. In the interpretation of condensation by Volmer theory there is always this element of uncertainty about the physical state of the nucleus : is it solid or liquid? The uncertainty is embarrassing because macroscopically the surface tension has different values for these states and a decision has to be made as to which to use in the theoretical formula. I doubt whether this difference is really meaningful in nucleation.

To overcome this difficulty a theoretical approach is required in which the structures and properties of the condensing particles are related to those of the molecules composing them. As a test of the usefulness of such a theory one would look for its ability to predict the rates of production of the particles and to relate these to measureable physical properties of the system during condensation. A primitive attempt at such a theory was given in ref. (1) of my paper, and Dr. A. A. Pouring and I have been using it in some calculations that should show, among other things, how sensitive the predictions of the path of condensation are to the molecular details. Whether the comparison of computed and measured values of experimental variables like pressure and temperature will provide a useful check on the adequacy of the cluster models also remains to be seen.

Dr. D. Stauffer (*Clark College, Atlanta, Ga.*) said: Buckle's eqn (1.9) shows that one can calculate some cluster properties from measured (pressure, density, temperature) relations (equation of state). Fisher's droplet model [1] gives good agreement with the measured equation of state both near the liquid-gas critical point [2] and at lower temperatures.[3] It also agrees with direct evaluations of cluster concentrations in a two-dimensional model.[4] Does Buckle's approach give an alternative droplet model which also can be tested using the measured equation of state? This would be very valuable as a replacement for the classical nucleation theory. I would also ask what is the relation between his eqn (2.15) and the "classical" approach (e.g. eqn (10) of Dunham).[5]

Dr. E. R. Buckle (*Sheffield University*) said: In reply to Kiang and Stauffer, I am not optimistic about making comparisons of experimental PV isothermals with theoretical cluster distributions (e.g., my eqn (1.3) and (1.9)) to obtain the properties of the clusters. Except at high pressures, for which the cluster models are not intended, or at the very high supersaturations which build up in a fast expansion, the concentrations of clusters fall too rapidly with size. The dependence of the distribution on the external variables should be more apparent experimentally as the system passes through the condensation threshold. During this stage the Volmer minimum in c_g and the relaxation hump that follows it move into the region of small cluster sizes and then back out again. The time available for observation is so short that measurements with high time-resolution are called for. It seems that the measurements should aim to resolve the sizes also if cluster properties are to be investigated. The results of methods, such as bulk scattering of light, which give only a mean particle size over a finite time interval would be very difficult to relate to such properties because of the complex form of the relaxing size distribution (the curve of c_g against g resembles in shape a PV isotherm of van der Waals at sub-critical temperatures).

In the method of Volmer the clusters in an equilibrium store are assumed to grow by molecular collisions and evaporation is ignored. The flux condensation is assumed to be that of eqn (2.12), and is therefore independent of cluster size. Becker and Doering's modification was to consider also evaporation but again there was no allowance for the possibility that the chance of capture or expulsion of molecules might vary with the size of particle. The theory of my paper shows that the introduction of size-dependent accommodation coefficients leads to the conclusion that the net flux on an aerosol particle is dependent on the size distribution and cannot be calculated from the laws for a macroscopic surface.

Dr. W. J. Dunning (*Bristol University*) said: It seems that the limiting process in Buckle's eqn (1.5) is not general but ancitipates a Volmer-like model in which the clusters are considered to be compact.

[1] *Physics*, 1967, **3**, 255.
[2] *Z. Phys.*, 1970, **235**, 130.
[3] *Phys. Letters*, 1972, **40A**, 345.
[4] *Phys. Rev.*, 1972, **B6**, 2777; also *J. Stat. Phys.*, 1972, **6**, 49.
[5] *J. Rec. Atm.*, 1966, **2**, 331.

Dr. E. R. Buckle (*University of Sheffield*) said : In a treatment of this kind there is one respect in which the clusters must be regarded as compact. The stepwise processes $A_{g-1}+A_1 = A_g$, are only amenable to a simple collision theory if the cluster lifetimes are long in comparison with the collision time. High vapour densities are excluded by this, and there is therefore some meaning in concepts such as the cluster-gas interface and the surface tension. It is a point of my paper that if clusters are to exist homogeneously at up to indefinitely large sizes the quantity ζ_g must obey the conditions $\zeta_g > 0$, $\Delta\zeta_g/\Delta g = 0$ in the limit as $g \to \infty$. But this requires $\omega_g \to \omega_\infty$ as $g \to \infty$ where ω_g approaches the constant ω_∞ from below. These conditions are satisfied if one makes the reasonable assumption that, in a growing cluster of iso-tropically bound atoms, the nearest-neighbour coordination number λ_g rises to a limit λ_∞. This represents the ordering process that accompanies the differentiation of the condensed phase.

With regard to the more diffuse entities, only at high vapour densities near the critical point would there be tenuous regions of high local density in significant concentrations. Under such conditions, however, long-range density fluctuations are already a characteristic of the *saturated* vapour and the concepts of nucleation theory are no longer useful.

Prof. M. Kerker (*Clarkson Coll. Techn., Potsdam*) said: With regard to the paper by Buckle, in our experiments on the formation of dibutylphthalate aerosol by cooling a mixture of vapour and NaCl particles (radii ranging from 30 to 100 Å), we observed that only a small fraction of the particles served as condensation nuclei.[1] Also, this number depended strongly upon the rate of cooling ; there were more aerosol particles of smaller average size when the cooling rate was greater. We assumed this was controlled by the rate at which the most effective classes of nuclei could relieve the rapidly increasing supersaturation. Is this observation pertinent to the dynamic processes which Buckle describes in homogeneous nucleation?

Dr. E. R. Buckle (*Sheffield University*) said: In reply to Kerker, if the particles coagulate while still at temperatures at which they are volatile it confirms that their sizes and individual properties are predetermined by the seed and are not influenced by the kinetic factors that determine size distributions in spontaneously-condensed aerosols. Yet the effect predicted for such an aerosol, that the rate of growth of a particle gets slower as its size increases, would lead to what Kerker has observed on changing the cooling rate : the faster the cooling of the vapour, the smaller and more numerous the particles become.

I believe this is purely coincidental, and the effects are characteristic of hetero-geneous nucleation. In experiments on the seeding of water from moist air expanded in the wind tunnel [2] the effectiveness of seed was greatest at low flow rates (i.e., slow cooling) and high humidities. Kerker describes how he makes allowance for the extra time particles have for coagulation if they are moving near the condenser wall. There may also be a connexion between the activity of the NaCl particles as condensa-tion nuclei and their position and speed relative to the wall. The proportion of seed particles that are effective as condensation centres would be expected to be sensitive to the radial velocity and temperature gradients, and therefore to the flow speed. Consequently I suspect the reason for what was observed is the non-uniform condi-tions.

[1] G. N. Nicholson and M. Kerker, *J. Colloid Interface Sci.*, 1973, **43**, 246.
[2] E. R. Buckle and A. A. Pouring, *Nature*, 1965, **208**, 367.

Dr. W. J. Dunning (*Bristol University*) said: With regard to Kiang's paper, how large do the droplets grow before they come to equilibrium with the reduced relative humidity and reduced activity? The authors have pointed out many possible sources of error and complication. Is the activity of, say, sulphuric acid derived from the concentration of sulphuric acid in the vapour phase? Would not this be a composite term including not only H_2SO_4 molecules but other species such as H_3OHSO_4?

It is assumed that the condition of a nucleus of aqueous sulphuric acid is the same as that of a random sample in the bulk solution. However, for bulk solutions, some of the sulphuric acid will be dissociated into ions. In nuclei containing, say, 5 sulphuric acid molecules and perhaps 30 water molecules, such dissociation will be inhibited since some of the resultant electrostatic field will stray outside the nucleus where the dielectric constant is low (~ 1). Further, the ions will tend to avoid approaching the surface of the nucleus and to occupy only the middle; this will affect the entropy of mixing. Such points may need consideration when the theory is developed further.

Dr. R. A. Cox (*AERE, Harwell*) said: With regard to the heteromolecular nucleation of $H_2SO_4 + H_2O$ vapour mixtures discussed in the paper by Kiang and Stauffer, a simple experimental test of the validity of the Flood–Neumann–Doering–Reiss–Doyle theory was suggested by Doyle.[1] His calculations indicated that appreciable nucleation rates would occur at sulphuric acid vapour activities of 10^{-2}-10^{-3} in air at 50 % relative humidity (RH; 25°C). This corresponded to the equilibrium vapour phase activity above an aqueous solution of H_2SO_4 of composition $\simeq 75$ % wt/wt H_2SO_4. Thus a sulphuric acid solution of this composition should fume in air at 50 % RH.

We have measured the concentration of condensation nucleii (CN) in an air-stream passing over concentrated H_2SO_4 solutions of various compositions using a Pollack CN counter. At 72 % wt/wt, no CN were detected even at 70 % RH. With 77 % wt/wt H_2SO_4, particles (300-600 cm^{-3}) were detected at 70 % RH, and at 83 % wt/wt the particle counts at 70 % and 5 % RH were 3×10^5 and 10^4 cm^{-3} respectively.

These experiments are only semi-quantitative since (*a*), the CN counter does not measure the number of nucleating embryos but only the number of particles which grow to sufficient size to register in the CN counter ($\gtrsim 25$ Å). Losses of particles of this size (and smaller) by diffusion to the containing walls will be appreciable. Also (*b*), equilibrium conditions of H_2SO_4 and H_2O vapour were not attained above the liquid surface and the departure from equilibrium cannot be assessed easily. Nevertheless, these results do indicate that the theoretical predictions are not grossly in error and that heteromolecular nucleation in $H_2SO_4 + H_2O$ mixtures can occur at an appreciable rate at extremely low partial pressures of H_2SO_4 vapour (i.e., approximately 10^{-9}-10^{-8} Torr at 50 % RH).

Prof. C. S. Kiang and **Dr. D. Stauffer** (*Clark College, Atlanta*) said: In reply to Dunning, 1-6 Å is a typical radius of the "critical" droplets at the saddle point. After this heteromolecular nucleation, the droplets grow until the H_2SO_4 gas is (nearly) exhausted, which happen for droplet sizes of typically 10-100 Å (see ref. (15) for details).

The H_2SO_4 activity was determined by thermodynamic relations and specific heat measurements (Giauque *et al.*, ref. (6)); the evaluation assumes the presence of only two gaseous species. We do not know the magnitude of the error involved in this approximation. In addition to these dissociation effects, which may differ in small

[1] *J. Chem. Phys.*, 1961, **35**, 795.

droplets from bulk phase dissociation effects, one also expects (ref. (2)) an enrichment of one phase near the droplet surface. For small droplets, the Gibbs adsorption equation describing this surface enrichment can be seriously wrong, in particular if applied to $H_2O + C_2H_5OH$ heteromolecular nucleation. Computer simulations of small liquid droplets (Monte Carlo, molecular dynamics, etc.) might eventually answer these questions; we cannot.

In reply to Cox, for a 72 wt % solution, the H_2SO_4 activity is 0.0007, for 77 % it is 0.0044, and for 83 % it is 0.04 according to Giauque et al. (ref. (6)).

Dr. D. Stauffer (*Clark College, Atlanta, Ga.*) said: The vapour pressure of 10^{-4} Torr for H_2SO_4 was questioned by Doyle,[1] who prefers 10^{-6} Torr; which is the better value?

Dr. C. N. Davies (*University of Essex*) said: I agree with Stauffer that there is doubt about the partial pressure of H_2SO_4 above aqueous solutions. It is possible that it could be measured by a technique similar to that described by Frostling.[1] Droplets as large as 2 μm diam. can be kept in suspension, with a greatly reduced loss by sedimentation, in a cylindrical chamber which is continuously rotated. By holding the atmosphere in the chamber at a constant relative humidity and sampling the aerosol over a long period it might be possible to measure the rate of evaporation of H_2SO_4 as a function of the ambient humidity.

Dr. R. G. Picknett (*Chem. Defence Est., Porton Down*) said: I would raise two points about the paper by Davies. The first concerns the evaporation coefficient, which must have a value near to unity if the interpolation formula, eqn (1.13), is to be applicable. Measurements of this parameter are sparse, but a value for water of only 0.04 has been reported, and so eqn (1.13) must be employed with caution. Extensive calculations of droplet evaporation have been made by N. L. Cross and myself in which we find that a 70 % difference in droplet lifetime is obtained when evaporation coefficients of 0.04 and 1.0 are used. This is for drops of 5 μm radius. My second point concerns the effect of self-cooling on the evaporation rate, which Davies correctly states is negligible for the substances other than water in table 2. This effect has also been investigated in the calculations made by N. L. Cross and myself. It is most important for droplet evaporation in vapour-free surroundings, and under these conditions it rapidly becomes significant as the vapour pressure increases above 0.1 mbar. If we take a vapour pressure of 1 mbar, 10 times as large, then a 5 μm radius droplet of a typical organic liquid will have the surface temperature depressed by about 0.3°C, i.e., sufficient to cause a material reduction in the rate of evaporation.

Dr. C. N. Davies (*University of Essex*) said: In reply to Picknett, it is difficult to measure the evaporation coefficient, α. Bradley et al.[2] gave 0.28 for di-n-butyl phthalate and 0.35 for butyl stearate droplets in air but it was subsequently decided that $\alpha \approx 1$ for di-n-butyl phthalate in air, hydrogen and freon,[3] for straight chain hydrocarbons in air,[4] and for branched-chain hydrocarbons and a straight-chain fluorocarbon in air.[5] For rhombic sulphur it was found that $\alpha = 0.73$.[6]

[1] J. Aerosol Sci., 1970, **1**, 341; and 1973, in press.
[2] R. S. Bradley, M. G. Evans and R. W. Whytlaw Gray, Proc. Roy. Soc. A, 1946, **186**, 368.
[3] J. Birks and R. S. Bradley, ibid., 1949, **198**, 226.
[4] R. S. Bradley and A. D. Shellard, ibid., 1949, **198**, 239.
[5] R. S. Bradley and G. C. S. Waghorn, ibid., 1951, **206**, 65.
[6] R. S. Bradley, ibid., 1951, **205**, 553.

Alty and Mackay [1] concluded that thermal accommodation of water vapour molecules striking a water surface was achieved but that the rate of re-evaporation of condensing molecules was high at vapour equilibrium so that the rate of evaporation of water molecules from the liquid phase was only 0.034–0.036 of the rate of impact from saturated vapour, according to kinetic theory. However, Jamieson,[2] using a dynamic technique, found α to be at least 10 times greater than this low value.

There has thus been a tendency for α for liquids to increase as experimental techniques improved and, recently, Jer Ru Maa,[3] using a jet tensimeter, has obtained results which lead him to conclude that $\alpha = 1$ for all liquids. Further references are given in table 1.8 of A. G. Amelin's book *Theory of Fog Condensation* (Moscow, 1972). Picknett's remarks on evaporation are interesting. For water, the temperature of a drop, regardless of its size, is equal to that of the ventilated wet bulb thermometer.

Prof. E. Rosner (*Yale University*) said: While the evaporation (or condensation) coefficient α for the *liquids* of interest to Davies may indeed be close enough to unity to ensure the utility of eqn (1.12), this assumption would certainly fail for the evaporation (or growth) of *crystalline* aerosols, especially when the dominant vapour species do not exist as structural entities in the condensed phase.[4] For example, low and sharply temperature dependent α-values have been measured for the individual faces of crystalline solids which (i) *dissociate* upon sublimation (e.g., AlN(s), Al$_2$O$_3$(s), NH$_4$Cl(s)), or (ii) whose vapours are *associated* (As(s) and P(s), giving tetramers in the vapour phase). Also of interest in this connection is the fact that for such solids melting is expected to be accompanied by a discontinuous increase ("jump") in α (observed [5] for the sublimation of polycrystalline Al$_2$O$_3$(s), Ga$_2$O$_3$(s) and 3Al$_2$O$_3$-2SiO$_2$(s)). Since this is probably a general phenomenon holding for phase changes even below the equilibrium transition temperature, it is interesting to consider its consequences for the relative evaporation (or growth) of aerosols for which the condensed phase may be either crystalline or amorphous. In the usual case for which $\Delta H_{\text{sublim}} > \Delta H_{\text{vap}}$, both high vapour pressure and high α would combine to cause rapid gasification of a liquid aerosol compared to its crystalline counterpart at the same surface temperature. For condensational growth from the vapour, however, these effects would oppose one another, causing loss disparity in condensation rates more than in gasification rates. Finally, since compact crystalline *aggregates* appear to be present (at least as intermediates) during the production of inorganic oxide aerosols in flames we should note that prior to complete sintering such an aggregate (i) would be characterized by an effective α higher than that corresponding to the surfaces of its crystalline constituent "primary" particles (owing to multiple vapour molecule/solid encounters during escape of condensation from/in the "labyrinth"); (ii) can lose or gain mass without a corresponding change in the *outer* dimensions of the aggregate (owing to a change in overall aggregate density, ρ).

Dr. C. N. Davies (*University of Essex*) said: Rosner had made some important points. However, the association of vapour molecules to form, e.g., tetramers will

[1] T. Alty and C. A. Mackay, *ibid.*, 1935, **149**, 104.
[2] D. T. Jamieson, *Nature*, 1964, **202**, 583.
[3] Jer Ru Maa, *Ind. Eng. Chem. Fund.*, 1967, **6**, 504; 1970, **8**, 564; 1970, **9**, 283.
[4] This has been reviewed by G. A. Somorjai and J. E. Lester in *Progress in Solid State Chemistry*, H. Reiss, ed. (Pergamon Press, Oxford, 1967), Vol. 4, pp. 1-52.
[5] R. P. Burns, J. Jason and M. G. Inghram, *J. Chem. Phys.*, 1964, **40**, 2739; see also R. P. Burns, *Ph.D. Dissertation* (Dept. Physics, Univ. Chicago, 1965).

reduce the kinetic impact rate by $\frac{1}{8}$ so that a corresponding reduction in the rate of vaporization occurs, quite apart from any effect due to α. If the vapour is dissociated, the impact rates of each type will usually differ so that the values of α need to adjust themselves accordingly.

Prof. M. Kerker (*Clarson Coll. Techn., Potsdam*) said: I would ask Davies, how would one transpose this calculation to a heterodisperse aerosol, assuming condensation to the wall was minimal and that the process was primarily distillation from smaller to larger particles due to the Kelvin effect? What would the vapour field " seen " by a particular particle be? How would the evaporization rate compare to that for the single particle model? Further questions are : (i) how sensitive would the evaporation rate be to the evaporation coefficient, particularly for small concentration gradients? (ii) Would one expect that " contamination " might significantly affect evaporation rates? (iii) May one neglect the latent heat effects, particularly in an aerosol having a particle concentration of the order of 10^6 particles cm^{-3}?

Dr. C. N. Davies (*University of Essex*) said: The vapour field " seen " by a particle depends on Kn. When Kn is large the particle " sees " a vacuum, roughly up to a distance Kna from its centre. When Kn is very small the concentration gradient outside the particle is such that

$$(n_r - n_\infty)/(n_s - n_\infty) = a/r,$$

where n_r is the concentration of vapour at radius r.

If the concentration of the aerosol is 10^6 particles/cm^3, then the volume per particle averages 10^{-6} cm^3, which is equal to a sphere of radius 62 μm. During quasi-steady evaporation of an isolated particle having $a = 0.31$ μm the concentration at the surface of a concentric sphere of radius 62 μm would be 99.5 % of the concentration at infinity. The evaporation under quasi-steady conditions of such a particle in an aerosol of 10^6 particles cm^3 therefore proceeds at the same rate as it would were the particle isolated. The establishment of quasi-steady conditions requires a time of the order of $\lambda/\bar{c}$, say, 10^{-10} s when Kn is large ; for diffusion controlled evaporation the time dependent term is $a/\sqrt{\pi\nabla t}$. Putting this equal to 0.01, so that the difference between the transient and quasi-steady rates of evaporation is negligible, gives $t = 10^{-4}$ s. Whatever the value of Kn, the time taken to establish quasi-steady conditions is negligible ; the rate of evaporation of a particle in the cloud will be the same as that of an isolated particle.

If the coefficient α is very small, the rate of evaporation is not controlled by diffusion but by the rate of escape of vapour molecules from the surface, even though Kn may be very small. This happens when water droplets are coated with a layer of long chain molecules.[1] As α decreases, therefore, the rate of evaporation becomes less dependent on the concentration gradient and more dependent on α/Kn ; such behaviour is unlikely to occur with drops of organic liquids.

Contamination can affect the evaporation of liquid droplets in two ways : (i) by lowering the vapour pressure due to the rising concentration of involatile contaminant as evaporation proceeds ; (ii) by forming a film on the surface of aqueous drops which impedes evaporation ; highly specific properties are required in the contaminant for this effect to be large.

Suppose the concentration of aerosol is 7.7×10^{-7} g/cm^3 ; the latent heat of vaporization of DBP is 79 cal/g so that complete evaporation will withdraw from the

[1] C. N. Davies, *Disc. Faraday Soc.*, 1960, **30**, 144.

gas phase 6.1×10^{-5} cal/cm^3. 1 cm^3 of air has a heat capacity of 3×10^{-4} cal/°C. The fall in temperature due to complete evaporation of the disperse phase is thus $3 \times 10^{-4}/6.1 \times 10^{-5} = 4.9$°C.

Dr. R. G. Picknett (*Chem. Defence Est., Porton Down*) said: Kerker has asked what happens to the evaporation process when a cloud of droplets is present. N. L. Cross and myself have performed calculations for monodisperse aerosols which we hope to publish soon. Provided the mass concentration of aerosol is less than about 1 mg/m^3, interaction of the vapour gradients adjacent to neighbouring droplets is negligible, and the only effect of the aerosol is to increase the background vapour concentration as the evaporation proceeds, thus slowing the process.

Prof. M. Kerker (*Clarkson Coll. Techn., N.Y.*) said: We have found our aerosols quite stable to evaporation as pointed out in the discussion on our paper. Since the mass concentration is 1 mg/l., the evaporation must proceed even significantly lower than Cross finds at 1 mg/m.

Prof. D. E. Rosner (*Yale University*) said: In quantitative treatments of the evolution of the aerosol size spectrum function $n(r, \mathbf{x}, t)$ under conditions for which the " growth " term $\partial(\dot{r}n)/\partial r$ plays an important role, it is common to assume that the individual particle growth rate $\dot{r}$ is a function of, at most, the prevailing particle radius r and local environmental variables at position $\mathbf{x}$ and time t. For example, in the continuum limit (Kn $\ll 1$) the Maxwell–Smoluchowski equation provides the proportionality $\dot{r} \propto r^{-1}$, but it is prudent to recall the assumptions underlying this simple result prior to its formal application to dilute (low volume fraction) aerosols in new situations. In a recent investigation [1] of the vaporization of isolated droplets in the continuum regime, conditions leading to the breakdown of the instantaneous $\dot{r} \propto r^{-1}$ law have been explored, with some results of potential significance to aerosol science/technology mentioned here. Briefly, for the validity of the $\dot{r} \propto r^{-1}$ law it is not sufficient that droplet and its local environmental conditions undergo negligible fractional changes in the characteristic diffusion time r^2/D_v (where D_v is the Fick diffusion coefficient for the evaporating/condensing vapour). It is also necessary that the velocity of the moving phase boundary be small compared to the characteristic vapour diffusion velocity. This leads to a necessary condition of the form:

$$\frac{\rho_\infty}{\rho_{\text{droplet}}} \left| \frac{\omega_{v,w} - \omega_{v,\infty}}{1 - \omega_{v,\omega}} \right| \ll 1,$$

where $\omega_{v,w}$ is the vapour mass fraction at the droplet surface and $\omega_{v,\infty}$ is the vapour mass fraction in the gaseous environment " far " from (i.e. several droplet radii away from) the droplet.[2] Ordinarily, the density ρ_∞ of the gaseous environment is much smaller than the density ρ_{droplet} of the droplet itself, and the local vapour mass fractions, ω_v, are everywhere much smaller than unity so that this condition for the validity of the quasi-steady approximation (leading to $\dot{r} \propto r^{-1}$) is satisfied. However, if one considers a spray of a liquid fuel, say, at a total pressure level comparable to the

---

[1] D. E. Rosner and W. S. Chang, *Combustion Sci. Techn.*, 1973, in press.

[2] Under conditions for which the Maxwell–Smoluchowski $\dot{r}$ expression is valid, the diffusional " driving force " parameter in the absolute value brackets is itself small compared to unity, and $-\dot{r}$ is linearly proportional to $\omega_{v,w} - \omega_{v,\infty}$. However, a generalization of the quasi-steady Maxwell–Smoluchowski expression is available for which the $\dot{r} \propto r^{-1}$ dependence is preserved even when the driving force parameter is not small. (See, e.g. D. B. Spalding, *Convective Mass Transfer—An Introduction* (McGraw-Hill, New York, 1963)).

thermodynamic critical pressure of the fuel, then for droplets whose temperature approaches their critical temperature this parameter becomes appreciable, and the quasi-steady approximation loses its utility. Interestingly enough this situation is encountered for diesel engine cylinders [1] into which kerosene ($p_c \approx 26$ atm, $T_c \approx 662$ K) is injected as a droplet spray. In such cases a fully transient treatment of the $\dot{r}$ function appearing in the aerosol evolution equation is evidently required.

[1] D. E. Rosner, *AIAA J.*, 1967, **5**, 163.

Inorganic Oxide Aerosols of Controlled Submicronic Dimensions

By F. Juillet, F. Lecomte, H. Mozzanega, S. J. Teichner, A. Thevenet and
P. Vergnon

Institut de Recherches sur la Catalyse (C.N.R.S.), Département de Chimie Physique,
69-Villeurbanne, France

Received 4th December 1972

Metallic oxides aerosols are prepared by decomposition of anhydrous chlorides in the diffusion flame of a hydrogen–oxygen reactor. The flow rate of the chloride vapour, the temperature of the flame and the residence time of the reagent in the flame determine the shape (spherical or polyhedral), the dimensions (in the range from 60 Å to 2000 Å) and in some cases the crystalline structure of the particles, which in all cases are non-porous.

These highly divided oxides exhibit unusual photocatalytic properties which are not encountered with aerosols in the micron range or with porous particles prepared in a conventional way. Titanium dioxide, in particular, enables the catalytic photo-oxidation (in the u.-v. range) at room temperature of organic and inorganic compounds. Paraffins and olefins are oxidized partially and/or totally whereas ammonia yields N_2O and N_2, carbon monoxide yields carbon dioxide and hydrogen sulphide yields sulphur dioxide and sulphur.

Industrial smokes inject into the atmosphere submicronic particles of metallic oxides which are often in contact with industrial gases containing hydrocarbons, ammonia, carbon monoxide, hydrogen sulphide, sulphur dioxide and oxides of nitrogen. Since the natural sedimentation of these aerosols is a slow process, their reaction with the above gases in the presence of oxygen and of u.-v. irradiation is of interest in the study of environmental problems.

Although the smokes of metallic oxides are usually prepared in the laboratory by electric arc or plasma methods, we preferred to generate the submicronic aerosols by the flame reactor method [1, 2] because it permits a good control of the size and the shape of the oxides, and also because it is more closely correlated to the industrial " involuntary " generation of particles in the smokes.

A special interest was attached to the shape of oxide particles generated in the flame reactor, because previous studies [3] have shown that surface properties of anatase aerosols are different for polyhedral or spherical particles. Indeed, spherical particles exhibit a statistical abundance of all crystallographic planes whereas polyhedral particles may have some privileged planes developed. Moreover, the number of discontinuities at the surface (corners, edges and steps) is also greater in the polyhedral particles and therefore point defects, because of poorly coordinated surface ions, seem to be more abundant in these particles.

The size of particles may also control the shape and the defect structure of the surface of particles because when only a small quantity of ions with a normal coordination number is present in a particle then only the most stable planes are likely to be developed.[4]

EXPERIMENTAL

The aerosol particles are obtained by decomposition of anhydrous metallic chloride vapour in the hydrogen–oxygen flame of a diffusion multitubular burner. The experimental device has been described in detail.[2, 5]   The flow rate of reacting gases, the concentration of the chloride in the feed and the temperature of the flame may be varied over a large range. For a given temperature of the flame (obtained by varying the H_2/O_2 ratio), an increase of the concentration of the chloride vapour carried out into the burner by the oxygen feed increases the diameter of particles of the aerosol collected in a electrostatic precipitator.   The particles are non-porous and practically monodispersed for each preparation.

The photocatalytic properties at room temperature of the aerosols were studied in a differential reactor, already described.[6]   A u.-v. source was used, in some cases with a monochromator or filters, such that the selected wavelength could pass through a silica window and irradiate the aerosol deposited on a porous film in the reactor in the form of a thin layer. The reaction products were analysed by gas chromatography.

RESULTS AND DISCUSSION

MORPHOLOGY OF AEROSOLS

Particles of Al_2O_3, TiO_2, SiO_2, ZrO_2, Fe_2O_3, Cr_2O_3, V_2O_5, SnO_2 and GeO_2, were prepared as required from corresponding volatile chlorides (or oxychlorides).[5]   The relationship between the concentration of the chloride in the feed and the diameter of particles for each temperature of the flame has been given elsewhere.[5]   In the present paper, particular attention is attached to the relationship between the shape and the diameter of particles with the surface activity of TiO_2 aerosols prepared in flames whose temperature is in the range of 1500 to 3000 K.   Typical flow rates of gases into the burner for a flame at 3000 K are of the order of 8×10^{-3} mol/s for hydrogen, 4×10^{-3} mol/s for oxygen, 1.2×10^{-3} mol/s for nitrogen.

For a cold flame (e.g., 1500 K) a proportion of the hydrogen is substituted by nitrogen.   Titanium tetrachloride vapour flow rate may vary over the range of 10^{-6} to 5×10^{-4} mol/s.

The residence time of the particles in the flame, which depends on the flow rate of the carrier gas and the cross-sections of the burner tubes, may vary between 0.3×10^{-2} and 15×10^{-2} s per 1 cm length of the flame.

It is assumed that the rate of transformation of the chloride vapour in the flame into the oxide is much higher then the rate of growth of the oxide droplets or particles. Consequently, the residence time of " initial " molecules of the oxide in an elementary volume of the flame depends on the flow rate of reagents into the burner.   On the other hand, the concentration of " initial " molecules of the oxide or its vapour pressure is determined by the concentration of metallic chloride vapour in the carrier (oxygen) gas.   An attempt is then made to determine the conditions of the formation in the flame of a particle of the oxide in connection with the concentration of " initial " molecules of the oxide and their residence time in the flame.

The electron micrograph of fig. 1a shows a titania aerosol obtained in a cold flame (1700 K) whereas fig. 1b shows the aerosol obtained in a hot flame (3000 K).   The overall rate of flow of feed gases (H_2, O_2, N_2) was 1.3×10^{-2} mol/s for both preparations (residence time 0.05 s/cm) and the flow of titanium tetrachloride was also identical at the low rate of 0.4×10^{-5} mol/s for both aerosols.   These results show that for any flame temperature, and for a low concentration of reacting species, the aerosol particles present have dimensions below 200 Å and their shape is that of a polyhedral type, exhibiting facets.   In this range of concentration of $TiCl_4$ the influence of the residence time is negligible.

When the titanium tetrachloride flow rate is increased almost 100 times (25 to 30×10^{-5} mol/s), fig. 1c (1700 K) and 1d (3000 K) show a remarkable difference in the morphology of particles.   For the cold flame (1c) the shape of aerosol particles is of the same type as previously shown (1a) though their diameter is now increased to

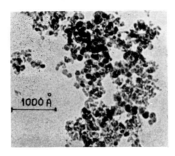

FIG. 1a.—Aerosol of titania prepared in a cold flame (1700 K). TiCl$_4$ flow rate: 0.4×10^{-5} mol s^{-1}.

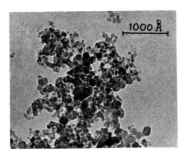

FIG. 1b.—Aerosol of titania prepared in a hot flame (3000 K). TiCl$_4$ flow rate: 0.4×10^{-5} mol s^{-1}.

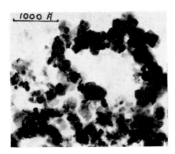

FIG. 1c.—Aerosol of titania prepared in a cold flame (1700 K). TiCl$_4$ flow rate: 30×10^{-5} mol s^{-1}.

FIG. 1d.—Aerosol of titania prepared in a hot flame (3000 K). TiCl$_4$ flow rate: 25×10^{-5} mol s^{-1}.

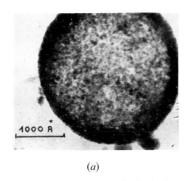

(a)

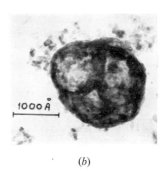

(b)

FIG. 2—(a) and (b): Formation of spherical particles of titania from polyhedral particles in a flame of intermediate temperature (2100 K): TiCl$_4$ flow rate: 25×10^{-5} mol s^{-1}.

[To face page 58

360-400 Å. The variation of the residence time only modifies the size of particles and not their morphology. For the hot flame (1*d*) the particles now present a perfectly spherical shape of a diameter of the order of 1500 Å. It is supposed that this spherical morphology results from the condensation of " initial " molecules of TiO_2 into liquid droplets (melting point of TiO_2 = 2200 K) which after cooling and quenching give solid particles with the initial shape of droplets. In this latter case the proportion of spherical particles in the aerosol increases when the residence time increases. The question now arises : why, in the case of a low concentration of titanium tetrachloride, and hence of " initial " molecules of TiO_2 (fig. 1*b*), the liquid droplets of a smaller diameter are not formed in the hot flame. The polyhedral shape of the particles seems indeed to indicate that condensation of " initial " molecules of TiO_2 proceed directly into a solid state, in the same manner as a for a cold flame (fig. 1*a*), below the melting point of TiO_2.

Because the flame reactor enables one continuously to vary the temperature of the flame, and the residence time in the flame, it was possible to set the boundary conditions between the spheres and the polyhedral particles. Fig. 2 shows the micrographs from which the mechanism of the formation of a spherical particle may be deduced. It must also be recalled that spherical particles of diameter smaller than 300 Å, have never been observed for any flame temperature,[5] which seems to show that the liquid state cannot be formed below some critical diameter of particles. Fig. 2*a* and 2*b* seem to indicate, moreover, that the liquid droplet is not obtained directly from the condensation of " initial " molecules of TiO_2, but only by the melting of a group or cluster of small solid polyhedral particles initially condensed. For an intermediate flame temperature (2100 K) and a high flow rate of titanium tetrachloride (30×10^{-5} mol/s) a sufficiently high concentration of small (polyhedral) particles is present in the flame to allow the formation of aggregates of particles which, at this temperature, will just be able to melt—resulting in a spherical cluster. This behaviour should be correlated with two observations : (i) the vapour pressure increases when the radius of particles decreases, and (ii) the vapour pressure in equilibrium with the condensed phase is smaller for solid than for liquid, hence a critical radius of curvature may exist below which only the solid phase is stable.

The crystalline structure of titanium dioxide seems also to depend on the dimensions and shape of particles. In cold flames, for polyhedral particles, anatase is principally formed. However, for hot flames, polyhedric particles may contain up to 30 % of rutile, whereas spherical particles contain almost 100 % of anatase.

It is therefore not surprising that particles of different morphology and structure exhibit different catalytic properties [3] and also photo-catalytic properties as shown in the next section.

PHOTOCATALYTIC OXIDATION IN THE PRESENCE OF SOME OXIDE AEROSOLS

It has been already shown that alumina, titania or zirconia aerosols (diameter of particles below 300 Å) may be reduced on their surface in vacuum at 500°C giving non-stoichiometric oxides.[7, 8] For titania, this reduction may be achieved at room temperature in vacuum if the solid is simultaneously irradiated in u.-v. (2000-3600 Å).[9] Moreover, titania aerosols exhibit at room temperature photo-catalytic behaviour in the partial and/or total oxidation of hydrocarbons.[5, 6] For this reason, a study of their behaviour in the photocatalytic oxidation of inorganic molecules was also undertaken.

It must be recalled that the photocatalytic activity, e.g., in the oxidation of iso-butane into acetone, expressed as a number of micromoles of acetone formed per minute per gram of catalyst spread out on the porous support in the differential reactor, is a linear function of the weight of the catalyst, up to some critical limit. It has been suggested [6] that this behaviour is related to the surface nature of the process and to the need for the u.-v. radiation, which is unable to reach the catalyst particles at the bottom of the bed if the thickness of the bed exceeds some critical limit. Furthermore, all the tests of photocatalytic activity were performed with the mass of the aerosol not exceeding the critical mass. In a typical test of CO oxidation, the composition of reacting feed was 12.5 % of O_2, 25 % of CO in 62.5 % of He as a carrier gas, with a flow rate of 1 l./h, onto 10 to 33 mg of aerosol uniformly deposited on a porous support (fiberglass) in the reactor.

Table 1 gives the results of the photocatalytic oxidation of CO at room temperature onto titania aerosols of various surface areas, prepared in the flame reactor.

TABLE 1.—PHOTOCATALYTIC ACTIVITY OF TiO_2 AEROSOLS

surface area/ $m^2 g^{-1}$	morphology	total mass in the bed/ mg	conversion %	activity [a] $\mu mol\ CO_2$ $min^{-1} m^{-2}$	activity/ $\mu mol\ CO_2$ $min^{-1} g^{-1}$	temperature o the flame/ K	structure % rutile
23.5	spheres	20	0.71	72	3.20	3000	2
32.5	spheres	35	2.39	118	3.70	3000	2
41.0	spheres	13	1.51	202	4.90	2700	3
68.0	polyhedr.	19	1.48	135	1.99	1900	6
70.0	polyhedr.	13	1.36	181	2.56	1900	8
98.0	polyhedr.	15	1.73	200	2.04	1700	6
140.0	polyhedr.	10	1.73	350	2.49	1700	6

[a] All experiments are performed with a constant intensity of u.-v. beam

If the photocatalytic activity, in micromoles of CO_2 per min and per m^2 (μmol $min^{-1} m^{-2}$) is plotted as a function of the surface area (fig. 3), two distinct plots are observed, for spheres and polyhedral particles. The activity per unit surface should be

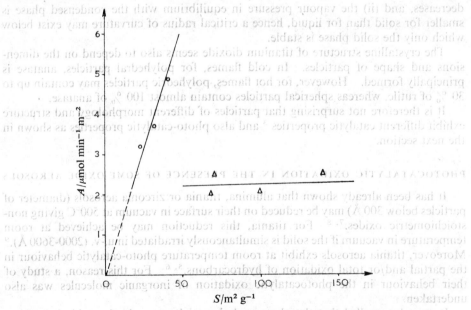

FIG. 3.—Photocatalytic activity for CO oxidation of spherical and polyhedral aerosols. ○, spheres; △, polyhedra

independent of the extent of the surface if the quality of this surface in catalysis remains constant. This is the case for polyhedral particles, whereas for spherical titania the quality of the surface in photocatalysis seems to increase with the specific surface area, i.e., when the particle size decreases. It is difficult to ascribe this behaviour to a different rutile content (table 1) of aerosols because their *surface* content is not known. However, if the photocatalytic activity depends on surface defect structure (point defects),[10] the polyhedral particles have some chance to exhibit the same surface concentration of defects, whereas for spherical (melted) particles the organization of the surface may be more difficult to achieve when the dimensions of the particles (for small particles of higher surface area) are close to the crystallographic distances in various planes of the lattice.[11]

As previously observed in the photocatalytic oxidation of hydrocarbons,[6] titania (anatase) obtained in a conventional manner, by hydrolysis of $TiCl_4$, does not exhibit any activity in the oxidation of CO. It must be recalled that this sample is porous and therefore not convenient for a surface photo process.

TABLE 2.—PHOTOCATALYTIC ACTIVITY IN THE OXIDATION OF CO OF VARIOUS AEROSOLS

nature	surface area/$m^2 g^{-1}$	activity a/μmol CO_2 $min^{-1} m^{-2}$
TiO_2	70	0.46
ZrO_2	37	0.016
SiO_2	220	0
Fe_2O_3	39	0
Al_2O_3	100	0.017
SnO_2	54	0.03
V_2O_5	34	0
Cr_2O_3	13	traces
Ga_2O_3	2	0.45

a The conditions of irradiation were different from those used for data in table 1 (decreased intensity of u.-v. radiation).

Among all the aerosols prepared in the flame reactor, titania exhibits the highest photocatalytic activity in the oxidation of CO. Table 2 gives the comparative values of the activity for some aerosols for which the morphological study was not undertaken.

The same oxides prepared in a conventional way by precipitation in aqueous media and calcining do not exhibit any measurable photocatalytic activity.

In contrast with the photocatalytic oxidation of hydrocarbons, where only titania aerosols were active, various oxides exhibit some, not negligible, activity in the CO oxidation.

Photo-oxidation of other inorganic substances was mainly studied on polyhedral titania (70 m^2 g). A mixture of ammonia (20 %) oxygen (40 %) and helium (40 %) was passed with a flow rate of 1.2 l./h through the differential photoreactor and a conversion of 5 % was registered. The reaction products are N_2 (85 %) and N_2O (15 %), apart from water. Nitrous oxide is neither photo-oxidized in the same conditions, nor can it be used as a source of oxygen in the photo-oxidation of hydrocarbons or CO. Blyholder and coworkers[12] have, however, observed a phot o-oxidation of CO by nitrous oxide in the presence of ZnO obtained by a conventional method. But this catalyst is also able to oxidize CO with N_2O in a thermal process at low temperature.

Finally, hydrogen sulphide, in a mixture of H_2S (20 %), O_2 (30 %) and He (50 %), with a flow rate of 1.2 l./h, was photo-oxidized on titania (70 m²/g) with a conversion of 6 %. In the exhaust gases sulphur dioxide and water vapour were identified but sulphur was deposited simultaneously onto the catalyst bed.

Experiments to determine the activity of aerosols other than titania in the photo-oxidation of NH_3 and H_2S are still to be attempted. However, it may be already concluded that the state (dimensions, morphology) of the oxide particles in industrial smokes is of paramount importance in their surface activity. In conclusion, it has been shown that it is not possible to extrapolate and compare data obtained for less divided oxides or for oxides prepared in a conventional way (mainly in aqueous media) so far as their photocatalytic activity is concerned.

[1] R. Caillat, J. P. Cuer, J. Elston, F. Juillet, R. Pointud, M. Prettre and S. J. Teichner, *Bull. Soc. Chim. France*, 1959, 152.
[2] J. Long and S. J. Teichner, *Rev. Int. Hautes Temp. Réfract.*, 1965, **2**, 47.
[3] J. Herrmann, S. J. Teichner and P. Vergnon, *J. Catalysis*, to be published.
[4] R. Van Hardeveld and F. Hartog, *Surface Sci.*, 1969, **15**, 189.
[5] M. Formenti, F. Juillet, P. Meriaudeau, S. J. Teichner and P. Vergnon in *Aerosols and Atmospheric Chemistry*, ed. G. M. Hidy (Academic Press, N.Y., 1972), p. 45.
[6] M. Formenti, F. Juillet, P. Meriaudeau and S. J. Teichner, *Chem. Techn.*, 1971, **1**, 680 and 5th *Intern. Congr. Catalysis* (Palm Beach, 1972).
[7] B. Arghiropoulos, J. Elston, P. Hilaire, F. Juillet and S. J. Teichner in *Reactivity of Solids*, ed. J. H. de Boer (Elsevier Pub. Company, Amsterdam, 1961), p. 525.
[8] J. Long, F. Juillet and S. J. Teichner, *Rev. Int. Hautes Temp. Réfract.*, 1965, **2**, 163.
[9] M. Formenti, H. Courbon, F. Juillet, A. Lissatchenko, J. R. Martin, P. Meriaudeau and S. J. Teichner, *J. Vac. Sci. Techn.*, 1972, **9**, 947.
[10] Ph. Roussel and S. J. Teichner, *Catalysis Review*, 1972, **6**, 133.
[11] O. M. Poltorak, V. S. Boroninet and A. N. Mitrofanova, *Proc. 4th Intern. Congr. Catalysis*, Moscow 1968, ed. J. W. Hightower (Houston, 1970), p. 1235.
[12] Ken-Ichi Tanaka and G. Blyholder, *J. Chem. Soc. D*, 1971, **14**, 736.

Formation of TiO$_2$ Aerosol from the Combustion Supported Reaction of TiCl$_4$ and O$_2$

By A. P. George, R. D. Murley and E. R. Place

Tioxide International, Central Laboratories, Portack Lane,
Stockton-on-Tees, Teeside

Received 18th *December*, 1972

The formation of particulate TiO$_2$ has been studied by the addition of small quantities (10^{-5}-10^{-3} mol fraction) of TiCl$_4$ vapour to a lean CO+O$_2$+N$_2$ flame with a maximum temperature of about 1400°C. Measurements of TiCl$_4$ concentration have been made as a function of height (residence time) by u.-v. absorption spectroscopy. The results demonstrate that chemical reaction is essentially complete 50 ms down stream of the CO flame-front, at which stage the TiO$_2$ particles have reached a diameter of 410 Å. Electron microscopic examination of samples of material from the flame shows that particle growth continues for a further 200 ms by a flocculation mechanism. This is a major factor determining the final particle size (630 Å). Agreement with theoretical flocculation predictions is reasonable both with respect to the development of the mean size and the size distribution. Results of sintering experiments carried out in the flame and of similar measurements carried out in the hot stage of an electron microscope demonstrate that the particles produced in this system exhibit a fusion temperature much below that of the bulk solid (1850°C). The occurrence of sintering in the flame is necessary to account for the form of the TiO$_2$ particles produced in this system.

The high-temperature oxidation of gaseous TiCl$_4$ according to reaction (1) forms the basis of an industrial process for the production of pigmentary TiO$_2$:

$$TiCl_4 + O_2 \rightarrow TiO_2(s) + 2Cl_2 \quad (\Delta H = -43.4 \text{ kcal/mol}). \tag{1}$$

The pigmentary properties of the TiO$_2$ are related directly to particle size and size distribution. Consequently it is important to understand the processes that determine these size characteristics. The relevant processes contributing to the final size are nucleation, growth by chemical reaction, and growth by flocculation. Although in principle the theory behind these processes is well understood, there is little practical evidence to confirm the behaviour of high-temperature, high-concentration, small-particle aerosol systems in which chemical reaction is occurring. The present study provides some practical information on these factors which, although obtained specifically for the TiCl$_4$+O$_2$ reaction system, are relevant to other aerosol systems in similar regimes.

The oxidation reaction only occurs at an appreciable rate at temperatures in excess of about 1000°C. Although the reaction is exothermic it does not become self-supporting in the manner of a combustion reaction. In order to establish a system amenable to study, it was desirable to avoid the complications inherent in preheating and mixing the reactants. This was achieved by utilizing a lean, flat, laminar CO+O$_2$ flame as the source of heat. In this way, premixed TiCl$_4$ was reacted with excess O$_2$ in an essentially plug-flow system, allowing residence time to be simply related to position. The use of CO as a fuel has the advantages that the flame produces no water or ionization and that the products are relatively inert. Water has a pronounced effect on the reaction and the generation of charged species could affect all stages of the particle formation process.

EXPERIMENTAL

The complete gas delivery and burner system is shown diagramatically in fig. 1 and details of the burner are shown in fig. 2. The burner consists of an hexagonal array of 271 stainless steel hypodermic tubes, 0.050″ o.d., 0.006″ wall thickness, the outer three rows, 144 in total, providing the sheath flame. The upper burner body is cooled by transformer oil circulating from a water-cooled heat exchanger. Flame stability is improved by the provision of a stainless steel gauze 2 cm above the burner mouth.

The flame temperature in this system can be controlled independently of the mixture composition by varying the total flowrate. All the measurements described refer to the

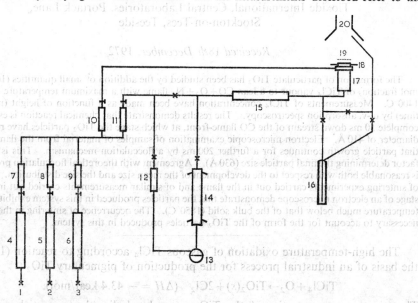

FIG. 1.—Schematic diagram of burner system : 1, 2, 3, Carbon monoxide, oxygen and nitrogen source ; 4, 5, 6, drying tubes ; 7, 8, 9, 10, 11, 12, flowmeters ; 13, TiCl$_4$ evaporator ; 14, ballotini-packed water condenser ; 15, mixing vessel ; 16, absorption vessel ; 17, burner ; 18, coolant inlet/outlet ; 19, stabilizing gauze ; 20, vent.

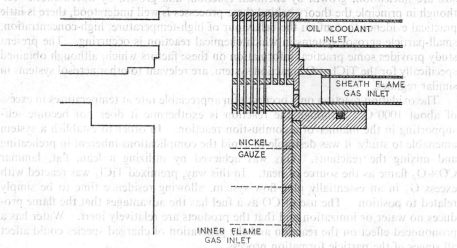

FIG. 2.—Details of multiorifice burner.

following flame conditions: molar ratio $CO/O_2/N_2 = 1/0.95/1.1$; flow to inner burner = 1 l. min^{-1}; flow to sheath burner = 3.3 l. min^{-1}; maximum flame temperature = 1650° K.

Additioning of the inner flame gases with $TiCl_4$ is achieved using a by-pass system, metered fractions of the gases passing through a $TiCl_4$ saturator. The two gas streams then re-unite and flow to the burner via a mixing tube containing ballotini and glass wool plugs where $TiCl_4$ hydrolysis products, formed by reaction with residual water vapour in the gases, are removed. The concentration of $TiCl_4$ in the feed gases is determined at the commencement and end of an experiment by passing them through an absorption vessel containing tetrachloroethylene for a known period of time. This effects total extraction of $TiCl_4$, the concentration of which is subsequently determined colorimetrically in aqueous phase as the peroxo complex. This level of $TiCl_4$ is reduced with respect to the flame as a consequence of losses incurred at the burner face where surface growth of TiO_2 takes place irrespective of flame conditions or $TiCl_4$ addition level. These losses were determined by mass balance, the solids produced in the flame being collected on a glass-fibre filter pad. As a check on completeness of reaction, the exhaust gases from these experiments were scrubbed with tetrachloroethylene when no unreacted $TiCl_4$ could be detected. The range of $TiCl_4$ concentrations, expressed as mol fraction of feed gases, established using this technique was 4.5×10^{-5}-$3.3 \ 10^{-3}$.

Particle samples were taken from the flame by direct deposition on to electron microscope grids, mounted on a brass holder. Samples were taken by sweeping the grid holder manually through the flame, with a sweep time of approximately 1 s, the number of passes required to give a particle number concentration sufficient for counting and size analysis varying from 1 to 4, dependent upon flame $TiCl_4$ concentration. The grid mounting and support produces rapid quenching of the sample and this method was found to be superior to a quartz probe technique, both in ease of operation and sample reproducibility.

Determination of the absorption spectra of $TiCl_4$ was carried out on the same burner. A deuterium arc lamp and slit collimator were mounted on an optical bench at one side of the burner in diametric opposition to a Hilger and Watt D292 grating monochromator. A constant slit width of 0.8 mm was used throughout. The light intensity at the mono-chromator exit slit was measured with an RCA IP 28 multiplying phototube, the output from which was displayed on a digital voltmeter. The reference spectrum for $TiCl_4$ was obtained on the burner with the flame unignited.

The fusion of flame-produced TiO_2 particles was examined initially by allowing them to deposit on a fine platinum wire at $\sim 900°C$, removing a sample for examination and then re-introducing the wire into the flame at $\sim 1300°C$, after which a further sample was taken. A more quantitative method was later applied in which the particles were deposited directly on palladium grids by brief exposure to a $TiCl_4$-additioned flame, after which the grids were placed in the electron microscope hot-stage and heated at a rate of approximately 20°C min^{-1} while maintaining a visual check upon the particles. The temperature range within which the particle clusters underwent a sudden and marked shrinkage was noted.

RESULTS AND DISCUSSION

A variety of experimental techniques have been applied to the study of this particular reaction system; those relevant to the present discussion have been detailed above.

The discussion centres on the measured particle size distributions of material sampled from the flame, a typical example of which is shown in plate 1. All distributions were obtained by sizing each particle present on the electron micrograph separately, irrespective of its position with respect to other particles. Table 1 shows the change of particle size and standard deviation with residence time. The variation of mean particle size with initial $TiCl_4$ concentration for samples taken at 2 cm is shown in fig. 3.

The results show clearly that the particles are growing in size as they travel down-stream from the burner and that the final size is related to reactant concentration.

TABLE 1.—VARIATION OF PARTICLE SIZE PARAMETERS AND GROWTH RATES AT TiCl$_4$ MOL FRACTION 2.0×10^{-3}

sampling position (cm above burner face)	0.5	1.0	1.5	2.0
estimated flame residence time/ms	50	100	160	230
$\bar{d}$ (geometric weight mean)/μm	0.041	0.055	0.062	0.063
standard deviation	1.372	1.349	1.329	1.354
$\bar{d}$ (geometric weight mean)/μm, calculated	—	0.061	0.072	0.080
standard deviation	—	1.340	1.321	1.302
apparent growth rate/(μm s^{-1})	4×10^{-1}	1.4×10^{-1}	5.8×10^{-2}	7.1×10^{-3}
growth rate/(μm s^{-1}) from Ghoshtagore	4.4×10^{-2}	3.1×10^{-2}	7.1×10^{-3}	4×10^{-4}

The main purpose of this work was to understand the processes leading to the initial distribution and the subsequent growth mechanism. The relevant stages to be considered are nucleation, growth by chemical reaction and flocculation.

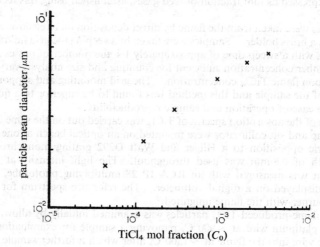

FIG. 3.—Variation of mean particle diameter with initial TiCl$_4$ concentration.

NUCLEATION

By the use of similar arguments to those proposed by Ulrich,[1] it can be shown that the critical nucleus size under the experimental conditions which apply here is less than the size of the TiO$_2$ molecule. This implies that nucleation does not present a barrier to particle formation, which is largely determined by the rate of chemical reaction. Collision processes between small particles is extremely rapid and, as shown by the application of simple flocculation theory,[1] the concentration of particles present rapidly becomes independent of the initial concentration of nuclei. Hence, providing that chemical reaction to produce new particles of TiO$_2$ is rapid compared with the processes of growth by release of TiO$_2$ at the surface of existing particles and growth by flocculation, then nucleation need not be considered further as a factor affecting the final stage of the aerosol produced. We find in accord with Ulrich [1] that, assuming instantaneous chemical reaction, the particle concentration and size are affected less than 1 % by the initial nucleus size and concentration after times of the order of 10^{-6} s. We are concerned here with events occurring at residence times of greater than 50 ms.

The collision rate between small particles can be drastically reduced if they acquire an electric charge. This phenomenon has been shown [2, 3] to occur in the formation of carbon particles but at the maximum temperatures encountered here the measured charge density is much less than that necessary to influence the collision rate of small particles. No particles smaller than 20 Å have been observed in any of the samples taken from the smallest residence time position (50 ms). It is concluded that chemical reaction leading to formation of new particles is complete by this stage.

CHEMICAL REACTION

Evidence from several experimental results suggests that chemical reaction is rapid compared with flocculation. In a one-dimensional system, such as the one studied here, material deposition is proportional to particle surface area giving a rate of particle growth independent of particle size. This implies an invariant size distribution about an increasing mean diameter. This behaviour is not observed in practice. As shown later, the results agree with the predicted behaviour of a flocculating system.

Chemical analysis of the gases present at the highest sampling point (230 ms) showed no detectable presence of $TiCl_4$. (The limit of sensitivity of the test gives a minimum value of 97 % for the extent of $TiCl_4$ disappearance at this point.) The disappearance of $TiCl_4$ in the early stages of reaction was followed by u.-v. spectroscopy. The results obtained are given in fig. 4. At a spatial resolution of 2 mm in

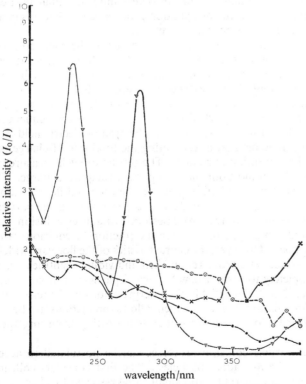

FIG. 4.—Absorption Spectra: ▽ $TiCl_4$ in $O_2 + N_2$ mixture corrected to flame conditions; $TiCl_4$ additioned flame, mol fraction 1.4×10^{-3}, × 2-3 mm above burner face; ● 3-4 mm above burner face; ⊙ 14-15 mm above burner face.

the flame the only position at which the absorption of TiCl₄ could be detected was at a height of 2-3 mm. Even with no allowance for the unknown increase in the absorption coefficient of TiCl₄ with temperature, comparison with the room temperature unreacted-TiCl₄ spectrum shows an average degree of reaction of about 70 % integrated over the residence time of 30 ± 10 ms. The estimate is even higher than this if reasonable allowance is made for the continuous background absorption probably arising from the presence of TiO₂ particles. Although disappearance of TiCl₄ cannot be related directly to the formation of TiO₂ it seems likely that this step may well be rate controlling in the reaction. (Ti—Cl bond energy 82 kcal/mol).

Values of apparent growth rate at the various sampling stations are given in table 1, assuming no nucleation and complete reaction at the 230 ms sampling point. Ghoshtagore [4] gives the following kinetic expression for the growth rate of TiO₂ under the conditions appropriate to the concentration conditions used here :

$$\frac{dr}{dt} = \frac{1.12 \times 10^7}{T} \exp \frac{(-8.96 \times 10^3)}{T} p(\text{TiCl}_4) \ \mu\text{m s}^{-1}.$$

The values calculated from this expression are given for comparison in table 1. The predicted values are much slower than those observed experimentally.

FLOCCULATION

The evidence so far presented suggests that neither nucleation nor growth by chemical reaction are dominant factors in determining the final particle size characteristics. Consideration of the flocculation process shows that this can account for the essential features of the experimental results.

The flocculation process comprises two components, the collision process and the behaviour of particles after collision. The first has been widely discussed in the literature, e.g., Fuchs.[5] The rate of collision is largely determined by the Brownian motion of particles. Only the presence of strong radial convective flows, as for chemical reaction at the surface,[6] and the effect of electric charges carried by the particle, are likely to cause a marked change in the collision frequency. Chemical reaction can be neglected in this system. Application of electric fields to the aerosol system provides a simple method of estimating the total rate of charge generation by measurement of the saturation current.[7] The results of such measurements on this system have shown that at most only half the particles acquire a charge. The presence of charge at this level has a negligible effect on the observed flocculation rates.

Equally important as the rate of collisions, especially when the particle characteristics are being considered, are the processes occurring after collision. A " sticking factor " is commonly employed to describe the fraction of collisions which result in the formation of a floc. However, the characteristics of the floc vary widely depending on whether the particles stick and retain their individual identities or, at the other extreme, fuse completely to form a new " single " particle of larger size, as happens with droplet suspensions. To assist in the interpretations of the results use was made of a computer flocculation model [8] which allows predictions to be made of the developing size distribution of an aerosol system starting from any specified initial size distribution.

Two classes of particle collision processes can be postulated to account for the observed growth of the individual particles. The first considers collisions between the observed particles and particles too small to be resolved by electron microscopy. If conditions at the first sampling point are considered and the limit of particle size that can be observed is put even as high as 10 Å, then the collision rate of such particles would be so rapid as to give growth to the final observed size of 630 Å in a time of 1 ms. No conditions can be found which would predict steady growth over the observed period of about 180 ms.

The second class of collisions concerns only the particles observed on the electron micrographs. If all the particles are considered to be present in the gas phase, then the computer predictions for the development of both the mean size and of the size distribution agree closely with the observed particle sizes. With a sticking coefficient of 1.0 the predicted flocculation rate is about 10 % too rapid, as shown in table 1.

The calculation assumes a high degree of fusion between impinging particles since otherwise the collision diameter would increase at a rate much faster than that of the mean mass diameter. Close examination of the electron micrographs of particle samples shows in most cases that there are a number of particles present which appear to show signs of having been formed from two individual particles which have fused together. The particles arrowed in plate 1 have this form.

Extrapolation of both theoretical [9] and experimental [10] data on the rate of sintering of particles suggests that this phenomenon may allow an appreciable proportion of the particles present to sinter in the time available. Evidence is also available [11] showing that particles of very small diameter exhibit properties of the liquid state at temperatures many hundreds of degrees below their bulk melting point. Experimental confirmation of this behaviour was found for the present system.

Particulate material collected on a platinum probe and then reheated in the flame gases demonstrated a tenfold increase in particle diameter. Direct observation of the fusion process utilizing a hot-stage electron microscope with a sample of particles collected directly on the grid demonstrated a sudden change in structure when the temperature reached $\sim 840°C$. Plates 2(a) and (b) show the sample before and after heat treatment. Heating effects of the microscope electron beam were shown to be negligible. On the basis of these results it appears plausible that at the temperatures of 1400-1100°C in the flame rapid fusion of particles takes place.

Further confirmation of the behaviour of the aerosol as a flocculating system has been obtained using the concept of the self-preserving size distribution. [12] It has been established that given sufficient time the size distribution of a flocculating system, expressed in non-dimensional terms, should approach an equilibrium form. The properties of the size distribution have been established by Hidy. [13]

Fig. 5 shows the measured size distributions obtained in these experiments, compared with the self-preserving distributions. The trend in development of the non-dimensional distribution is similar to that observed by Ulrich [1] and the final form lies close to the self-preserving distribution for high values of Knudsen number, the regime which applies to the present particles.

Finally, results obtained for the variation of particle size at constant residence time with initial reactant concentration given in fig. 3 also demonstrate the appropriate behaviour for a flocculation controlled system. Theory predicts a relationship,

$$d = kC_0^n,$$

where n can lie between 0.33 for small particles to 0.4 for the simple Smoluchowski equation. The value of n found experimentally over an eighty-fold range of concentrations varies between 0.33 and 0.38 depending on the mean size parameter used. The predicted value of the constant k using small particle theory is 0.93 compared with the experimental value of 0.43. This discrepancy has not yet been resolved.

The remaining item is related to the appearance of groups of particles in the samples which were taken. These are clearly observable in certain of the electron microscope pictures, and their presence was originally taken as evidence of flocculates in the gas phase. This factor proved to be the major obstacle in the interpretation of the results, but there is now some circumstantial evidence to demonstrate that the groups of particles seen in the samples are an artefact of the method of collection.

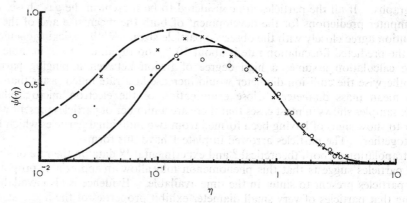

FIG. 5.—Self-preserving size-distribution function : × flame residence time 50 ms ; ● flame residence time 110 ms ; ⊙ flame residence time 180 ms. —— theoretical distribution, Knudsen number > 10, from Ulrich ; – – – – theoretical distribution, Knudsen number 0.0, from Hidy.

The major points in favour of this argument are : (i) the crystal size distribution of the material in the groups is the same, within experimental accuracy, as the isolated particles ; (ii) the apparent degree of flocculation is highest at the earliest sampling time, which is contrary to expectation ; (iii) light-scattering measurements [14] on a similar type of system show particle sizes close to that of the single crystals, rather than the groups observed on the sampling grids ; (iv) flocculation theory cannot explain the apparent amount of flocculation seen on the earliest sample, i.e., the maximum flocculation rate is too slow to give the observed result.

CONCLUSIONS

In the system considered, flocculation is the process which essentially determines the particle size distribution. Although the findings refer specifically to this system, flocculation will always eventually determine an aerosol-particle size-distribution unless factors such as particle charging reduce the collision rate to a negligible value.

However, in this system the fusion of particles after collision also plays a major role in that it determines whether the flocculation process leads to groups of small particles or simply larger particles. The fusion behaviour of small particles relevant to high temperature aerosols requires further examination before further conclusions can be made.

The authors thank the Directors of Tioxide International for permission to publish this paper. The assistance of Mr. M. J. Westwood with respect to the calculation of theoretical flocculation rates and to Mr. W. Brander who carried out most of the experimental work is gratefully acknowledged.

[1] G. D. Ulrich, *Comb. Sci. Tech.*, 1971, **4**, 47.
[2] E. R. Place, F. J. Weinberg, *11th Symp. Int. Combustion* (The Combustion Institute, Pittsburgh, 1967), p. 245.
[3] J. Lawton and F. J. Weinberg, *Electrical Aspects of Combustion* (Clarendon Press, Oxford, 1969), p. 247 ff.

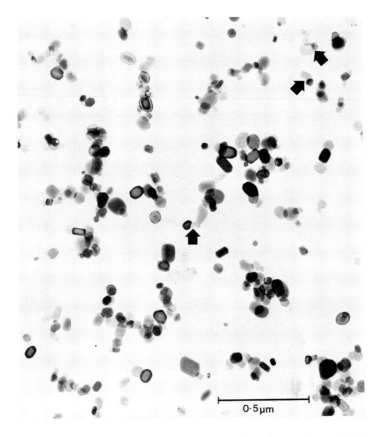

PLATE 1.—Electron micrograph of sample taken at 1.5 cm above burner face, at TiCl$_4$ mol fraction 2.0×10^{-3}.

[*To face page* 70

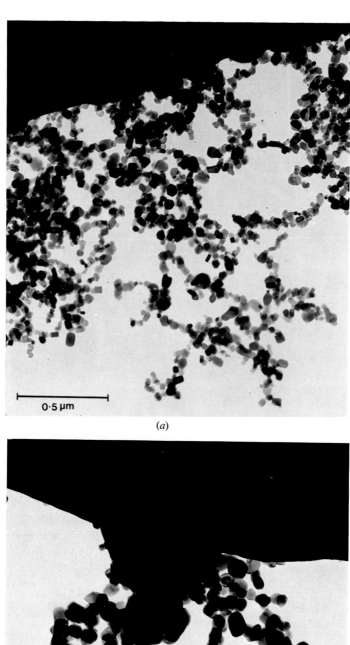

(a)

(b)

PLATE 2.—Sample of particulate TiO_2 (a) as taken from the flame; and (b) after heating to 840°C.

[4] R. N. Ghoshtagore, *J. Electrochem. Soc.*, 1970, **117**, 529.
[5] N. A. Fuchs, *The Mechanics of Aerosols* (Pergamon Press, Oxford, 1964), chap. 7, p. 338.
[6] P. A. Tesner, *7th Symp. Int. Combustion* (Butterworths, London, 1959), p. 546.
[7] J. Lawton and F. J. Weinberg, *Electrical Aspects of Combustion* (Clarendon Press, Oxford, 1969), chap. 5.
[8] M. J. Westwood, private communication.
[9] W. D. Kingery and M. Berg, *J. Appl. Phys.*, 1955, **26**, 1205.
[10] H. V. Anderson, *J. Amer. Cer. Soc.*, 1967, **50**, 235.
[11] N. A. Fuchs, A. G. Sutugin, *Highly Dispersed Aerosols* (Ann. Arbor, London, 1970), p. 85.
[12] D. L. Swift, S. K. Friedlander, *J. Colloid Sci.*, 1964, **19**, 621.
[13] G. M. Hidy, *J. Colloid Sci.*, 1965, **20**, 123.
[14] A. R. Jones (Imperial College, London), private communication.

GENERAL DISCUSSION

Dr. E. R. Buckle (*Sheffield University*) (*communicated*): Would Teichner clarify his argument for the conclusion that there is a lower limit to the size at which particles can exist in liquid form? I am confused by the use of the terms " residence time " and " flow rate ". Is it the mass flow rate (mol/s) of TiCl$_4$ and not the flow speed that is substantially different for the cases contrasted in fig. 1*a*, *b* and fig. 1*c*, *d* of his paper? The flow speed (cm/s) is specified by giving the residence time (0.05 s/cm) only for fig. 1*a*, *b*, although it is said that residence times, in general, varied from 0.003-0.15 s/cm. The point is important because the concentration of vapour, as well as the temperature and residence time, affects the sizes of particles in a condensation aerosol, and it may also affect their morphology. The larger *size* in fig. 1*c* is understandable if the mass flow rate is greater while the residence time remains substantially the same since a higher concentration of vapour tends to encourage growth. However, this also depends on the temperature, and the growth of the nuclei in the flame at 3000 K was clearly faster still (fig. 1*d*).

The different *shapes* may relate to the quenching process. The cooling rates of particles from these high temperatures are controlled by radiation, and therefore the size of a particle can be decisive in determining its final crystal form. While it is doubtful if the distinction of particles as liquid or solid can have any meaning when the diameter is only 10 nm, say, it is reasonable to suppose that the sub-micron particles studied here will be capable of melting, and, therefore, of freezing.

In view of the high melting point of TiO$_2$, the condensate at 1700 K cannot begin as liquid so the nucleus grows in the vapour as a solid particle. These particles are probably monocrystals. At 3000 K the nuclei grow into droplets, but at low vapour concentrations their size will be limited. Small, *molten* particles stand a better chance than large ones of crystallizing from a single nucleus if growth is controlled by heat transfer. The large liquid particles formed at higher vapour concentrations will not cool so rapidly because of their smaller surface-to-volume ratio. There is therefore a greater likelihood that they will crystallize around many centres, and polycrystalline particles tend to take on a spherical outline. Spherical particles of doubly-refracting metallic halides that were condensed from the vapour at temperatures above the melting point showed extinction of plane-polarized light in zones resembling those in the particles of fig. 2*b* here. The halide particles [1] condensed as droplets, and I wonder whether the particle of fig. 2*b* might have been formed in the same way. How accurately was the flame temperature known in this case?

Prof. S. J. Teichner (*University of Lyon, France*) (*communicated*): In reply to Buckle, the residence time is calculated from the inverse of the flow speed and is expressed in s/cm length of the flame. In fig. 1*a*, *b* and 1*c*, *d* the mass flow rate is given in mol TiCl$_4$/s. According to the value of the mass flow rate of TiCl$_4$, two cases should be considered. (i) For a low mass flow rate of TiCl$_4$ (0.4×10^{-5} mol s^{-1}), only polyhedric particles are formed for any flame temperature (below or above the melting point of TiO$_2$), and for any residence time in the flame used. (ii) For a high mass flow rate of TiCl$_4$ ($20\text{-}30 \times 10^{-5}$ mol s^{-1}), the temperature of the flame and the residence time directly influence the shape of particles.

(*a*) For a low flame-temperature (below the melting point of TiO$_2$) only polyhedric

[1] E. R. Buckle and C. N. Hooker, *Trans. Faraday Soc.*, 1962, **58**, 1939.

particles are formed. Their diameter increases with both (i) increasing $TiCl_4$ mass flow rate, and (ii) increasing residence time at constant $TiCl_4$ flow rate. For instance (fig. 1c) the residence time is of 0.12 s cm^{-1} and the particle diameter is 300-400 Å. When, for the same mass flow rate (and the same temperature) the residence time is decreased to 0.003 s cm^{-1}, the diameter of particles decreases to 100 Å.

(b) For a high flame-temperature (above the melting point of TiO_2) and for a large mass flow rate of $TiCl_4$ (25×10^{-5} mol s^{-1}) (value equivalent to the mass flow rate of particles in fig. 1c) and for a residence time of 0.15 s cm^{-1} (a value also equivalent to that of particles of fig. 1c), spherical particles are obtained (fig. 1d). This shows that in order to obtain spherical particles two conditions must be fulfilled : (i) the temperature of the flame should be above that of the melting point of the oxide, (ii) the mass flow rate, or, to be more exact the concentration of the species in the flame, should be above some critical value for a given residence time.

Concerning the comment on the origin of the sphericity of particles, which would be correlated with the presence of many nuclei, it has been observed (i) that for spherical particles X-ray (line-broadening) diffraction gives evidence of the presence of a monocrystalline solid and not of a polycrystalline solid which then tends to take a spherical outline ; (ii) polyhedric particles, on the other hand, of dimensions (700 Å) well above that of spheres (300 Å) can also be prepared, provided the conditions previously described are fulfilled.

Dr. B. Waldie (*Heriot-Watt University*) said: George, Murley and Place have presented electron micrographs of particles and data on weight mean particle sizes obtained from electron micrographs. Would they indicate how the shapes of particles were taken into account in obtaining size data from micrographs. The micrograph in plate I does not appear to be shadowed, but unless shadowing were used then size data in only two dimensions could be obtained. The variations in intensity of the images in plate I suggest that there could be considerable variation in particle dimensions in the direction of viewing. This problem of particle shape was encountered in some previous measurements of rates of coagulation in combustion generated oxide aerosols.[1, 2] There, simple electron micrographs gave circular images which one was tempted to assume represented spherical particles. In fact, shadowing showed the particles to be non-spherical and shape correction factors were obtained from the lengths and shapes of the shadows. The particle sizes were generally larger than those in the present paper because the residence times were about an order of magnitude greater.

Teichner has enquired about the possibility of using scanning electron microscopy. This technique was used in the previous study,[1, 2] and for agglomerates around 1 μm, it tended to confirm the shape factors deduced from shadowed micrographs. A scanning electron micrograph was obtained [2] in which constituent particles down to about 0.1 μm could be distinguished on the outside of agglomerates of around 1 μm size. Subsequent improvements in the resolution of scanning electron microscopes could perhaps enable shape data to be obtained for the upper part of the particle size range reported in the paper of George et al.

Prof. S. J. Teichner (*University of Lyon, France*) said : In reply to Waldie, the technique of replica examination is also a convenient way of determining the shape of

[1] B. Waldie, *Ph.D. Thesis* (University of Newcastle upon Tyne, 1968).
[2] B. Waldie and I. Fells, *Experimental and Theoretical Studies of Gaseous Suspensions of Thermionic Emitting Particles for use as MHD Working Fluids in Electricity from MHD*, Vol. II (Int. Atomic Energy Agency, Vienna, 1968), p. 1161.

particles. For spherical particles of titania aerosol (fig. 1*d* of my paper) of a diameter of 1500 Å, a perfectly spherical shape was observed. For polyhedric particles (fig. 1*a*, *b*, *c*) for which there is no doubt of the absence of spherical shape, the most convenient way of determining their mean diameter *d* is from the surface area *S* measured by the gas adsorption method ($d = 6/\rho S$, where ρ is the density of the material). The particles of course, should not be porous. Their diameter thus determined does not change very much for different geometric forms.

Dr. D. Stauffer (*Clark College, Atlanta, Ga*) said: If one wants to produce monodisperse aerosols in the size range below 100 Å, is TiO_2 a practical choice?

Prof. S. J. Teichner (*University of Lyon, France*) said: In reply to Stauffer, titanium dioxide aerosols have been studied in our laboratory for many years in connection with their increasing density or sintering properties,[1] catalytic properties,[2] electrical properties and defect structure [3] and photo-catalytic properties.[4] Titania may be also prepared as particles of 50 Å diam. only (320 m²/g). However, obtainment of such a highly divided state does not seem to be restricted to titania. Preliminary results concerning silica and alumina give evidence for formation of particles of 100 Å diam. Probably other aerosols (ZrO_2, SnO_2, Fe_2O_3, FeO, V_2O_5, Cr_2O_3) could also be obtained as particles in this diameter range.

Mr. E. R. Place (*Tioxide Int. Ltd., Billingham*) said: We have previously shown by shadowing micrograph samples that the particles are spheroidal. Shape is taken into account during the sizing technique in which particles are characterized by the diameter of a sphere of equivalent volume. The particles are assumed to be prolate spheroids with their axis in the plane of the micrograph.

Dr. W. J. Dunning (*Bristol University*) said: With regard to the paper by Place, under usual conditions of crystal growth, low-index planes require two-dimensional nucleation or emergent screw dislocations to bring about their growth. High-index planes do not require these and hence normally grow much more rapidly; thus corners are filled in and the crystal becomes a polyhedron bounded by low-index planes. If, under your conditions, the supersaturation of TiO_2 is so high that nucleation does not present a barrier to particle formation, then two-dimensional nucleation or dislocations are not necessary for the growth of low-index faces. Low-index faces then grow as rapidly as high-index faces and the crystal is no longer polyhedral but spherical.

There seems to be a large proportion of spherical particles and of particles with rounded surfaces in his Plate 1. The proportion of round particles should be higher the shorter the residence time. For longer residence times the supersaturation may fall to a level where surface nucleation becomes a barrier to growth and then the proportion of polyhedral crystals should be high. Was such an effect observed?

[1] P. Vergnon, M. Astier, D. Beruto, G. Brula and S. J. Teichner, *Rev. Int. Hautes Tempér. Réfract.*, 1972, **9**, 27; P. Vergnon, M. Astier and S. J. Teichner, *Sintering and Related Phenomena* (Plenum Publ. Corp. (N.Y., London), 1973, **6**, p. 301.)

[2] J. Long and S. J. Teichner, *Bull. Soc. Chim.*, 1965, 2625; M. Th. Vainchtock, P. Vergnon, F. Juillet and S. J. Teichner, *Bull. Soc. Chim.*, 1970, **8-9**, 2806, 2812.

[3] J. M. Herrmann, P. Vergnon and S. J. Teichner, *Bull. Soc. Chim.*, 1972, **9**, 271; P. Meriaudeau, M. Che, P. C. Gravelle and S. J. Teichner, *Bull. Soc. Chim.*, 1971, **1**, 13; P. C. Gravelle, F. Juillet, P. Meriaudeau and S. J. Teichner, *Disc. Faraday Soc.*, 1971, **52**, 140.

[4] M. Formenti, F. Juillet, P. Meriaudeau and S. J. Teichner, *Chem. Tech.*, 1971, **1**, 680.

The slower rates of growth found by Ghoshtagore may be due to adsorption of impurities on the crystal face or lower supersaturation.

Mr. E. R. Place (*Tioxide Int. Ltd., Billingham*) said: In reply to Dunning, we find that particles on the whole tend to be more crystalline at shorter residence times. We discount nucleation as an important process for the range of residence times for which we have samples. Nevertheless, the change in particle characteristics is puzzling since for flames where the maximum temperature is higher than the bulk melting point, crystalline particles are first formed which do not assume a spherical droplet shape until a later stage.

Prof. M. Kerker (*Clarkson Coll. Techn., Potsdam*) said: This is a comment on Dunning's question as to whether there is X-ray evidence for polycrystallinity. We always obtained spherical particles of NaCl, AgCl, and V_2O_5 when these aerosols were formed by cooling of the hot vapours. Some crude X-ray and electron diffraction measurements of the NaCl showed no evidence of crystallinity. If the NaCl particles, collected by thermal precipitation upon an electron microscope grid, were permitted to set for some time in the laboratory prior to electron microscopic observation, particularly upon a humid day, they changed from spheres to polyhedra including cubes which did give sharp X-ray patterns. We assumed that this change occurred by resolution into a surface layer of water and diffusion to a crystallizing centre.

Dr. S. C. Graham (*Shell Res. Ltd., Chester*) said: Place states that his experimental value of n in the equation $d = kC_0^n$ varies between 0.33 and 0.38 depending on the size parameter used. To the extent that the TiO_2 particles are spherical and that coagulation is the only process occurring, I would consider the only appropriate size parameter to be the mean particle volume or, equivalently, the diameter of a particle with the mean volume. This and no other size parameter is directly related to the total particle number density, independently of the particle size distribution, and the rate of change of the number of particles is equal to the particle collision rate.

In fig. 3, his experimental points do give a near-linear plot with a slope n of 0.33 yet as he points out, free molecule theory requires a slope of $6/5 \times 1/3 = 0.4$, and the particles are certainly too small for Smoluchowski's equation (which requires a slope 1/3) to be valid. The cause of the anomalously low values of n may be that the sticking efficiency on collision decreases as the particle size increases.

Ignoring van der Waals forces, his value of $0.43/0.93 = 1/2.16$ for the ratio of observed to predicted value of k corresponds to an experimental collision rate lower than that calculated from the theory by a factor of ten (2.16^3) which implies an overall sticking efficiency significantly less than unity. It is interesting to note that in our paper on lead aerosols the reverse situation exists in that the observed rate exceeds the theoretical value by a factor of about 4.5.

Mr. E. R. Place (*Tioxide Int. Ltd., Billingham*) said: In reply to Graham, in the expression used to relate diameter with reactant concentration, $d = kC_0^n$, the mean value of d used to characterize the size distribution is complex. I agree that the diameter of the particle with the mean volume is the correct average value which relates to particle concentration. However, the size dependence of the flocculation rate constant is incorporated in this expression. In the kinetic regime a mean volume diameter and a mean cross-sectional area diameter (relating to the collision cross section are involved), i.e.,

$$\frac{d\bar{d}_v}{dt} = \frac{2Cx_0}{\Pi\rho}\left[\frac{6kT}{\rho}\right]^{\frac{1}{2}}\frac{\bar{d}^2}{\bar{d}_v^{\frac{7}{2}}}$$

C = sticking coefficient, x_0 = initial reactant mass concentration, $\bar{d}$ = mean linear diameter and $\bar{d}_v$ = mean volume diameter. Under the experimental conditions, Knudsen numbers are in the range 3-30 suggesting that particles will be flocculating to some extent in the transition region between kinetic and continuum conditions.

Re-examination of the predicted relationships gives $d = 0.62\ C_0^{0.4}$ from kinetic and $d = 0.72\ C_0^{0.33}$ from simple continuum theory. The experimental results lie between these limits with the flocculation rate about 25 % lower than that predicted by kinetic theory. The different relationships obtained using the different mean diameters are thought to reflect the errors in the sizing technique. Higher order means will be increasingly sensitive to small counting errors at the large diameter tail of the distribution.

In reply to Kerker, X-ray line broadening measurements give a crystal size which corresponds approximately to those measured from electron microscopy.

Prof. C. S. Kiang (*Clark College, Atlanta, Ga.*) said: Does Place have any information on the experimental measurements of the bulk surface tension for TiO_2?

Mr. E. R. Place (*Tioxide Int. Ltd., Billingham*) said: In reply to Kiang, no—a crude theoretical estimate giving a value of 1500 erg/cm² can be found in *Problemy Mettalurgii Titana* (Moscow, 1967), p. 63-79, by S. G. Moinov and V. A. Reznichenko.

Dr. E. R. Buckle (*Sheffield University*) (*communicated*): In the paper by George *et al.*, the authors discount the nucleation process as rate-determining on the grounds that the nucleus would have to be of sub-molecular size. Would the authors explain how they arrive at this conclusion as it underlies their explanation of the experimental results as dependent on flocculation or fusion of particles?

It is easy to show by Volmer's theory that the volume of a nucleus is given by

$$v^* = 2W^*/w'', \tag{1}$$

where W^* is the reversible, isothermal work of nucleus formation and w'' is the reversible work per unit volume for the phase change in bulk. The value of w'' is set by the experimental conditions but W^* depends on the rate of nucleation, J. J has to be specified before W^* can be calculated. The rate of nucleation may be written as

$$J = K\exp(-W^*/kT), \text{ m}^{-3}\text{ s}^{-1},$$

where the value of K depends on the choice of kinetic model. Then if V is the sample volume, the nucleation frequency is

$$I = JV, \text{s}^{-1},$$

and

$$W^* = kT\ln(VK/I). \tag{2}$$

The "experimental value" of I therefore affects v^*, and an unrealistic result for v^* could reflect a wrong choice for I.

Mr. E. R. Place (*Tioxide Int. Ltd., Billingham*) said: In reply to Buckle, we have considered primarily the development of the size distribution from the 50 ms residence time position, the earliest point at which we have experimental results on particle size, by all possible mechanisms. We conclude that growth by chemical reaction is not taking place both because no $TiCl_4$ is present and because the change in size distribution to the next sampling point is in the opposite sense to that required by a surface growth mechanism. We can include in growth the accretion at the surface of either gas phase TiO_2 or any nucleus precursor material. If nucleation is slow (large nuclei) then growth at the particle surface already present should be rapid in comparison. We do not observe this. Rapid nucleation (small nuclei) would imply a high concentration of small particles which are not seen on the size distribution. If they are sufficiently small not to be resolved then they must be removed extremely rapidly by flocculation. The variation in particle diameter over an eighty-fold change in reactant concentration implies an approximately constant number concentration of particles at the final sampling point. It seems unlikely that a nucleation-controlled system would give this result.

We conclude therefore that nucleation is not occurring in the region of measurement to any significant extent. As a consequence of this we suggest that nucleation occurs earlier in the system. It is under these conditions of very rapid nucleation with a large driving force due to fast chemical reaction that we estimate that the nucleus size could be submolecular. Although I agree with the relations derived by Buckle, surely it is the stable nucleus size which physically determines the nucleation rate and not vice versa.

Dr. E. R. Buckle (*Sheffield University*) (*communicated*): With reference to the last point raised by Place my meaning was that his count of nuclei must be correct before he can derive from theory the properties of the nucleus, including its size.

Condensation and Evaporation of Metallic Aerosols

By E. R. Buckle and K. C. Pointon

Department of Metallurgy, The University, Sheffield S1 3JD

Received 22nd January, 1973

The heat-pulse cloud chamber has been used to study the condensation of metallic aerosols in the presence of purified argon. Multiplication, growth and evaporation of Ca, Cd, Pb and Zn particles vary with the background temperature in the chamber. The volatile Cd and Zn resemble the alkali halides in that growth occurs readily in suspension when a sufficient vapour pressure is maintained, and particles are formed that settle out at appreciable speeds. These particles fall from the cloud independently.

With Pb, the vapour pressure in the vicinity of the melting point is much lower, and nucleation in the vapour at the high temperatures close to its point of generation is followed by the rapid arrest of growth and evaporation as the particles move away into the chamber. This results in the freezing-in of large numbers of minute particles, and a smoke is formed in which there is little evidence of further change. When the temperature of the chamber is reduced to room temperature, the particles are exceedingly fine and numerous when first condensed but the smoke thins out, apparently by agglomeration. Observable motion in the smoke, apart from the Brownian motion, is dependent on convection in the supporting gas; the particles move by streaming and do not fall out.

The present cloud chamber is modelled on the original design of Buckle and Ubbelohde,[1] with certain adaptations necessary for its use with metals and for the general improvement of operation. A substantial advantage is obtained by the use of probes which obviate the need to dismantle the chamber for sampling the fall-out and renewing the metal supply. The technique is basically as before, and involves the repeated production of aerosols as the temperature of the background is slowly varied. Highly supersaturated vapour is produced by passing current through a coil in a supersaturator probe so as to flash-heat the metal sample above the background temperature. After formation, the vapour rapidly cools to form a suspension of droplets or solid particles by condensation. The suspension is viewed telescopically under intense illumination and the behaviour of the particles observed. Other probes are used to sample the fall-out and control the motion of the aerosol.

EXPERIMENTAL

DESIGN OF CLOUD CHAMBER

The chamber is assembled inside a horizontal tube furnace with a Pt–Rh winding. This provides a steady background temperature controllable to ± 1 K between 400 and 1800 K. The chamber is a muffle of refractory alumina, 76 cm long and of 52 mm bore, extended at one end via a water-cooled brass head by a Pyrex manipulation section (fig. 1a, 2). The free ends of the extended muffle terminate in brass heads, each of which is fitted with a window for viewing the interior of the chamber and two probe carriers. The head mounted on the alumina muffle is also water-cooled. Nine recrystallized alumina crucibles are assembled end-to-end in the muffle, dividing the chamber into a further nine sections and reducing heat loss from the interior. The middle section functions as the generating chamber, and communicates with the heads by means of two Vitreosil pipes passing through axial holes drilled in the floors of the alumina crucibles. Additional holes carry alignment rods and probes.

78

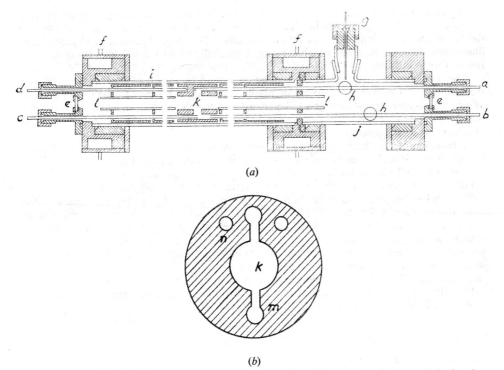

FIG. 1.—(a), longitudinal section of cloud chamber; (b) radial section of generating chamber
a, supersaturator probe; b, substrate probe; c, exhaust probe; d, thermocouple; e, chamber
window; f, water cooling; g, sample feeder; h, observation window; i, muffle containing crucibles;
j, glass section; k, generating chamber; l, viewing pipe; m, probe recess; n, alignment hole.

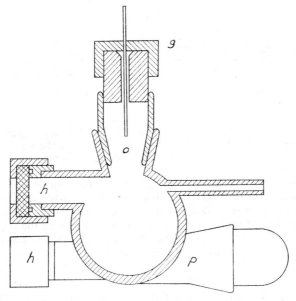

FIG. 2.—Glass manipulation section. o, supersaturator access turret; p, substrate access turret.

The central crucible is also modified by reducing the bore to match the pipe-section with alumina cement, leaving grooves in which the probes are recessed. This construction avoids the formation of turbulent eddies in the aerosols. The central section is observed and illuminated through the pipes, which are coated internally with carbon from a sooty flame to reduce their reflectivity.

The temperature is probed in the generating section by means of a sheathed Pt/Pt-Rh thermocouple. Gas inlets controlled by needle valves are connected to the end-heads and allow oxygen- and water-free argon to be passed into the chamber from either end, after the initial evacuation of air. An exhaust probe extends into the central chamber for local pumping during observations on aerosols.

The design of an efficient supersaturating device has involved considerable experimentation. A simple design consists of a twin-bore alumina tube carrying leads of 1 mm thick Ni welded to a small heating coil of tungsten. The coil is supplied with current from a Variac. To minimize its effect on the chamber temperature, the power dissipated in the coil must be sufficiently low in comparison with the average power input to the furnace windings. At the same time, to avoid the shorting of the coil and its subsequent failure, it is necessary to protect it from the test metal which otherwise spreads along the coil when molten. A satisfactory design is shown in fig. 3a. The coil is of Mo, tightly wound and closely spaced and supported on a former of alumina. It fits into the lower bore of a piece of twin-bore alumina tubing, and the upper bore is exposed over the middle 1 cm of its length by grinding to form a slot. The ends of this bore are sealed with alumina cement. The metal sample is held in the slot, and the whole assembly attached to the probe, after welding the coil to the leads, by a tightly fitting sleeve of Pt–Rh.

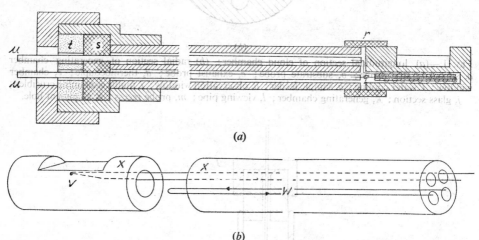

(a)

(b)

FIG. 3.—(a), supersaturator probe; (b), substrate probe (exploded view). q, Mo coil; r, Pt–Rh sleeve; s, Nitrile rubber gasket; t, insulating compression disc; u, Ni lead; v, thermocouple; w, coolant gas circuit; x, Pt–Rh connecting sleeve not shown.

The substrate probe (fig. 3b) consists of a short piece of alumina thermocouple sheathing on which a flat surface has been cut. This is connected to a 4-bore capillary probe, again with a Pt–Rh sleeve to provide rigid support at high temperatures. A thermocouple in contact with the under surface of the flat gives the temperature of the upper surface with reasonable accuracy. The substrate can be cooled below the chamber temperature by a gas stream conducted via the other two bores of the probe.

OPTICAL TECHNIQUE

The viewing technique is the same as before.[1] A large converging lens is used to collect as much light as possible from the diffuse source of a 250-W Hg arc-lamp and to focus it to form a secondary light source of about 2 mm diam. on an iris diaphragm. The illuminated aperture is focussed with a converging doublet of short focal length on to a second diaphragm consisting of two blades with V-notches enabling the aperture to be narrowed down to give an extremely small tertiary point-source. A final doublet of weak convergence collects the light from this source into a very narrow beam which enters the cloud chamber after passing through a filter to select the 5461 Å mercury line.

The use of silica windows to isolate the central section [1] was abandoned because of the obscuring effect of metallic condensate strongly illuminated by the incoming light beam. Confinement of clouds to the generating section was achieved by a new technique of gas flow, described below. The advantage to visibility was substantial because the Airy patterns of the cloud particles could be viewed with the telescope directed at a lower angle to the light beam.

PROCEDURE

To prepare for a condensation run, the furnace is set to heat the chamber to a steady temperature about 300 K below the melting point of the metal (table 1). The chamber is evacuated to a pressure between 1 and 10 N m^{-2} and filled with purified argon to atmospheric pressure. The argon stream is continued during the loading of the supersaturator probe. The slot of the supersaturator is positioned in the manipulation section directly below the vertical turret. Test metal in the form of wire is then fed through the seal in the turret to the heated probe until the slot is full of molten metal. The probe is then pushed into the gener-ating chamber and the gas flow discontinued, leaving the whole cloud chamber under a slightly positive pressure.

TABLE 1.—VAPOUR PRESSURES OF THE METALS [4,5] AT SIGNIFICANT TEMPERATURES
(T_f = m.p., T_b = b.p.)

metal	$0.8\ T_f$/K	T_b/K	$p^\circ(0.8\ T_f)$/N m^{-2} †
Ca	893	1756	7
Zn	554	1180	8×10^{-2}
Cd	475	1038	6×10^{-2}
Pb	480	2020	3×10^{-11}
Al	746	2740	3×10^{-11}

† value for liquid extrapolated from T_f

Using the Variac, the metal is flash-heated to several 100 K above the background temp-erature until a suspension of condensed particles appears. The particles show a tendency to move out of the central chamber into the viewing pipes where the temperature is unknown. This is prevented by a slow flow of argon along the pipes. The gas enters at the inlets at each end and is drawn into the central section by the exhaust probe. By careful setting of the needle valves the gas flow may be tuned and the metallic vapour and suspended particles caused to circulate slowly in the central section. Particles can be held almost stationary for periods of up to 30 s, depending on the volatility, if they occupy positions toward the centre of the rotating cloud. A temperature scanning procedure [1] is used to establish the properties of the metallic aerosol that depend on the growth, evaporation and physical state of the particles in them.

RESULTS

Before commencing work on the metals, the performance of the apparatus, and in particular the new design of supersaturator, was tested on one of the salts studied by Buckle and Ubbelohde.[1] KI was chosen as a representative salt with a suitable vapour pressure curve and clear-cut cloud phenomena. The critical solidification temperature T_s was reported [1] as 799 K.

As the temperature of the cloud chamber was raised from 770 to 800 K marked changes in the behaviour of the KI clouds were seen. Dense clouds of tiny particles which responded slowly to changes in the supersaturator current gave way at higher temperatures to clouds in which the particles evaporated or grew rapidly as the supply of vapour was varied. The particles in clouds showed twinkling when the background was at 795 K but the effect had vanished when the temperature reached 797 K. T_s therefore lies between these values as judged from the readings on a thermocouple recessed in the wall of the open-ended generating chamber. The small discrepancy with the value previously reported was not considered to be serious enough to warrant further refinements to the method at this stage, and work on the metals was begun after expelling the residual salt under vacuum at high temperature. The correlation $T_s \sim 0.8\ T_f$ was used as a guide in the search for critical effects in metallic clouds.[2, 3]

GENERAL OBSERVATIONS ON METALLIC AEROSOLS

The work so far has been restricted to telescopic observations. The Airy patterns formed by the particles are similar to those seen with salt aerosols, the brightness of the central disc and the number of concentric haloes indicating the relative size. Depending on conditions, particles appear thinly in small numbers when the size is large, and densely in large numbers when the size is small.

Large particles that grow quickly are lost by sedimentation. Such particles may be seen to move independently. When small, particles occur in more or less persistent streams, or " curtains ", and show the eclipsing effect [1] as well as Brownian motion within the curtain. The curtains move by streaming in various ways depending on the pattern of convection in the chamber. When the gas flow is suitably tuned the appearance of the curtain in motion is suggestive of the rotation of a stellar nebula. Such conditions of motion are optimum for the observation of single particles in a cloud which is not too dense.

The effect known as " twinkling " [1] has not been observed to be a general property of metallic aerosols formed by condensation. With Zn, and also with Cd, the vast numbers of particles that are formed at temperatures below $0.8\ T_f$ and which may be attributed with confidence to condensation show an indistinct flicker, but it has not been possible to detect a sudden onset of this effect. Large, twinkling particles are sometimes seen in small numbers during the early stages of formation of a cloud. It is believed that these are ejected along with the vapour as the sample on the supersaturator becomes finally molten. The ejection is not visible with the present design, the probe being recessed in the roof, but it was clearly observed in the work on salts. Such particles drop out very quickly and may be distinguished from the condensate if turbulence is avoided. A shower of particles has also been observed after tapping the probe.

ZINC

At temperatures in the vicinity of $0.8\ T_f$ (table 1), large particles are easily grown in large numbers. The aerosol motion is controllable by gas-flow tuning, and the lifetimes are substantial (at least 60 s). These particles flicker when seen in isolation. At 500 K the numbers are greater, and at 475 K there are small as well as large particles present. The proportion of small particles increases on further cooling, and at 390 K stable, dense suspensions of minute particles are formed.

CADMIUM

From $0.8\ T_f$ down to 430 K the aerosols are densely populated with particles that fall out rapidly (in a few seconds). Growth is difficult to induce and the continued operation of the supersaturator merely produces more particles. At the same time, the particles appear to diminish in size by evaporation. Flickering is also observed with this metal. There is no change down to 400 K beyond an increase in number density and a decrease in the size of the particles.

With the chamber at room temperature the particles formed by condensation are exceedingly faint but stable. Quantities of larger particles are also formed that possibly originate from unmelted Cd expelled from the probe. These show unusual behaviour in apparently shrinking in size as they fall directly and rapidly towards the floor of the chamber. Similar properties are shown by the particles which fall when the probe is tapped, and as the size diminishes so does the speed of descent. There is apparently a connexion between these effects and the presence of residual metallic vapour. If the chamber is flushed with argon and probe particles again dislodged without passing current, the effects are not observed.

LEAD

Aerosols of Pb behave differently from those of Zn and Cd. At $0.8\ T_f$, ejected particles appear first, then curtains of minute particles formed by condensation. The fine particles are very persistent but do not grow in the vapour. Even above the melting point (601 K), growth is too slow to relieve the supersaturation when the probe is kept hot. Instead, the number of particles increases.

As the temperature is lowered from $0.8\ T_f$ the concentration of particles formed in a cloud is increased and the particle size is decreased. The clouds are also less persistent. At room temperature a smoke is formed in which the Airy discs are initially barely visible. The smoke slowly thins out and the particles that remain become brighter, indicating growth. Brownian motion continues and there is no loss by sedimentation. The impression is that the process of enlargement is visible at room temperature because of the high density of the initial smoke, whereas at higher temperatures the process is still operative but the brightening of the Airy disc cannot be discerned. It is difficult to compare by eye the brightness of the discs when the particles are thinly dispersed.

CALCIUM

The behaviour of Ca in the chamber also has unique features. A complication is the low vapour density. This leads to the stratification of the particles and inhibits circulation. The same tendency possibly accounts for their persistence at high temperatures when they might be expected to evaporate more readily. The data of table 1 suggest that Ca should behave as a volatile metal like Zn and Cd, but substantial growth of the particles could not be induced, even at $0.8\ T_f$.

Another problem was reaction of Ca with the alumina of the probe. This interfered as the chamber temperature approached T_f, and when the melting point of Ca was reached (1116 K) the reaction became self-sustaining and generated curtains of condensate even when the current was off. It is possible that at these high temperatures Al is vaporized and condenses along with the Ca. It would be expected (table 1) that pure Al vapour would condense only to minute particles.

DISCUSSION

In the work on salts [1, 6, 7] it was established that the cloud lifetimes always tended to decrease as the background temperature was increased. The rise of the temperature through the twinkling threshold T_s could in many cases be correlated

with a sharp fall in the lifetime. The effect was attributed to the increased evaporation of particles which remain liquid throughout the period of observation.

It was also observed with salts that when the chamber temperature was much
lower than T_s the clouds formed were persistent and composed of multitudes of minute
particles. This may be explained as follows. Assuming that the test material is
always heated to the boiling point by the supersaturator, the saturation ratio $p/p°$,
where $p°$ is the vapour pressure at the chamber temperature T, can approach very
high values when T is low (see, e.g., table 1). The result is a high concentration of
nuclei which have little prospect of growth.

From the few results we have obtained so far it would appear that there is an
essential difference between the properties of aerosols of metals and salts. If the
metal is involatile at the melting point (Pb, table 1) the growth-rate of particles, even
when liquid, is so slow that at high temperatures one merely generates increasing
numbers of them without effecting much enlargement. At low temperatures (Pb at
room temperature) the number density of particles is much greater, so great, in fact,
that even in the first faint smoke, agglomeration takes place. It is tentatively proposed that it is this that leads to the brightening of the images observed through the
telescope.

This interpretation will be tested by examination of fall-out. It would be in
keeping with microscopical observations on metallic condensate sampled from
various other sources, such as exploding wires.[8] Particle aggregation in the fall-out
from fine smokes has not been observed with the halides of the metals,[1, 6, 7] but it has
with oxides,[8] which, again, are often relatively involatile compounds.

On theoretical grounds,[9] collision leading to fusion between particles in a volatile
aerosol is a rare event in comparison with growth. As defined in this way, therefore,
coagulation should not contribute to the relief of supersaturation by providing a short
cut to the aggregation of molecules. It was also argued that under uniform conditions
of supersaturation growth should be severely limited. If this conclusion is valid, the
observed formation of micron-size particles in metallic aerosols is to be attributed to
their nucleation and growth under conditions of steep temperature and concentration
gradients near the supersaturator. The possibility that they are heterogeneously
nucleated on foreign particles already of appreciable size is unlikely if these do not also
originate at the supersaturator.

We are grateful to the Science Research Council for support, including a maintenance award to K. C. P.

[1] E. R. Buckle and A. R. Ubbelohde, *Proc. Roy. Soc. A*, 1960, **259**, 325.
[2] D. Turnbull and R. E. Cech, *J. Appl. Phys.*, 1950, **21**, 804.
[3] E. R. Buckle, *Nature*, 1960, **186**, 875.
[4] O. Kubaschewski, E. Ll. Evans and C. B. Alcock, *Metallurgical Thermochemistry*, (Pergamon,
    Oxford, 4th ed., 1967).
[5] J. F. Elliott and M. Gleiser, *Thermochemistry for Steelmaking* (Addison-Wesley, Reading,
    Mass., 1960), vol. 1.
[6] E. R. Buckle and C. N. Hooker, *Trans. Faraday Soc.*, 1962, **58**, 1939.
[7] E. R. Buckle, *Condensation and Evaporation of Solids*, ed. E. Rutner *et al.* (Gordon and Breach,
    New York, 1964), p. 537.
[8] J. Harvey, H. I. Matthews and H. Wilman, *Discuss. Faraday Soc.*, 1960, **30**, 113.
[9] E. R. Buckle, this Discussion.

Coagulation of Molten Lead Aerosols

By S. C. Graham and J. B. Homer*

Shell Research Ltd., Thornton Research Centre, P.O. Box 1, Chester CH1 3SH

Received 4th December, 1972

A study is made of the kinetics by which particles in a high-temperature aerosol coagulate. The experimental method uses a light-scattering technique coupled to a shock tube, and allows a continuous record to be made of the changes in particle volume during the coagulation process. The theory of free-molecule coagulation of aerosols with a self-preserving size distribution has been developed to include the effects of dispersion forces and a comparison made between theoretical and observed rates of coagulation of a molten lead aerosol at temperatures around 940 K. Observed rates are found to be a factor of two faster than theory would predict.

In this paper we describe a study of the coagulation of very finely dispersed aerosols that coagulate on a millisecond time-scale. We have developed an experimental method that enables a continuous record to be made of the changes in particle volume during such coagulation, and the results afford a test of whether current coagulation theory[1-5] is capable of predicting the coagulation rates of very small particles. The study is made specifically on lead aerosols at temperatures around 940 K, and the work is an extension of our previous study [6] on the rates of condensation of lead vapour.

The lead aerosols are generated in a shock tube by the thermal decomposition of tetramethyl-lead (TML) highly diluted with argon, and " ideal " conditions are chosen where virtually all the lead condenses within 0.5 ms and remains at a constant particulate volume for the remaining 3 ms of available flow time. The molten lead particles collide and coalesce during this period and grow to diameters of 10-20 nm before the end of the flow. Since such diameters are less than one-fifth of the mean free path of the argon diluent, we may expect [3,7] the coagulation process to have the characteristics of the free-molecule rather than the diffusion-controlled regime. Furthermore, the observed change in particle volume is so high that we expect a self-preserving size distribution to be developed very early in the flow. We have therefore developed the theory of free-molecule coagulation of aerosols with a self-preserving size distribution to describe the rate of coagulation of these aerosols.

The experimental method for measuring the change in particle volume during the flow is based on a light-scattering technique using an argon-ion laser as the light source. The rates of coagulation are recorded and compared with those predicted by the theory.

THEORY

COAGULATION

The theory of aerosol coagulation is developed here to provide an appropriate equation relating the mean particle volume to the coagulation time. Within the free-molecule regime, coagulation theory defines the collision parameter [ref. (3), p. 303] as

$$\beta(v, \tilde{v}) = \left(\frac{3}{4\pi}\right)^{1/6}\left(\frac{6kT}{\rho}\right)^{1/2}(v^{1/3}+\tilde{v}^{1/3})^2\left(\frac{1}{v}+\frac{1}{\tilde{v}}\right)^{1/2} \quad (1)$$

For an isodisperse system, in which the particles coalesce on every collision, this leads [ref. (2), eqn (7) ref. (8), eqn (22)] to a coagulation rate of

$$\frac{dN_\infty}{dt} = -\frac{1}{2}\left(\frac{3}{4\pi}\right)^{1/6}\left(\frac{6kT}{\rho}\right)^{1/2}(4\sqrt{2})\phi^{1/6}N_\infty^{11/6}. \tag{2}$$

Using the relationship $N_\infty \bar{v} = \phi$, eqn (2) may be expressed in the alternative form,

$$(\bar{v})^{-1/6}\frac{d\bar{v}}{dt} = \frac{1}{2}\left(\frac{3}{4\pi}\right)^{1/6}\left(\frac{6kT}{\rho}\right)^{1/2}4\sqrt{2}\phi. \tag{3}$$

In the above equations, v is the volume of a particle, k is Boltzmann's constant, T is the absolute temperature, ρ is the density of the particulate phase, N_∞ is the total particle number density at time t, $\bar{v}$ is the mean particle volume at time t and ϕ is the particulate volume fraction.

A system of coagulating lead particles (droplets) in a stagnant gas, in which gravitational effects and the loss of particulare material through particle wall collisions are negligible, is one in which we may expect the particle size distribution to tend towards a "self-preserving" form.[3,5] Whilst the nature of such self-preserving size distributions has been described by Friedlander[5] and others[9,10] for coagulation in the Brownian diffusion regime, it is only recently that approximations to the self-preserving distribution for the free-molecule regime have been published by Lai, Friedlander et al.[1] and by Ulrich.[2]* The rate of coagulation for such systems is given by

$$\frac{dN_\infty}{dt} = -\frac{1}{2}\left(\frac{3}{4\pi}\right)^{1/6}\left(\frac{6kT}{\rho}\right)^{1/2}\alpha\phi^{1/6}N_\infty^{11/6}, \tag{4}$$

where

$$\alpha = \int_0^\infty\int_0^\infty (\eta^{1/3}+\tilde{\eta}^{1/3})^2\left(\frac{1}{\eta}+\frac{1}{\tilde{\eta}}\right)^{1/2}\psi(\eta)\psi(\tilde{\eta})\,d\eta\,d\tilde{\eta}, \tag{5}$$

and where η is the reduced particle volume and $\psi(\eta)$ the reduced distribution function defined in eqn (7) of ref. (1) by

$$\alpha\left\{2\psi(\eta)+\eta\frac{d\psi(\eta)}{d\eta}\right\}+\int_0^\eta [\tilde{\eta}^{1/3}+(\eta-\tilde{\eta})^{1/3}]^2\left(\frac{1}{\tilde{\eta}}+\frac{1}{(\eta-\tilde{\eta})}\right)^{1/2}\psi(\tilde{\eta})\psi(\eta-\tilde{\eta})\,d\tilde{\eta}$$

$$-2\psi(\eta)\int_0^\infty (\eta^{1/3}+\tilde{\eta}^{1/3})^2\left(\frac{1}{\eta}+\frac{1}{\tilde{\eta}}\right)^{1/2}\psi(\tilde{\eta})\,d\tilde{\eta} = 0. \tag{6}$$

As part of this work we derived the ordinary integro-differential equation (6) independently of Lai, Friedlander et al.[1] and obtained a numerical solution to this equation which we believe to be more accurate for values of $\eta \geq 0.15$ than either of the published distributions.[1,2] An important difference between our computed distribution and that of Lai, Friedlander et al.[1] is that in our analysis the two fundamental constraints:

$$\int_0^\infty \psi(\eta)\,d\eta = 1 \quad\text{and}\quad \int_0^\infty \psi(\eta)\eta\,d\eta = 1$$

---

* Ulrich under-estimated the rate density of collisions between equal-sized particles by a factor of two, which may account for some of the difference between his computed distribution (fig. 1(b)) and ours (fig. 1(c)).

are both satisfied with a high degree of accuracy (1 part in 10^4). Details of our numerical results will be published elsewhere [11] but the three distributions are illustrated in fig. 1. Throughout this paper wherever numerical values of η are required, they are calculated from our own computed distribution shown in fig. 1(*b*). Of particular importance in these calculations are the integrals α and $\int_0^\infty \psi(\eta)\eta^2 \, d\eta$ for which values were derived from fig. 1(*b*) and to be 6.4 and 1.84 respectively.

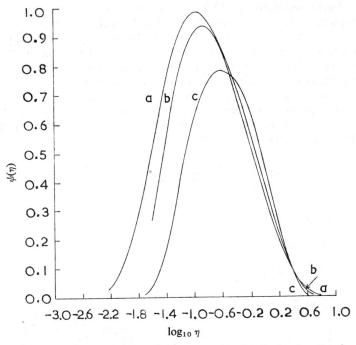

FIG. 1.—Results of computations of the self-preserving size distribution function for free-molecule aerosols: (*a*) Lai, Friedlander *et al.*[1], (*b*) this work, and (*c*) Ulrich.[2]

Eqn (4) can be modified to include the effect of inter-particle dispersion forces which for lead aerosols can be significant.[12] We can take these forces into account if we assume that they modify the collision parameter according to

$$\beta(v, v) = \left(\frac{3}{4\pi}\right)^{1/6}\left(\frac{6kT}{\rho}\right)^{1/2} G\left(\frac{v}{\tilde{v}}\right)(v^{1/3} + \tilde{v}^{1/3})^2\left(\frac{1}{v} + \frac{1}{\tilde{v}}\right)^{1/2}. \tag{8}$$

Eqn (4) then becomes

$$\frac{dN_\infty}{dt} = -\frac{1}{2}\left(\frac{3}{4\pi}\right)^{1/6}\left(\frac{6kT}{\rho}\right)^{1/2} \alpha'\phi^{1/6}N_\infty^{11/6}, \tag{9}$$

where

$$\alpha' = \int_0^\infty\int_0^\infty G\left(\frac{\eta}{\tilde{\eta}}\right)\psi'(\eta)\psi'(\tilde{\eta})(\eta^{1/3} + \tilde{\eta}^{1/3})^2\left(\frac{1}{\eta} + \frac{1}{\tilde{\eta}}\right)^{1/2} d\eta \, d\tilde{\eta}, \tag{10}$$

and where $\psi'(\eta)$ is now a function of $G(\eta/\bar{\eta})$ and satisfies the equation,

$$\alpha'\left\{2\psi'(\eta)+\eta\frac{d\psi'(\eta)}{d\eta}\right\}+\int_0^\eta G\left(\frac{\eta}{\eta-\bar{\eta}}\right)[\bar{\eta}^{1/3}+(\eta-\bar{\eta})^{1/3}]^2\left[\frac{1}{\bar{\eta}}+\frac{1}{(\eta-\bar{\eta})}\right]^{1/2}\psi'(\bar{\eta})\psi'(\eta-\bar{\eta})\,d\bar{\eta}-$$

$$2\psi'(\eta)\int_0^\infty G\left(\frac{\eta}{\bar{\eta}}\right)(\eta^{1/3}+\bar{\eta}^{1/3})^2\left(\frac{1}{\eta}+\frac{1}{\bar{\eta}}\right)^{1/2}\psi'(\bar{\eta})\,d\bar{\eta}=0, \quad (11)$$

so that for every different function $G(\eta/\bar{\eta})$ there will be a correspondingly different self-preserving size distribution.

Recently, Fuchs and Sutugin [4,13] have shown that interparticle dispersion forces substantially increase the rate of coagulation of sodium chloride aerosols in the free-molecule regime. They show that for collisions between spheres of equal size the coagulation rate is enhanced by a factor which is dependent only on the ratio (A/T), where A is the Hamaker [12,14] constant and T is the absolute temperature. We have extended their treatment to include collisions between unequal spheres and find that the collision cross-section is increased by a factor G, being the value of $F(\sigma, \mu)$ evaluated at $\partial F(\sigma, \mu)/\partial\sigma = 0$. Here $\sigma = (r_1+r_2)/\rho'$ and $\mu = (r_1-r_2)/(r_1+r_2)$, where r_1 and r_2 are the particle radii and ρ' is the distance of closest approach of the two spheres during a near collision. $F(\sigma, \mu)$ is given by

$$F(\sigma, \mu) = \frac{1}{\sigma^2}\left[1+\frac{A}{3kT}\left\{\tfrac{1}{2}(1-\mu^2)\sigma^2\left[\frac{1}{(1-\sigma^2)}+\frac{1}{(1-\mu^2\sigma^2)}+\ln\left(\frac{1-\sigma^2}{1-\mu^2\sigma^2}\right)\right]\right\}\right]. \quad (12)$$

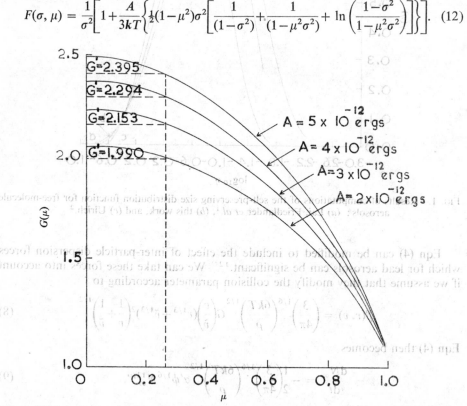

FIG. 2.—The dependence of the collision cross-section enhancement ratio, $G(\mu)$, on the difference in particle size, for various values of the Hamaker constant A and for a temperature of 940 K. μ is $(r_1-r_2)/(r_1+r_2)$ where r_1 and r_2 are the radii of the two particles. G' is the approximate coagulation rate enhancement due to dispersion forces for an aerosol with the self-preserving size distribution as defined in eqn (6).

Fortunately, however, G is only weakly dependent on μ in the important region near $\mu = 0$ as shown by the plots of $G(\mu)$ for various values of A/T in fig. 2, and thus for all reasonable values of the Hamaker constant for liquid lead (no reliable value being available [15, 16]), the effect of $G(\mu)$ on the form of the self-preserving size distribution may be ignored. Within this approximation the dispersion forces increase the coagulation rate by the factor G' where

$$G' = \frac{1}{\alpha} \int_0^\infty \int_0^\infty \psi(\eta)\psi(\tilde{\eta})G\left(\frac{\eta}{\tilde{\eta}}\right)(\eta^{1/3} + \tilde{\eta}^{1/3})^2 \left(\frac{1}{\eta} + \frac{1}{\tilde{\eta}}\right)^{\frac{1}{2}} d\eta \, d\tilde{\eta}, \tag{13}$$

and where

$$G\left(\frac{\eta}{\tilde{\eta}}\right) \equiv G(\mu) \quad \text{and} \quad \frac{\eta}{\tilde{\eta}} = \left(\frac{1+\mu}{1-\mu}\right)^3.$$

The corresponding rate equation is obtained by insertion of G' into eqn (4), which, on substituting $\phi/\bar{v}$ for N_∞, gives, on integration,

$$\bar{v}^{5/6} - \bar{v}_{t=0}^{5/6} = \frac{5}{12}\left(\frac{3}{4\pi}\right)^{1/6}\left(\frac{6kT}{\rho}\right)^{1/2} G'\alpha\phi t, \tag{14}$$

so that for $\bar{v} \gg \bar{v}_{t=0}$, to a good approximation,

$$\bar{v} = \left[\frac{5}{12}\left(\frac{3}{4\pi}\right)^{1/6}\left(\frac{6kT}{\rho}\right)^{1/2} G'\alpha\phi\right]^{6/5} t^{6/5}. \tag{15}$$

This is the required equation which describes the expected change of mean particle volume with time.

LIGHT SCATTERING BY SMALL PARTICLES

Because of their small size the lead particles are within the small-particle limit of Mie theory [17, 18] for visible radiation. Within this limit a spherical particle scatters light in proportion to the square of its volume.[17] The intensity of light scattered by an aerosol of such particles (Rayleigh scattering) is thus proportional to $\int_0^\infty n(v) v^2 \, dv$ where $n(v) \, dv$ is the number density of particles with volumes between v and $(v+dv)$. For an aerosol with the self-preserving size distribution given in fig. 1(b) this integral simplifies [see eqn (7)] to

$$\int_0^\infty n(v)v^2 \, dv = \phi\bar{v} \int_0^\infty \psi(\eta)\eta^2 \, d\eta = 1.84\phi\bar{v}, \tag{16}$$

so that for an aerosol with a constant particulate volume fraction the scattered light intensity is directly proportional to the instantaneous mean particle volume. This relationship is one that allows a direct experimental check on the growth of mean particle volume during the coagulation process as described by eqn (15).

Because of the essential similarity of particulate and molecular Rayleigh scattering,[17] the measurement of the latter proves to be extremely useful in aligning and calibrating the optical detection system. In addition, information on the shape of the aerosol particles can be obtained from the dependence of the scattered light intensity on the orientation of the plane of polarization of the incident light, in the same way as such measurements on gases can be used to determine anisotropies of molecular polarizabilities.

EXPERIMENTAL

Lead aerosols were generated in the shock tube by the decomposition of TML in dilute mixtures with argon in the manner previously described.[6] The operation of the 76 mm i.d. shock tube and of the recording oscilloscopes is similar also to that previously reported.[6]

The optical system for the light scattering measurements was set up as indicated diagrammatically in fig. 3. A Laser Sciences Inc. 2-W, argon-ion laser gave a monochromatic beam of 800 mW at 488.0 nm. The plane of polarization of the beam is rotated from the vertical to the horizontal by the polarization rotator and is then focused at the centre of the shock tube. The light scattered perpendicular to the beam and to the axis of the shock

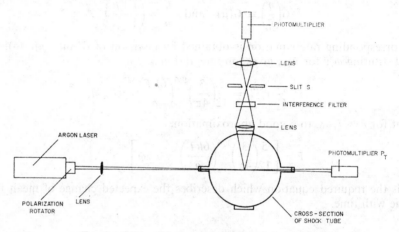

FIG. 3.—Schematic diagram of the optical system.

tube by molecules or particles at this focus is collected by a lens and passes through an interference filter (band pass 1.0 nm) to eliminate thermal radiation. The scattered light is focused to give an image at a slit S, whose width is carefully matched to that of the image in order to prevent, as far as possible, the thermal radiation and stray laser light from reaching the detecting photomultiplier P_s, and the photomultiplier output is displayed and photographed on an oscilloscope.

Alignment and calibration of the detection system were conducted before each shock in the following manner. The shock tube was filled with filtered argon to a pressure of 800 Torr and the slit S (fig. 3) was traversed in a horizontal plane until a position was found which gave a maximum in the detected signal. In this condition, simultaneous measurements of the output voltages, V_s^{Ar} and V_T^{Ar} of the two photomultipliers P_s and P_T respectively were taken. These measurements were then repeated with the shock tube evacuated to give V_s^{Vac} and V_T^{Vac}. The scattered light signals from the lead aerosols are calibrated using the value of $(V_s^{Ar}/V_T^{Ar}) - (V_s^{Vac}/V_T^{Vac})$. The shock tube was then charged with a TML+argon mixture and a shock fired without further adjustment to the optical sytem, the values of V_s and V_T during the shock flow being displayed and photographed on an oscilloscope. The sensitivity of the technique was such, that when the apparatus was initially set up, the ratios (V_s^{Ar}/V_T^{Ar}) and (V_s^{Vac}/V_T^{Vac}) were themselves in the ratio 20:1.

During the initial setting-up of the apparatus a check was made on the validity of the detection system by measuring the relative scattering cross-sections of CCl_4 and Ar and these were found to be in the ratio 34:1, as against a ratio of 38:1 calculated from literature [19-21] values.

RESULTS

LIGHT-SCATTERING MEASUREMENTS ON LEAD AEROSOLS

A quantitative treatment of the time variation of the intensity of light scattered by a coagulating aerosol is feasible only for the period that the aerosol has the self-preserving size distribution and a constant volume fraction of particulate lead. The extent to which this ideal condition is approached depends critically on the rate of formation of lead vapour via the decomposition of TML and on the rate of nucleation of this vapour. Ideally, these rates should be very fast in comparison with the available observation time, for only after the nucleation of lead is complete will the size distribution of the lead particles begin to approach the self-preserving form. In practice, the two rates are highly temperature-dependent though in opposite ways.[6] The rate-determining step in the formation of lead vapour is the initial step in the decomposition of TML, and this decomposition has been shown [6] to display first-order kinetics. In contrast, the nucleation rate is critically dependent on the super-saturation ratio and, as shown previously,[6] this ratio must exceed ~ 50 for rapid nucleation to occur during the available observation time. For a total lead concentration of 7×10^{15} atom/cm³, corresponding to a particulate volume fraction of 2.4×10^{-7}, near ideal coagulation can be expected to occur somewhere in the temperature range 870-1010 K, the lower temperature corresponding to a limiting TML half-life of ~ 1.0 ms, the upper temperature corresponding to a limiting super-saturation ratio of ~ 50. Experimentally, for this lead concentration, near ideal coagulation was observed within the much narrower temperature range 920-960 K.

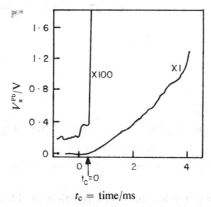

$t_c = \text{time/ms}$

FIG. 4.—Oscilloscope trace of the scattered light signal for a shock recorded under " near ideal " conditions. The output voltage V_s^{Pb} has been displayed simultaneously at the two different sensitivities 1 V/cm and 0.01 V/cm. Zero time is assigned to the time of arrival of the shock front at the point of observation. Zero coagulation time is indicated as $t_c = 0$. For this shock, $T = 930$ K, $[Pb] = 7 \times 10^{15}$ atom/cm³, $[Ar] = 1.4 \times 10^{19}$ atom/cm³.

Fig. 4 shows an example of an oscilloscope trace recorded for such a condition and demonstrates the overall sensitivity of the technique. This trace records a change in V_s^{Pb} by a factor of ~ 1000 during the shock flow corresponding to a tenfold increase in mean particle diameter. As required by eqn (15), the corresponding plot of $\log_{10} V_s^{Pb}$ against $\log_{10} t$ is linear with a slope of $\frac{6}{5}$ as shown in fig. 5 and these results represent, to our knowledge, the first time that this relationship has been tested directly. A similar time-dependence was found for all aerosols with total lead concentrations of $\sim 7 \times 10^{15}$ atom/cm³ in the temperature range 920-960 K, the observed slopes ranging from 1.18 to 1.22. Outside this temperature range very different patterns of behaviour were observed.

At temperatures progressively lower than 920 K, the critical supersaturation ratio is reached at progressively lower lead vapour concentrations, so that coagulation is initiated well before the decomposition of TML is complete. Because condensation of lead vapour is rapid after nucleation, a condition is quickly reached where the growth of the particulate volume fraction of lead is limited by the rate of decomposition of TML. A record from a typical low-temperature shock is illustrated in fig. 6(a) where the "acceleration" of V_s^{Pb} is clearly greater than that of a $t^{6/5}$ dependence and arises, at least in part, because the rate of aerosol coagulation increases with increasing particulate volume fraction. At temperatures below 820 K, no scattered light signals were observed, confirming the absence of particles under these conditions.

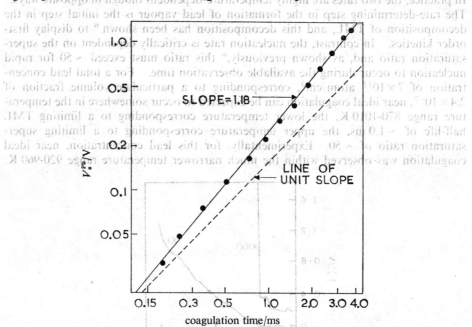

FIG. 5.—A plot of $\log_{10} V_s^{Pb}$ against $\log_{10} t$ from the oscilloscope record of fig. 4.

At temperatures above 960 K, the decomposition of TML is very fast but the "ideal" conditions of coagulation cease to be achieved because the nucleation process becomes the limiting factor. Whilst rapid homogeneous nucleation occurs at high supersaturation ratios of lead vapour, at progressively lower supersaturations (higher temperatures) the induction period before significant nucleation occurs, lengthens, and if sufficient particulate impurities are present (e.g., dust or PbO) heterogeneous nucleation may take over as the dominant nucleation process. We may then expect that condensation of vapour on to a relatively small number of particles may become the dominant growth process of the aerosol rather than coagulation. Experimentally, we have found that at temperatures above 960 K (corresponding to a supersaturation ratio of $\leqslant 250$), the scattered light records showed increasingly erratic variations indicative of heterogeneous nucleation (fig. 6(b)) and on increasing delay between the arrival of the incident shock wave and the onset of a rapidly increasing light intensity in keeping with a decreasing homogeneous nucleation rate. No particulate scattering was detected for shocked gas temperatures above 1100 K.

An investigation of the shape of the coagulating lead particles was made by the dependence of the scattered light intensity on the angle between the plane of polarization of the incident beam and the scattering plane. When the two planes were

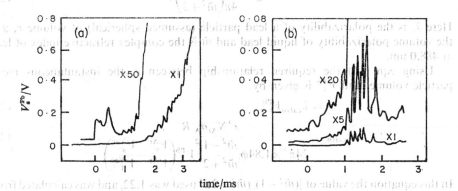

FIG. 6.—Oscilloscope trace of the scattered light signals for shocks recorded at (*a*) $T = 830$ K, [Pb] $= 6.8 \times 10^{15}$ atom/cm^3, and [Ar] $= 1.4 \times 10^{19}$ atom/cm^3; (*b*) $T = 966$ K, [Pb] $= 6.2 \times 10^{15}$ atom/cm^3, and [Ar] $= 1.26 \times 10^{19}$ atom/cm^3.

parallel, the pattern of the scattered light intensity for shocks in the near-ideal range was identical to that observed for the perpendicular configuration (fig. 4) but was uniformly weaker by a factor of 95. To within experimental error this is the same as the ratio of 100 : 1 which we observed for molecular Rayleigh scattering by SF$_6$ and by CCl$_4$, and thus confirms the interpretation of the scattered light signals from the coagulating lead aerosols as Rayleigh scattering from spherical particles.

DETERMINATION OF ABSOLUTE PARTICLE SIZES AND COAGULATION RATES

So far, the interpretation of the scattered light measurements has required only that the intensity of this light be proportional to the output voltage of the detecting photomultiplier. However, these measurements are potentially capable of yielding absolute values of particle sizes and coagulation rates but to do so requires a calibration of the scattered light intensity. We used the calibration procedure based on the detection of molecular Rayleigh scattering which allows the determination of the instantaneous differential cross-section per unit volume of aerosol, σ_{Pb}^{*}, from the voltage V_s^{Pb}.

The value of σ_{Pb}^{*} is given by

$$\frac{\sigma_{Pb}^{*}}{(3/8\pi)N_{Ar}\sigma_{Ar}} = R\left(\frac{V_s^{Pb}}{V_T^{Pb}}\right)\bigg/\left(\frac{V_s^{Ar}}{V_T^{Ar}} - \frac{V_s^{Vac}}{V_T^{Vac}}\right). \tag{17}$$

Here σ_{Ar} is the total scattering cross-section of the argon atom at 488.0 nm and N_{Ar} is the density of argon (atom/cm^3) at which the voltages V_s^{Ar} and V_T^{Ar} were recorded. V_T^{Pb} is the output voltage of the photomultiplier used to record the intensity of the transmitted beam after the plateau of constant absorption [6] had been reached. R is the ratio of the photomultiplier gains used during the measurement of V_s^{Ar} and V_s^{Pb}, respectively.

The cross-section σ_{Pb}^{*} is related to the particle size distribution and to the optical properties of liquid lead through the equations

$$\frac{8\pi}{3}\sigma_{Pb}^{*} = \frac{2^{7}\pi^{5}}{3\lambda^{4}}\int_{0}^{\infty} n(v)|\tilde{\alpha}_{v}|^{2}\,dv \tag{18}$$

$$\tilde{\alpha} = \tilde{\alpha}_{v}/v, \tag{19}$$

$$\tilde{\alpha} = \frac{3}{4\pi}\left(\frac{\tilde{m}^{2}-1}{\tilde{m}^{2}+2}\right). \tag{20}$$

Here $\tilde{\alpha}_{v}$ is the polarizability of a lead particle (assumed spherical) of volume v, $\tilde{\alpha}$ is the volume polarizability of liquid lead and $\tilde{m}$ is the complex refractive index of lead at 488.0 nm.

Using eqn (16) the required relationship between v, the instantaneous mean particle volume, and V_{s}^{Pb} is given by

$$\bar{v} = k_{calib}V_{s}^{Pb}, \tag{21}$$

$$k_{calib} = \frac{\lambda^{4}N_{Ar}\sigma_{Ar}R}{24\pi^{3}\times 1.84\phi\left|\dfrac{\tilde{m}^{2}-1}{\tilde{m}^{2}+2}\right|^{2}V_{T}^{Pb}\left(\dfrac{V_{s}^{Ar}}{V_{T}^{Ar}}-\dfrac{V_{s}^{Vac}}{V_{T}^{Vac}}\right)}. \tag{22}$$

In this equation the value of $|(\tilde{m}^{2}-1)/(\tilde{m}^{2}+2)|^{2}$ used was 1.22, and was calculated from Hodgson's [23] optical measurements on liquid lead at 1059 K. The value 6.45×10^{-27} cm^{2} used for the cross-section of argon at 488 nm was calculated from the measurements of Buckingham and Bridge [21] at 632.8 nm.

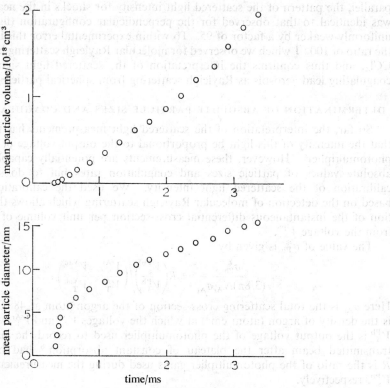

FIG. 7.—Variation in mean particle volume $\bar{v}$ and mean particle diameter $(6\bar{V}/\pi)^{\frac{1}{3}}$, with time calculated from the observed variation of V_{s}^{Pb} with time shown in fig. 4 and 5.

PARTICLE SIZES

The knowledge of k_{calib} allows the determination of the mean particle volume at any instant from V_s^{Pb} and an illustration of the change in mean particle volume during the shock flow time is shown in fig. 7 for a typical shock recorded under near-ideal conditions. The results of fig. 7 are taken specifically from the experimental record of fig. 3, where the lower limit of detectibility by light scattering corresponds to a mean particle diameter of 1.2 nm, and in which the conditions correspond closely to a similar experiment recorded and analyzed in depth in previous work.[22] The particle size deduced in the present work is commensurate not only with the size of particles (diameter 10-20 nm) removed from the shock tube after the experiment [6] but also with that predicted by the condensation model.[22]

COAGULATION RATES

As shown earlier in eqn (15), the rate constant k_{coag}, satisfying the equation $\bar{v} = k_{coag} \, t^{6/5}$, has the form

$$k_{coag} = \left[\frac{5}{12} \left(\frac{3}{4\pi} \right)^{1/6} \left(\frac{6kT}{\rho} \right)^{1/2} G' \alpha \phi \right]^{6/5}. \tag{23}$$

Experimental values of k_{coag} were obtained in the following manner. For each plot of $\log_{10} V_s^{Pb}$ against $\log_{10} t$ (fig. 5, for example), the best straight line of slope 6/5 was drawn through the experimental points and the value of the intercept, $\log_{10} k_{graph}$, satisfying the equation $\log_{10} V_s^{Pb} = \log_{10} k_{graph} + (6/5) \log_{10} t$ was obtained graphically. The required experimental value of k_{coag} is thus given by the product $(k_{calib} k_{graph})$. The results for five shocks recorded under near-ideal conditions are compared in table 1 where a Hamaker constant for lead of 4×10^{-12} erg has been assumed, and where it is seen that the experimental values of $(k_{calib} k_{graph})$ exceed the values of k_{coag} calculated from eqn. (15) by a factor of ~ 2.

TABLE 1.—RESULTS OF FIVE SHOCKS RECORDED UNDER NEAR-IDEAL CONDITIONS WHERE $[Pb] = 7 \times 10^{15}$ atom/cm^3 AND $[Ar] = 1.4 \times 10^{19}$ atom/cm^3

The mean value of $k_{calib} k_{graph}/k_{coag}$ for these records is 2.19 ± 0.22

T/K	$10^{18} k_{calib}/$ (cm^3/V)	$10^3 k_{graph}/$ (V/s$^{6/5}$)	$10^{15} k_{calib} k_{graph}/$ (cm^3/s$^{6/5}$)	$10^{15} k_{coag}/$ (cm^3/s$^{6/5}$)	$\dfrac{k_{calib} k_{graph}}{k_{coag}}$
960	2.29	1.01	2.31	1.04	2.22
920	2.41	1.20	2.89	0.99	2.91
930	2.22	0.90	2.00	1.00	2.00
920	1.70	1.22	2.06	0.99	2.09
940	5.22	0.33	1.74	1.02	1.71

This unexpected result cannot be attributed solely to experimental error, and an explanation must be found in either an overestimation of k_{calib} or an underestimation of k_{coag}. Of the constants required in the analysis, those with the greatest uncertainty are perhaps $|(\tilde{m}^2 - 1)/(\tilde{m}^2 + 2)|^2$ and A, the Hamaker constant. Optical properties are sensitive to the presence of impurities, and it is possible that the optical properties of the coagulating lead aerosols are different from those reported by Hodgson [23] for pure lead at 1059 K, namely, $\varepsilon_1 = -10.87$, $\varepsilon_2 = 14.10$ where $\varepsilon_1 - i\varepsilon_2 = \tilde{m}^2$. The magnitude of both ε_1 and ε_2 are large and, as a result, the value of

$$\left| \frac{\tilde{m}^2 - 1}{\tilde{m}^2 + 2} \right|^2 \equiv \frac{[(\varepsilon_1 - 1)(\varepsilon_1 + 2) + \varepsilon_2^2]^2 + 9\varepsilon_2^2}{[(\varepsilon_1 + 2)^2 + \varepsilon_2^2]^2} = 1.22$$

is also large and is insensitive to small changes in either ε_1 or ε_2. However, the possibility that small quantities of impurities (e.g., of oxygen, or carbon derived from TML) are present in the particulate lead phase and have modified substantially the values of ε_1 and ε_2 cannot be dismissed. Indeed, a similar implication arose from our results of the light absorption of those aerosols [6] from which the absorbance can be calculated to be a factor of 1.34 greater than would be predicted from Hodgson's values. As to the uncertainty in the Hamaker constant, there is no reliable value for lead, and the value of 4×10^{-12} erg used to determine k_{coag} in table 1 is based on the known values for A of several metals.[15] This value gives a ratio, A/T, of 4.2×10^{-15} erg/°C, and Fuchs and Sutugin have shown [13] that, for $A/T \geqslant 3.3 \times 10^{-15}$ erg/°C, further enhancement of free-molecule collision cross-sections is insensitive to increases in A/T, and this is certainly borne out in fig. 2.

CONCLUSIONS

The experiments have been successful in measuring the rate of coagulation of an aerosol at high temperature and in yielding a time-resolved absolute measure of the mean particle size. The particle size deduced for the lead aerosol is commensurate with the previous interpretation of the system. The rates of coagulation display the $t^{6/5}$ dependence of a free-molecule aerosol but the absolute rates apparently exceed those calculated by a factor of two. This difference is not large. It may be due either to a deficiency in the collision model used to calculate the theoretical coagulation rate or, quite conceivably, to an over-estimation of the calibration constant which relates the recorded light intensity to the mean particle volume.

We gratefully acknowledge the assistance of Mr M. A. McLeod in the experimental work and of Dr A. Robinson in the computational analysis.

[1] F. S. Lai, S. K. Friedlander, J. Pich and C. M. Hidy, *J. Colloid Interface Sci.*, 1972, **39**, 395.
[2] G. D. Ulrich, *Combustion Sci. Techn.*, 1971, **4**, 47.
[3] G. M. Hidy and J. R. Brock, *The Dynamics of Aerocolloidal Systems*, (Pergamon Press, New York, 1970).
[4] N. A. Fuchs and A. Sutugin in *Topics in Current Aerosol Research*, ed. G. M. Hidy and J. R. Brock, (Pergamon Press, New York, 1971).
[5] D. L. Swift and S. K. Friedlander, *J. Colloid Sci.*, 1964, **19**, 621.
[6] J. B. Homer and I. R. Hurle, *Proc. Roy. Soc. A*, 1972, **327**, 61.
[7] N. A. Fuchs, *The Mechanics of Aerosols*, (Pergamon Press, New York, 1964).
[8] J. R. Brock and G. M. Hidy, *J. Appl. Phys.*, 1965, **36**, 1857.
[9] G. M. Hidy, *J. Colloid Sci.*, 1965, **20**, 123.
[10] G. M. Hidy and D. K. Lilly, *J. Colloid Sci.*, 1965, **20**, 867.
[11] S. C. Graham and A. Robinson, to be published.
[12] H. Hamaker, *Physica*, 1937, **4**, 1058.
[13] N. A. Fuchs and A. Sutugin, *J. Colloid Sci.*, 1965, **20**, 442.
[14] J. Gregory, *Adv. Colloid Interface Sci.*, 1970, **2**, 396.
[15] J. Visser, *Adv. Interface Sci.*, to be published.
[16] G. Böhme, H. Krupp and W. Schnabel in *Molecular Processes on Solid Surfaces*, ed. Drauglis (McGraw-Hill, New York, 1969), p. 611.
[17] H. C. van de Hulst, *Light Scattering by Small Particles* (John Wiley and Sons Inc., New York, 1957).
[18] M. Kerker, *The Scattering of Light and Other Electromagnetic Radiation*, (Academic Press, New York, 1969).
[19] B. Linder, *J. Chem. Phys.*, 1960, **33**, 668.
[20] R. R. Rudder and D. R. Back, *J. Opt. Soc. Amer.*, 1968, **58**, 1260.
[21] A. D. Buckingham and N. J. Bridge, *J. Chem. Phys.*, 1964, **40**, 2733.
[22] J. B. Homer and A. Prothero, submitted to *J. Chem. Soc.*
[23] J. N. Hodgson, *Phil. Mag.*, 1961, **6**, 509.

GENERAL DISCUSSION

Mr. K. C. Pointon (*Sheffield University*) said: Our method is likely to produce pure particles because, if the background temperature is sufficiently low, they will have crystallized before touching any foreign surface. The shapes and sizes of fall-out particles were examined by scanning electron microscopy. Particles in the clouds are allowed to settle on to a flat tip of highly polished silica held by the substrate probe. The probe is then withdrawn from the generating chamber into the glass manipulation section where a layer of 60 : 40 Au–Pd, approximately 100 Å thick, is deposited on the silica surface by vacuum evaporation. This is to protect the fall-out from reaction with the atmosphere during transfer to the electron microscope.

Fig. 1 and 2 are micrographs of fall-out from Zn aerosols produced at a background temperature of 0.74 T_f. The Au–Pd film deposited on the substrate shown in fig. 1a and 1b was thick and has exfoliated; most of the Zn particles have adhered to the Au–Pd layer, but where particles have remained on the silica surface, holes have been plucked in the exfoliated film. The Zn particles are typically 1-5 μm diam. and have well-developed crystal faces, although the particle shape is sometimes complex. A polyhedral crystal with a hexagonal profile would appear to be typical of the crop of particles formed by condensation in the cloud chamber.

Kimoto et al.[1, 2] have observed the same well-defined crystal habit for Zn particles prepared by evaporation in purified argon at low pressure. Their crystallites were equiaxed and the morphology was consistent with the normal c.p.h. lattice of Zn. Kimoto reports that a small amount of oxygen in the argon caused a remarkable deterioration in the crystal habit of the particles; they became very irregular and rough. Most of the particles shown in fig. 1 and 2 are well formed crystallographically which suggests they are pure.

If twinkling results from the scattering of light by reflection at crystal faces, a spheroidal particle with a large number of flat faces would be expected to twinkle rapidly and rather weakly. This may explain the indistinct flickering observed. It would be difficult to understand, however, why the Zn particles in the form of hexagonal prisms, clearly visible in fig. 2b, did not show a distinct twinkling effect.

From the telescopic observation that the Airy images of the particles in a Pb smoke became brighter as the smoke thinned out, we believe Pb aerosols must agglomerate considerably at high particle densities. We have yet to test this interpretation by examination of Pb fall-out. Fall-out from clouds of Zn aerosols shows that agglomeration was a rare event (fig. 2a, b). This is in keeping with the absence of a brightening effect in this case.

Dr. S. C. Graham (*Shell Res. Ltd., Chester*) said: I do not consider that small metal particles with $x < 0.1$ where $x = \pi d/\lambda$, would give preferential back scattering at visible wavelengths.

As indicated in my reply to Kerker's question following my paper with Homer, the critical terms in the expansion of Q_{sca} as a power series in x are the lowest order contributions to the expressions for the electric and magnetic dipole terms a_1 and b_1, respectively. In the limit as $x \to 0$ (*m* unspecified),

$$Q_{sca} = (6/x^2)(|a_1|^2 + |b_1|^2)$$

where $|a_1|^2 = |s|^2 x^6$ and $|b_1|^2 = |s|^2 u^2 x^{10}$.

[1] K. Kimoto, Y. Kamiya, M. Nonoyama and R. Uyeda, *Jap. J. Appl. Phys.*, 1963, **2**, 702.
[2] K. Kimoto and I. Nihida, *Jap. J. Appl. Phys.*, 1967, **6**, 1047.

S7—4

Thus the importance of $|b_1|^2$ which causes the high back scattering is determined by the ratio

$$|b_1|^2/|a_1|^2 = |u|^2 x^4.$$

For the simple Rayleigh $Q_{sca}(= 6/x^2|\rho|^2 x^6)$ to be accurate to 1 % one must have, at least, an approximate upper limit on x, viz., $x \leqslant 0.1$. But, for $x = 0.1$, the ratio $|b_1|^2/|a_1|^2$ reaches 1 % when $10^{-4} |u|^2 = 10^{-2}$, i.e., $|u|^2 = 100$, so that

$$\left|\frac{m^2+2}{30}\right| = 100, \quad \text{or} \quad |m^2+2|^2 = 9 \times 10^4.$$

Assuming that m has the approximate form $m = (1/\sqrt{2})|m|(1-i)$ which is a good approximation for metals at infra-red and longer wavelengths where such high m values are found (ref. (17)), chap. 14), then $|m^2+2|^2 = |m|^4+4 = 9 \times 10^4$ so that $|m| = 17.3$ and $m = 12.3-12.3i$. If one takes $x \leqslant 0.31$ as the limit of the Rayleigh scattering domain for real m then $|b_1|^2/|a_1|^2$ reaches 10^{-2} for $|m^2+2|^2 = 9 \times 10^2$, or $m^2 \approx 30$.

There are few if any metals with such high values of m^2 at visible wavelengths and at $x = 0.3$, the simple Rayleigh expression will certainly not be accurate to within 1 % even for real m values. Though metals do not have such high values of m at visible wavelengths, much higher values are found at longer wavelengths. For example, van der Hulst (ref. (17), pp. 268 and 288) quotes an m value of $37-41i$ for platinum at $\lambda = 10 \ \mu m$ and $236-236i$ for silver at $\lambda = 30 \ \mu m$.

For larger values of x, particularly $0.5 \leqslant x \leqslant 5$, different considerations apply and the back scattering efficiencies of metals at visible wavelengths vary in a manner similar to that found for a perfectly reflecting sphere and I am grateful to Kerker for drawing my attention to this possibility.

Van der Hulst (ref. (17), chap. 14, especially pp. 284-287) has shown for spheres with $m = 3.41-1.94i$ (not untypical of the m values of metals at visible wavelengths) that the scattering efficiency/steradian in the backward direction rises monotonically from $x = 0$ to a large maximum near $x = 1$, with a deep minimum at $x = 1.65$ followed by further less extreme maxima and minima. For $m = \infty$ (and for $m = \infty - i\infty$) a similar series of maxima and minima are found at similar x values. However, at any given x, the magnitude of the back scattering efficiency is invariably greater for $m = \infty$ than for $m = 3.41-1.94i$ and presumably for any other finite value of m also.

Because these maxima and minima, which are very unlike the resonances observed for particles with real m, are well spread out with respect to the x co-ordinate, and because the x values at which they occur are insensitive to the value of m, it is possible that the variation in back scattering efficiency as a function of x could be used to determine the size of particles in an aerosol. In principle, measurements could be made on individual particles, or on a number of particles provided that the aerosol was not too polydisperse. For a particle or particles with rapidly changing sizes (coagulation or condensational growth) one would make observations at a fixed wavelength. For particles of a constant size, one would vary x by varying the frequency of the incident radiation. Are such measurements of back scattering efficiencies possible and, if so, valuable in Pointon's experimental system?

Prof. M. Kerker (*Clarkson Coll. Techn., Potsdam*) said: Has Pointon looked at the small metallic particles with white light, and if so, what is the colour? It would be interesting to observe whether these particles behave as Rayleigh scatterers or whether,

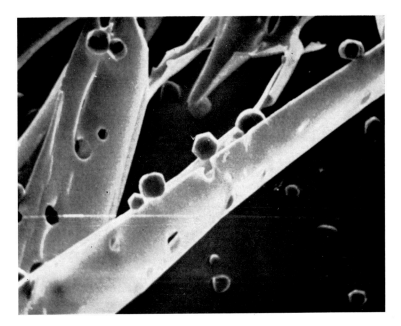

(*a*) magnification 2300 ×

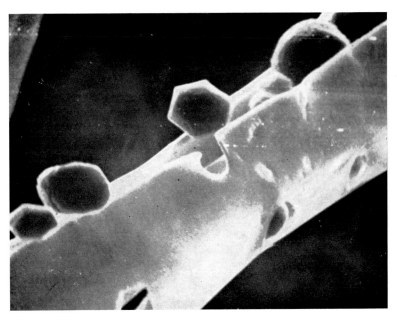

(*b*) magnification 5700 ×

FIG. 1.—Fall-out from Zn aerosols at a background temperature of 0.74 T_f.

[*To face page* 98

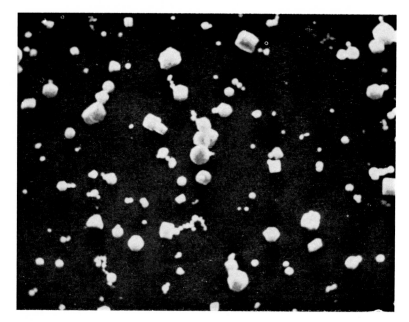

(*a*) magnification 2300 ×

(*b*) magnification 5700 ×

Fig. 2.—Fall-out from Zn aerosols at a background temperature of 0.74 T_f.

as for small perfectly reflecting particles, they scatter preferentially in the backward direction.

Mr. K. C. Pointon (*Sheffield University*) said: In reply to Kerker, we have not used white light, only green light. Particles that are easily visible with the telescope are 1 μm or larger in diameter. The size of the Airy disc, however, is not determined by the size of the particle but by the telescopic aperture. Therefore, the brightness of the particle determines whether it is visible. The angle between the light incident on the particles and the light received by the telescope has been varied over a substantial range by introducing vitreosil light pipes and angled metallic reflectors into the generating chamber. There is a great improvement in the brightness of particles when the viewing direction is nearly in line with the incident beam. We normally observe the particles against a dark background so that they appear self-luminous. By chance, we observed an interesting effect which might relate to Kerker's question about colour. When Ca vapour falling from the supersaturator crossed the path of green light entering the eye after reflection from the wall of the viewing pipe, it extinguished the light. The vapour looked like a stream of black treacle. We do not know whether this effect was the result of atomic absorption or multiple scattering from particles in the very earliest stages of growth.

Dr. S. C. Graham (*Shell Res. Ltd., Chester*) said: With regard to the extinction of the stray green light ($\lambda = 5461$ Å), by the Ca vapour or calcium particles, surely such extinction is due to absorption rather than scattering as the former is relatively so much greater for small particles than for large ones. Because Pointon's observations are normally made against a dark background he would not normally observe such absorption.

Dr. E. R. Buckle and **Mr. K. C. Pointon** (*Sheffield University*) (*communicated*): In reply to Graham, the extinction could still be due to back-scattering. How could light of this wavelength be absorbed by Ca vapour? The effect is interesting because it may indicate that ultra-fine particles are formed in the vapour immediately after it leaves the supersaturator. Using the telescope, we do not see any particles against a dark background at this stage, so that they could either be very small, strongly back-scattering, or both.

Dr. S. C. Graham (*Shell Research Ltd., Chester*) (*communicated*): In reply to Buckle and Pointon, I do indeed think that the " stream of black treacle " observed by Pointon was extinction caused by particles and not by calcium vapour. If the particles were sufficiently small (particle circumference/wavelength $\lesssim 0.2$) which seems probable as simultaneous scattering was not observed, then this extinction would be due to the true absorption of light within the particles rather than to scattering of light away from the forward direction (see, Van der Hulst, *Light Scattering by Small Particles*, chap. 14). I do not agree that the scattering of 5461 Å radiation by calcium particles into the *backward* hemisphere will ever be substantially greater than scattering into the forward hemisphere.

Dr. E. R. Buckle (*Sheffield University*) said: I would ask Graham two questions about his paper with Homer. First, his analysis of the light scattering data in terms of coagulation kinetics relies, as he states, on the attainment of a self-preserving size distribution. The mathematical analysis depends on the *assumption* that the size distribution function can be put into a form in which the time and the particulate volume are separable (see eqn (18) of Dunning's paper). Is there any independent evidence that this is a reasonable assumption on which to base the interpretation of your experiments? The second question is about the slope of the plot in fig. 5. I think it correct to conclude only that this is in keeping with the form of the expression for the classical free-particle collision parameter (eqn (1)), since one obtains $\bar{v} \propto t^{6/5}$ from eqn (3) without making the assumptions that lead to eqn (15). When he tested the experimental value of the coefficient, k, of $t^{6/5}$ against the one in eqn (15) there was a discrepancy. A feature of this comparison worries me. The theoretical coefficient k_{coag} from eqn (15) depends on the hypothesis of a self-preserving distribution, but so does the "experimental" one, $k_{\text{exp}} = k_{\text{calib}} k_{\text{graph}}$ because k_{calib} (eqn (22)) is derived from eqn (16). Therefore the quantities compared both depend on this hypothesis. Is this connected with his difficulty in getting an exact match of the theory with the experimental results?

Dr. S. C. Graham (*Shell Res. Ltd., Chester*) said: With regard to Buckle's first question, when free-molecule or diffusion-controlled (Smoluchowski) coagulation is simulated on a computer by feeding in an initial distribution and then following the

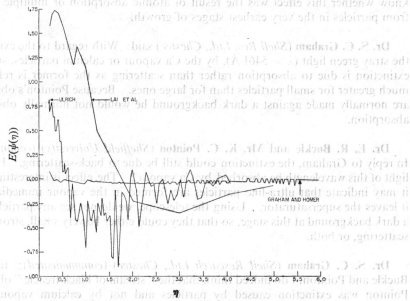

FIG. 1.—The error function $E(\psi(\eta))$ plotted against η.

change in number concentration of each particle size using the known expressions for the collision rate density for particles of different sizes, it is found that after sufficiently long " coagulation " times the computed distributions (expressed in dimensionless form) tend towards the solution of the corresponding integro-differential equation which was derived (unlike the computed distributions) using the self-preserving hypothesis. To my knowledge, no-one has yet proved that the limiting asymptotic form of the computed distributions *has to be* the corresponding self-preserving size distribution but there exists considerable verification that this is the case, particularly for diffusion-controlled coagulation.

The closeness of our computed distribution to the self-preserving distribution can be examined by feeding the computed value of ψ, designated ψ_{comp}, for each η into eqn (6) of our paper and plotting the resultant error function, $E(\psi_{comp})$, (i.e., the l.h.s. of eqn (16)) as a function of η. If ψ_{comp} is identical to the self-preserving distribution, then the error function is the straight line $E(\psi_{comp}(\eta)) = 0$. The following figure illustrates $E(\psi_{comp}(\eta))$ for our own computed distribution as well as for those of Ulrich and of Lai, Friedlander et al., and shows how close our computed distribution is to the self-preserving distribution.

With regard to the second question, Buckle is correct that the $t^{6/5}$-dependence of the particle volume is a basic feature of free-molecule coagulation and is not special to the self-preserving hypothesis. However, we do not observe $\bar{V}$ (mean volume) directly but rather a scattered light intensity I, where

$$I \propto \int \psi(\eta)\eta^2 \, d\eta \bar{V}.$$

This last equation is true for any arbitrary dimensionless size distribution ψ_{arb}, where ψ_{arb} is defined by $n(v, t) = (N_\infty^2/\phi)\psi_{arb}(\eta)$.

Now if ψ_{arb} were not the self-preserving distribution, one would expect $\int \psi(\eta)\eta^2 \, d\eta$ to be time-dependent and thus a graph of $\log I$ against $\log t$ would not give a linear plot of slope 6/5 even if a graph of $\log \bar{V}$ against $\log t$ were to give such a plot. Therefore, the fact that we do observe experimentally a linear plot of slope 6/5 for $\log I$ against $\log t$ strongly suggests (a) that $\int \psi(\eta)\eta^2 \, d\eta$ is a constant independent of time and (b) that $\bar{V}$, the mean volume, varies as $t^{6/5}$.

Incidentally, the "classical" approximation that every particle has the same volume (which is clearly impossible for a coagulating aerosol) is equivalent to defining a "classical" size distribution ψ_{class}, where $\psi_{class}(\eta) = \delta_{1,\eta}$ where δ is the Dirac delta function. Because at any instant $\eta = 1$, it follows that every function of ψ_{class} is time-independent and thus ψ_{class} is in a sense self preserving. However, ψ_{class} has no special significance and it is not the solution of any physically significant equation.

From the above, in order to relate I to $\bar{V}$ at any instant we have to make an assumption about the particle size distribution, given that we have experimental evidence as well as theoretical grounds for believing $\int \psi(\eta)\eta^2 \, d\eta$ to be a constant independent of time. There are no good reasons for assuming that $\psi = \delta_{1,\eta}$ but there are good grounds for believing ψ to be the self-preserving size distribution (i.e., the solution to eqn (6) of our paper). In particular, the lead particles are formed at extremely high supersaturations so that homogeneous nucleation is rapid and gives a large number of very small particles. These are precisely the conditions that are required to allow the self-preserving size distribution to develop early in the coagulation process.

We therefore assume that we have the self-preserving size distribution and examine the consistancy of this assumption, in particular by comparing the "experimental" coagulation rate constant with the theoretical one, and we find that the ratio of the two,

$$k_{calib}k_{graph}/k_{theor} = k_{experimental}/k_{theor} \approx 2.$$

If we made the classical approximation $\psi_{class}(\eta) = \delta_{1,\eta}$, this ratio would have the approximate value $2 \times 1.84 \times (1.13)^{6/5} \times (2.294/2.327)^{6/5} \approx 4$.

In this last equation, we have

$$\frac{\int \psi(\eta)\eta^2 \, d\eta}{\int \psi_{class}(\eta)\eta^2 \, d\eta} = \frac{1.84}{1},$$

$$\frac{\int_0^\infty \int_0^\infty \psi(\eta)\psi(\tilde{\eta})(\eta^{\frac{1}{3}}+\tilde{\eta}^{\frac{1}{3}})^2 \left(\frac{1}{\eta}+\frac{1}{\tilde{\eta}}\right)^{\frac{1}{2}} d\eta\, d\tilde{\eta}}{\int_0^\infty \int_0^\infty \psi_{class}(\eta)\psi_{class}(\tilde{\eta})(\eta^{\frac{1}{3}}+\tilde{\eta}^{\frac{1}{3}})^2 \left(\frac{1}{\eta}+\frac{1}{\tilde{\eta}}\right)^{\frac{1}{2}} d\eta\, d\tilde{\eta}} = \frac{6.4}{4\sqrt{2}} = 1.13$$

and finally

$$\left(\frac{G'}{G'_{class}}\right)^{6/5} = \left(\frac{2.294}{2.327}\right)^{6/5}.$$

Prof. M. Kerker (*Clarkson, Coll. Techn., Potsdam*) said: Has Graham given consideration to the possibility, because of the high complex refractive index, that these particles might not scatter according to Rayleigh's limiting equation for a small dielectric particle? It might be useful to carry out a " Mie " calculation for comparison with the Rayleigh theory. This might be the source of the discrepancy between the observed and calculated coagulation rates.

Dr. S. C. Graham (*Shell Research Ltd., Chester*) said: In reply to Kerker, the scattering efficiency of a sphere (Mie theory) is given by

$$Q_{sca} = \frac{2}{x^2} \sum_{n=1}^{\infty} (2n+1)\{|a_n|^2+|b_n|^2\}. \tag{1}$$

Expanding the Mie coefficients a_n and b_n in powers of x, the first few terms (ref. (17) of our paper, pp. 143-4) are

$$a_1 = isx^3(1-tx^2+isx^3)+ \ldots; \quad b_1 = isux^5 + \ldots; \tag{2}$$
$$a_2 = is\omega x^5 + \ldots; \quad b_2 = \ldots;$$

where

$$s = \frac{2}{3}\left(\frac{m^2-1}{m^2+2}\right); \quad t = \frac{3}{5}\left(\frac{m^2-2}{m^2+2}\right); \quad u = \frac{1}{30}(m^2+2); \quad w = \frac{1}{10}\left(\frac{m^2+2}{2m^2+3}\right). \tag{3}$$

The Rayleigh scattering formula refers to the limiting value of Q_{sca} as $x\to 0$ and $mx\to 0$, where

$$\sum (2n+1)\{|a_n|^2+|b_n|^2\} \to 3|a_1|^2 \to 3|s|^2x^6.$$

Whilst s, t and w assume small limiting values as $m\to\infty$, u increases rapidly and without limit so that the expansion of the b_n as a power series in x cannot be used even as $x\to 0$.

However, for lead at $\lambda = 488$ nm, $m^2 = -10.9-|4|i$ so that $|b_1|^2$, which has the value

$$|-8.9-14.1i|^2x^{10}/(30)^2 = (0.31)^2x^{10},$$

is still small. For $x\leqslant 0.1$ which corresponds to the upper size limit of the lead particles at the end of the shock flow, the contribution of this term to Q_{sca} is $<1\%$ and is quite negligible. However, the use of the Rayleigh formula does introduce errors $>1\%$ for lead particles with greater than 0.1. Thus

$$|a_1|^2 \approx |s|^2x^6(1-tx^2-isx^3)(1-t^*x^2+is^*x^3)$$
$$\approx |s|^2x^6(1-2\,Re(t)x^2)$$

and for $m^2 = -10.9-4i$

$$2\,Re(t) = 1.35.$$

The term $|b_i|^2$ gives the contribution from the oscillating magnetic dipole, and as van der Hulst has shown (ref. (17), p. 160) it is the interference between the induced oscillating electric and magnetic dipoles which gives a very small particle with $m = \infty$ its characteristically high back-scattering efficiency.

For light scattered perpendicular to an incident linearly polarized beam and scattered perpendicular to the polarization of the incident beam, the relationship between the (differential) scattering cross-sections of a Rayleigh particle and a perfectly reflecting particle ($m = \infty$) of the same size is particularly simple. For a Rayleigh particle this cross-section is given by

$$C_{\text{diff, sca}(\theta=\phi=\pi/2)} = a^2 \left| \frac{m^2-1}{m^2+2} \right|^2 x^4,$$

and for the latter

$$C_{\text{diff, sca}(\theta=\phi=\pi/2)} = a^2 x^4$$

(ref. (17), pp. 12, 127 and 159).

In conclusion, the value of m for lead at 488 nm is not large enough to invalidate the use of simple Rayleigh formulae to calculate total and differential scattering cross-sections of particles with sizes satisfying the condition $x \equiv \pi d/\lambda \leqslant 0.1$.

Formation of Soot Particles

BY P. A. TESNER

All-Union Research Institute for Natural Gas
Moscow obl. Razvilka VNIIGAS, U.S.S.R.

Received 1st January, 1973

Probable mechanisms are discussed of the formation processes of pyrolytic carbon films and soot particles, based on experimental investigations of their formation rates. Both are two-stage processes including nucleation and growth of nuclei. The formation of pyrolytic carbon from methane at temperatures below 1300 K is a molecular process. The activation energy of the formation of a plane nuclei is about 80, and of their growth about 50 kcal/mol. The formation of soot particles may take place in two ways differing in the nature of the nuclei as well as in the structure of the soot particles obtained.

The formation of soot particles during the burning and thermal decomposition of hydrocarbons is of a dual nature, the strictly physical laws of the creation of a new dispersed solid phase being complicated by a chemical process. The process as a whole is difficult to investigate and has not yet been adequately studied. Discussed below are recent experimental results on the kinetics of both formation and growth of soot particles as well as some ensuing conceptions about the mechanism of such processes.

STRUCTURE OF SOOT PARTICLES

The soot particles have a very compact structure. The density of their material [1] equals 2.0 g/cm³ which is only 10 % less than that of three-dimensionally-ordered graphite (2.26 g/cm³). Following Biscoe and Warren [2] and on the basis of the results of X-ray investigations, it has been assumed until recently that the soot particles comprised separate, irregularly located crystallites consisting of several approximately parallel graphite layers. Such a structure was termed " turbostratical ".

The application of high-resolution electron microscopes [3, 4] provided proof, but graphite layers, and not crystallites serve as building blocks for soot particles. These layers are bent to conform to the shape of the particles and have the form of shells replicating the outer surface of the particle. Thermal soot particles consist of concentric spherical shells. In particles of other types of soot, only the external shells repeat the shape of the outer surface, the internal structure of such particles containing obviously several centres of growth. The distance between the layers has a spread conforming to the general distribution law.

The compact and largely regular structure of the soot particles should be taken into account when considering the growth mechanism. It is evident, for instance, that one cannot logically imagine the creation of such a structure by consecutive association of more or less large blocks. Most probably, such a structure is the result of a molecular growth process for which the term " chemical crystallization " would perhaps be the most exact one. Experimental results have actually proved this.

GROWTH OF SOOT PARTICLES

The growth process of a soot particle is similar to that of a pyrolytic carbon film on a wall. It can be experimentally investigated in the absence of soot particle formation within a wide range of temperatures. The growth stage of soot particles has therefore been better investigated than the formation stage. Nevertheless, reliable data about the kinetics of pyrolitic carbon growth during the thermal decomposition of methane are available up to 1300 K only.[5] The growth rate of pyrolytic carbon is of the first order and is considerably inhibited by hydrogen. This inhibition effect can be well described by the Langmuir equation and can be attributed to a chemisorption of hydrogen. The growth rate of soot particles (in g cm^{-2} s^{-1}) can be expressed as follows:

$$W = 260 \, p_{CH_4}[1 - Bp_{H_2}/(1 + Bp_{H_2})] \exp(-66\,000/RT) \tag{1}$$

where p_{CH_4} and p_{H_2} are the partial pressures of methane and hydrogen, respectively, and R has units of cal mol^{-1} K^{-1}.

The inhibiting effect of hydrogen decreases when the temperature rises. The constant B in the Langmuir equation equals 40 at 1073 K and 25 at 1173 K. The activation energy of the process equals 66 ± 2 kcal/mol within a temperature range 1000-1300 K.

The growth rate of a pyrolytic carbon on a plane surface is governed by the same laws as that of the growth on the surface of soot particles and possesses the same activation energy but the rate constant is about 5 times higher. Possible causes of such a discrepancy are discussed below.

The growth rate of a pyrolytic carbon film is closely associated with the size of the crystallites being formed. Any individual hydrocarbon has at every temperature some constant average crystallite size for a stationary growth rate. It is reasonable to believe that the microcrystalline structure of the pyrolytic carbon film will reflect the molecular mechanism of its formation from molecules of the gaseous phase. Let us assume that each of the crystallites is being formed as a result of the growth of a nucleus in a basic plane, and that this growth continues until the crystallites, which expand towards each other, meet. Thus, the size of the crystallites depends on the rate of two processes, namely, the formation of nuclei and their growth. Consequently, if the growth rate and the average crystallite size are known from experiments, the formation rate of nuclei as well as the growth rate of crystallites can be determined by calculation.

So, for instance, the growth rate of a film obtained from methane on a plane surface at 1273 K in absence of hydrogen equals 250 Å/s, the average size of the crystallites L_a being 600 Å. These values correspond to a nuclei formation rate of $C = 2.6 \times 10^9$ nuclei cm^{-2} s^{-1} and to a crystallite growth rate of $W = 22$ Å/s.

The elementary collision theory permits one to determine from these data the activation energy of the nuclei formation as well as that of the crystallite growth. Assuming that a planar nucleus consists of a single atom of carbon, the activation energies of the nuclei formation E_n and crystallite growth E_g can be found from the equations:

$$E_n = 2.3 \, RT \log(N_f/C), \tag{2}$$

$$E_g = 2.3 \, RT \log(N_f/N_g), \tag{3}$$

where N_g = rate of film growth (atoms cm^{-2} s^{-2}) and N_f = number of collisions of methane molecules upon the surface (molecules cm^{-2} s^{-1}).

Substituting the values cited above for methane at 1073 K gives $E_n = 81$ and $E_g = 52$ kcal/mol. Consequently, the experimentally activation energy of the film growth process ($E = 66$ kcal/mol) represents the gross activation energy of both elementary processes.

According to these concepts, the formation of pyrocarbon is a peculiar branched-chain molecular process taking place on surfaces. The carbon atoms are built-in into a planar graphite lattice as a result of the interaction of methane molecules with surface carbon atoms which have free-valence electrons. The hydrocarbon radicals of the gaseous phase do not participate in this process. On the contrary, some of the methane molecules decompose on the growing carbon surface and produce new radicals while others break down directly into carbon and hydrogen. Thus, the solid surface generates either CH_3 or CH_2 radicals.[5]

This mechanism considered explains the difference of the pyrocarbon formation rates on the surface of soot particles and on a plane surface as being due to different sizes of the crystallites. Owing to the small dimensions of the soot particles, the crystallites cannot reach their stable size corresponding to the given temperature, and this slows down the total growth rate. It is also possible that the growth rate of a curved graphite layer is less than that of a planar one. This molecular growth mechanism of pyrocarbon during the thermal decomposition of methane is common for other hydrocarbons. This can, however, be regarded as true only for temperatures below 1300 K.

There are not enough reliable data on the kinetics of the growth at higher temperatures,[6] largely resulting from the undetermined composition of the gas interacting with the wall. Existing data on the formation kinetics and structure of the pyrocarbon, nevertheless, allows one to state that the chain process of its growth takes place at temperatures up to about 2500 K. Actually pyrocarbon films obtained at high temperatures show a pronounced texture and an anisotropic microcrystalline structure [7] not differing substantially from those produced at lower temperatures. And kinetic data for the rate of pyrocarbon growth for methane and acetylene at 1800 to 2100 K allows one to conclude that, for films growing at such temperatures, one active collision of a molecule upon the surface takes place per 10^3 to 10^4 molecular collisions.

There is no reason definitely to claim that the growth of the film at higher temperatures is such a strictly molecular process as that below 1300 K. On the contrary, one may believe that radicals contained in the gaseous phase can play a more or less important role under such conditions.

FORMATION OF SOOT PARTICLES

The classical scheme of aerosol formation including nucleation and growth is fully applicable to soot formation processes. But, unlike condensation, nuclei of soot particles are products of a chemical reaction. And since the number of molecules required to form a nucleus cannot enter the reaction simultaneously, there is no doubt that the nucleation of a soot particle is of a complex nature and comprises a number of consecutive elementary acts. The understanding of the soot particle generation mechanism requires measurements of the process rate under various conditions. The obtaining of such data involves considerable difficulties due to the high rates of the process. Nevertheless, available results of such measurements, although far from complete, can be considered important.

They are briefly summarized: (i) the formation rate of soot particles has a sharp maximum corresponding to a small degree of total decomposition of the hydrocarbon.[9, 10] (ii) The soot particle formation process is characterized by the presence of concentration thresholds and an induction period.[6] (iii) The initial growth rate of soot particles is considerably (in some instance, by two orders) higher than the stabilized growth rate of a pyrocarbon surface.[11]

(iv) During the thermal decomposition of diluted acetylene, soot particles may form by two substantially different processes. The activation energy of one of them is 33 and of the other 175 kcal/mol.[11] (v) For self-combustion of acetylene, the dispersity of the soot formed will be the greater, the higher the temperature in the front of the flame. A maximum dispersity will be reached in detonation of acetylene, when—due to minimum losses of heat from the front by radiation—the temperature reaches its highest value. The specific surface of soot obtained from detonation of acetylene attains 180 m²/g (average particle size 170 Å). The specific surface of detonation soot does not depend on the initial pressure.[12] (vi) The absolute rate of soot particle formation in the diffusion-type burning of an acetylene + hydrogen mixture equals 10^{15} particles cm^{-3} s^{-1}. When acetylene detonates at an initial pressure of 10 kg/cm², this rate exceeds 10^{19} particles cm^{-3} s^{-1}.

All the experimental facts and theoretical considerations suggest the following model. The formation of soot particles is, like any process of the initiation of a new dispersed phase, limited by the nucleation. Nuclei may be of two types, namely, either complex unsaturated polymer molecules, or simple radicals. The properties of the primary nucleus define the process of its further growth and the properties of the soot particles produced. A rough analogy may here be drawn between a nucleus and a DNA molecule in which a genetical code is incorporated.

The " molecular nucleus " obtained as a result of reactions including condensation, aromatisation and dehydrogenation, continues to grow by virtue of the same reactions. The product will be a soot particle having an indefinite structure, being X-ray amorphous, and containing a considerable amount of volatiles. Such a process was investigated by Homann et al.[13, 14] in rich premixed flames of acetylene, and was observed by Johnson and Andersen [15] as well as by Tesner and Altshuler [11] during the thermal decomposition of acetylene. It seems that the growth rate of these soot particles considerably exceeds that of the pyrocarbon.

A " radical nucleus " initiates a quite different chain of transformations which finally produce soot particles with a compact, regular, and well-investigated structure. The first step of these transformations should be the conversion of the radical nucleus into a nucleus having a physical surface, i.e., into one which is similar to the nucleus of an aerosol particle produced by condensation. Such a nucleus is a soot particle of a minimum size and its further growth process is similar to the pyrocarbon growth described above.

The formation process of a nucleus from a radical-nucleus has not yet been investigated and is most difficult to investigate. Taking into account all that is known about radical processes, this stage may be conceived as follows. The initial interactions between the radical nucleus and the original hydrocarbon molecules are radical reactions resulting in the formation of new radicals. It is quite clear that the activity of the radicals falls in the course of this process by formation of carbon–carbon bonds. Hence, the rate of their interaction with the original molecules will decrease too. At a certain moment the radical nucleus will lose its radical properties, attain the properties of a physical surface, and become a soot particle of minimum size thereby representing a nucleus.

Consequently, in contrast to the usual radical chain, in the chain under consideration more and more heavy and less active radicals will be formed and its propagation rate will gradually slow down. So, for instance, for acetylene the elementary reaction act and the chain leading to the formation of a nucleus are as follows:

elementary act :

$$C_n + C_2H_2 \rightarrow C_{n+2} + H_2,$$

chain :

$$C_2 \rightarrow C_4 \rightarrow C_6 \rightarrow \cdots \rightarrow C_n$$

radical nucleus   nucleus

The formation of a great number of soot particles from radical nuclei may be described by equations similar to those of a branched chain process with mutual termination of chains.[9] The termination represents in this process the destruction of radical nuclei on the surface of the particles formed. Concerning the branching, which was postulated in order to explain the experimentally observed increase of the particle formation rate, its mechanism is not understood.

A comparison of calculations and experimental data permits the determination of the activation energy of the formation of radical nuclei. For the formation of soot from acetylene its value is around 170 kcal/mol. Obviously, the C_2 radical is the only one requiring such an activation energy for its formation from acetylene.

The chain-type scheme of the nucleation and growth described above cannot be regarded as strictly proved but it explains satisfactorily the experimentally observed regularities. This scheme does not take into account the coagulation of the growing particles which actually takes place and results at late stages of particle growth in the formation of a chain-like structure.

The regions of existence of both soot formation processes described above are still indefinite. Probably the first process initiated by a molecular nucleus takes place at lower temperatures and at small concentrations of hydrocarbons. It seems that industrial soot production technology is probably based on an application of the second process, since the structure of all industrial soots is practically identical and they do not contain any considerable amounts of volatiles.

Finally, a great resemblance must be noted between the formation mechanisms of pyrocarbon and soot. Both are two-stage processes limited by nucleation. And both are branched chain processes. The growth process of a carbon surface is similar to a planar model of the three-dimensional soot formation process. The difference consists in that the growth of crystallites on a surface is limited by their coming into contact. The formation rate of planar nuclei and their growth rate at a constant hydrocarbon concentration in the gaseous phase is constant. But the growth of nuclei in volume is not limited, although the generated surface of the particles results in the destruction of radical nuclei and in the slowing down of the particle formation rate.

[1] A. Voet, Rubber Chem. Technol., 1964, 37, 630.
[2] J. Biscoe and B. E. Warren, J. Appl. Phys., 1942, 13, 364.
[3] R. D. Heidenreich, W. M. Hess and L. L. Ban, J. Appl. Cryst., 1968, 1, 1.
[4] P. A. Marsh, A. Voet, T. J. Mullens and L. D. Price, Carbon, 1971, 9, 797.
[5] P. A. Tesner, M. M. Polyakova and S. S. Mikheeva, DAN S.S.S.R., 1972, 203, 402.
[6] P. A. Tesner, Formation of Carbon from Gas Phase Hydrocarbons (Chimia, Moscow 1972).
[7] J. C. Bokros, Deposition, Structure, Properties of Pyrolytic Carbon. Chemistry and Physics of Carbon, ed. P. L. Walker (Marcel Dekker, New York), vol. 5, p. 27.
[8] B. N. Altshuler and P. A. Tesner, Gasovaya Promishl., 1969, 6, 41.
[9] P. A. Tesner, T. D. Snegiryova and V. G. Knorre, Combustion Flame, 1971, 17, 253.
[10] P. A. Tesner et al., Combustion Flame, 1971, 17, 279.
[11] P. A. Tesner and B. N. Altshuler, DAN S.S.S.R., 1969, 187, 1100.
[12] P. A. Tesner et al., Combustion and Explosion. (Proc. 3rd All-Union Symp. Combustion and Explosion). (Nauka, Moscow 1972), p. 725.
[13] K. H. Homann, Combustion Flame, 1967. 11, 265.
[14] K. H. Homann and H. G. Wagner, Proc. Roy. Soc. A, 1968, 307, 141.
[15] G. L. Johnson and R. C. Anderson, Proc. 5th Conf. Carbon, 1962, 1, 395.

Coagulation of Carbon Particles in Premixed Flames

By J. B. Howard, B. L. Wersborg and G. C. Williams

Fuels Research Laboratory, Dept. of Chemical Engineering, Massachusetts Institute of Technology, Cambridge, Massachusetts

Received 4th December, 1972

The size distribution, number concentration, and fraction charged of carbon particles at successive stages of formation in a low pressure flat flame were measured using molecular beam sampling, involving electrical beam deflection and electron microscopy of beam deposits and an optical absorption technique. Observed cluster-type structure within roughly spherical particles and decreasing particle number concentration following rapid nucleation, indicate the particles do indeed coagulate during growth. Particle size and number concentration data confirm this conclusion, although the experimental coagulation rate exceeds by a factor of about 10 the kinetic theory collision rate approximately adjusted for electrostatic forces, based upon the measured extent of particle charging, and Van der Waals attraction. Calculations, based upon extrapolation of the experimental coagulation rate constant into the flame region of significant particle nucleation and surface reaction, indicate that the particles nucleated first can grow predominantly by surface growth to a volume mean diameter of about 100 Å and that the number of primary particles per spherical unit within the final chainlike clusters is of order 10. Thus crystallites, the number of which is of order 10^3 per spherical unit, do not represent former particles.

Although the chemistry of dispersed carbon formation in flames has been the object of many investigations, coagulation of the particles has received little attention. Coagulation is known to occur in the final stages of carbon formation, but its role during particle nucleation and growth by surface reaction has remained obscure. The nucleation step would involve coagulation if nucleation amounts to a continuous transition from large hydrocarbon molecules to small soot particles of continuously decreasing number concentration, as advocated by Homann.[1] Bartholomé and Sachsse [2] and Fenimore and Jones [3] assume that carbon particles can grow by coagulation to a size too large to permit their burnout. If at least some of the carbon particles are charged, coagulation may be influenced by interparticle electrostatic forces. This influence and the importance of ionic nucleation have been discussed previously.[4-6]

Recently,[7] the following quantitative connection between particle growth by surface reaction and coagulation was derived by relating the rate of change of the volume mean particle radius a_3 to particle number concentration n, rate of appearance $\dot{N}_u$ of the smallest particles of radius a_0, and surface growth rate $\dot{S}_i$ of particles in the ith class having area mean radius a_i:

$$\frac{d[\ln(a_3)]}{dt} = \frac{1}{na_3^3}\sum_i n_i a_i^2 \dot{S}_i + (a_0/a_3)^3 \dot{N}_u/3n - \tfrac{1}{3}\frac{d[\ln(n)]}{dt}. \tag{1}$$

The surface growth rate at a given flame position may be assumed to be independent of particle size. Also, $\dot{N}_u$ and coagulation rate $\dot{N}_c$ are related by

$$\dot{N}_u = dn/dt + \dot{N}_c. \tag{2}$$

Denoting the area mean radius as a_2, eqn (1) then becomes

$$\frac{d[\ln(a_3)]}{dt} = (a_2^2/a_3^3)\dot{S} + (a_0/a_3)^3 \dot{N}_c/3n + [(a_0/a_3)^3 - 1]\frac{d[\ln(n)]}{3dt}. \qquad (3)$$

These equations show that the rate of change in particle radius is in general different from the surface growth rate, and they provide a means for distinguishing between the contributions of coagulation, surface growth, and nucleation.

The objective of the present investigation was to measure the rate of carbon particle coagulation under well known flame conditions and to assess quantitatively the role of coagulation during particle nucleation and growth. To these ends, particle size distribution, number concentration, and fraction of particles charged were measured at different stages of carbon formation in a unidimensional, low pressure flame using molecular beam sampling, electron microscopy, and optical absorption. These and other experimental results are compared with the theoretical coagulation rate based upon kinetic gas theory and a simple account of interparticle Van der Waals and electrostatic forces.

The sampling and analysis of carbon particles from flames using multistage molecular beam sampling and electron microscopy were improved until 15 Å diameter particles could be included in the measurements. Details of the apparatus and experimental techniques were described earlier.[7] In general, a flat premixed acetylene-oxygen flame maintained at 20 Torr, equivalence ratio 3, and cold gas velocity of 50 cm/s on a 7 cm diameter burner was probed along its centre line at different heights above the burner using a quartz nozzle expanding into the beam system. By opening a shutter for an adjusted length of time, the sample beam was admitted to the detection stage, operated at 8×10^{-6} Torr, in which particles were deposited directly onto electron microscope grids. A second sample was taken under identical conditions, except that an appropriate electric field was applied across the beam to deflect all charged particles. The difference between the deposit intensities in the two cases permitted calculation of the fraction of particles charged. The intensity was obtained, together with particles size and size distribution, by a particle count and diameter measurement on electron micrographs. The intensity measurements gave relative particle number concentrations from which approximate absolute values were obtained by calculating a calibration factor from the beam geometry traced by soot deposits.

The absolute value of particle number concentration was also determined by optical absorption measurements[8] in a second flame produced under identical conditions on a 10 cm diameter burner. The attenuation signal was obtained using a laser source ($\lambda = 6328$ Å) and two photomultiplier detectors. Temperature profiles were obtained using SiO_2-coated thermocouples. The absorption technique requires knowledge of the extinction cross section of young carbon particles which, because of their substantial hydrogen content, differ optically from the older carbon particles for which optical properties are available. This information was obtained using the molecular beam system to collect particle samples on glass slides and adjacent electron microscope grids. Subsequent measurement of the attenuation of the laser beam by the slide deposits, and of particle size distribution and number per unit area in the deposits using the electron microscope grids, permitted calculation of the extinction cross section.

Under the flame conditions here studied, visual observation of flame luminosity indicates that carbon formation starts at 1.5 cm height above the burner. Electron micrographs of representative carbon particles collected at different heights above

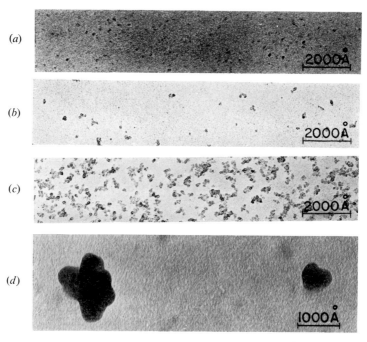

PLATE 1.—Carbon particles at different growth stages (a, b and c at 4 cm, 6 cm and 7 cm height above the burner of a 20 Torr C_2H_2—O_2 flame, magnification 90 000 × ; d at onset of chaining in a 1 atm C_3H_8—O_2 flame, magnification 158 000 ×).

the burner are shown in plate 1.   Up to 4 cm, the particles are mainly spherical (*a*) whereas chainlike clusters become noticeable at 6 cm (*b*) and predominant at 7 cm (*c*).   In (*d*) are shown enlarged particles from a propane-oxygen flame at 1 atm.

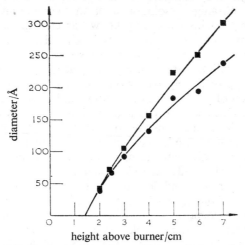

FIG. 1.—Mean particle diameter [volume mean diameter (■), number mean diameter (●)].

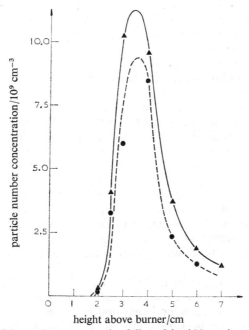

FIG. 2.—Particle number concentration [all particles (▲), uncharged particles (●)].

Their shape, which is representative of that which prevails just before chaining becomes predominant, may be interpreted as evidence for the fact that carbon particles will collide at all stages of formation, but the earliest collisions are hidden by large simultaneous surface growth which tends to fill in the boundaries between particles.

This behaviour leads to a gradual transition from roughly spherical clusters to the familar chainlike clusters. Thus, the spherically appearing units within the chains may not be used to calculate surface growth rates or the number of nuclei, as these units themselves are generally composed of several primary units. This interpretation is supported by ultrahigh resolution electron micrographs [9] on which may be recognized particle domains commonly known as crystallites, arranged around different growth centres within one " spherical " unit. The growth centres appear to have nucleated independently and grown for some time as separate particles, and to have coagulated while surface growth possibly accompanied by some migration was sufficiently rapid approximately to even out the cluster surface.

In the determination of particle size distribution and number concentration from electron micrographs, clusters were counted as single particles and non-spherical clusters were assigned the diameter of the volume equivalent sphere. By analyzing about 100 particles per micrograph, measurement error was kept below 10 % for diameter, and 20 % for relative number concentration. Owing to the difficulty of seeing the smallest particles under the electron microscope, error in the case of absolute number concentration undoubtedly exceeds 20 %. The size distributions thus measured progress from approximately Gaussian at 2 cm height above the burner to approximately lognormal at 7 cm. The relative standard deviation is about 0.2 and independent of mean particle size so long as the particles are spherical, but it rapidly approaches about 0.5 with the appearance of chainlike clusters. Mean particle size and number concentration at different heights above the burner are shown in fig. 1 and 2. From a small concentration at 2 cm, particle number increases rapidly at first, peaks shortly after 3 cm, and then decreases. This behaviour is assumed to reflect the opposing effects of nucleation and coagulation, the number increasing effect of nucleation being dominant at first, but subsequently negligible in comparison with the decreasing effect of coagulation. In view of the error in these data, the exact position of the particle number peak should be located by more accurate measurements.

The absolute number concentrations measured by absorption (not shown) at 4 and 5 cm height above the burner differ by less than 20 % from those determined by electron microscopy, which is within the error limit of the latter technique. The absorption values at 3 cm height above the burner are, however, twice as large. The difference could be due to absorption by large gas phase hydrocarbons or to incomplete detection of small particles on the micrographs.

A similar decrease in particle number with increasing height above the burner was observed before by Bonne, Homann and Wagner.[10] Their remarkable study does not use the concept of a volume equivalent particle diameter for chainlike clusters. Thus, their number concentration measurements describe the number of approximately spherical units within a chainlike cluster which stays nearly constant in the tail of the flame.

The measured concentration of neutral particles is given by the dashed line in fig. 2. The difference between these results and the corresponding total concentration values is the concentration of positively and negatively charged particles. The polarity of the charge, and charge per particle, where studied by reducing the deflecting field strength in a stepwise manner and collecting the particles on grids adjacent to the deposition area of neutral particles. This measurement gave intensity problems which prohibited a reliable count of particle density on the grids due to the difficulty of identification. Only chainlike clusters could reliably be distinguished from background grain and contamination ; these particles were exclusively positively charged. The results do indicate, however, that all charged particles under the flame conditions studied are predominantly of positive polarity with one charge per particle, but a few negative particles and a few particles with two charges cannot be excluded. Our present charge measurements, which use a Faraday cup instead of the electron microscope grids, indicate that carbon particles under different flame conditions can be predominantly neutral, positively charged, or negatively charged. The charging state is a strong function of flame temperature which in turn is influenced by the cold gas velocity and gas composition.

Experimental coagulation rate constants were obtained by assuming a mono-disperse system and expressing the coagulation rate in the form of the Smoluchowski [11] equation

$$\dot{N}_c = \tfrac{1}{2}Kn^2 \tag{4}$$

where K is the coagulation rate constant. Combining eqn (2) and (4) gives

$$d(1/n)/dt = K/2 - \dot{N}_u/n^2 \tag{5}$$

which shows there exists a linear relationship between n^{-1} and t when the rate of nucleation is sufficiently small, the slope of the line being $K/2$. Inverse particle

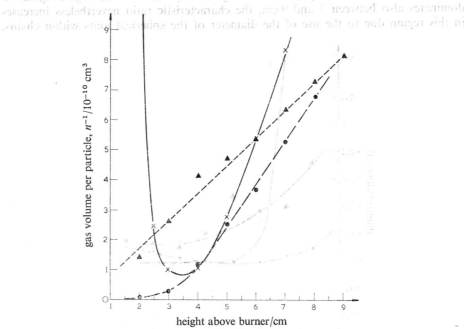

FIG. 3.—Gas volume per particle at different growth stages [electron microscope data of this study ($\times$); calculation from electron microscope data of Homann and Wagner ($\blacktriangle$); calculation from absorption data of Bonne and Wagner ($\bullet$)].

number plots are shown in fig. 3 for the electron microscopy data of both this study and that of Homann and Wagner [12] and absorption data of Bonne and Wagner.[13] Particle number concentrations of Bonne, Homann and Wagner were calculated from their values of soot mass fraction and particle diameter. Differences between the present data and those of the previous studies are due in part to the facts that the previous workers used an equivalence ratio of 3.5 and Bonne and Wagner, in the calibration of their absorption measurements, did not allow for change in the extinction cross section of young carbon particles with change in particle composition.

The approximately straight part of the curves downstream of about 4 cm height above the burner indicates a predominant coagulation of carbon particles to larger clusters; twice the slope of each line is the experimental coagulation rate constant for the flame conditions and zones represented.

Additional information is derived from eqn (3) which, in the region where surface growth and nucleation are negligible compared with coagulation, reduces to

$$d[\ln(n)]/3d[\ln(a_3)] = -1. \tag{6}$$

Values of the characteristic ratio identified by eqn (6) at different heights above the burner are shown in fig. 4. The numerical evaluation of particle number concentration extrapolates the values of this study to 8 cm height above the burner and shows that the characteristic ratio is scattered due to measuring errors. Its average is almost exactly -1, indicative of predominant particle coagulation, downstream of 4.5 cm height above the burner. The characteristic ratio calculated from the absorption measurements of Bonne and Wagner [13] is -1 from 4 to 6 cm height above the burner. In this region, the particles are approximately spherical and their size and number concentration change predominantly by coagulation. Although coagulation dominates also between 7 and 9 cm, the characteristic ratio nevertheless increases in this region due to the use of the diameter of the spherical units within chains,

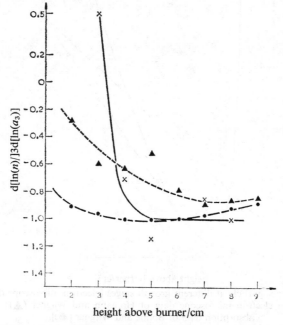

FIG. 4.—Characteristic ratio for particle coagulation [electron microscope data of this study ($\times$); calculation from electron microscope data of Homann and Wagner ($\blacktriangle$); calculation from absorption data of Bonne and Wagner ($\bullet$)].

which remained nearly constant, instead of the volume equivalent diameter of the cluster. Similar to the values obtained by electron microscopy in the present study, the deviations from -1 in the region from 2 to 3 cm are due to surface growth and nucleation influences. The values obtained for the study of Homann and Wagner [12] are rather scattered, which may be due to the fact that particles less than 40 Å diameter were not included in the electron microscope analysis.   Thus, experimental coagulation rate constants are only obtained from the measurements of Bonne and Wagner between about 4 and 7 cm height above the burner and from the present data downstream of the 4.5 cm position.   The values found are given below in terms of the kinetic theory collision model.

Carbon particles in low pressure flames are under free molecular flow conditions and therefore constitute a highly dispersed aerosol.[14]   If the size distribution is approximated as monodisperse, the coagulation rate constant is

$$K = 16a^2 y(\pi kT/m)^{\frac{1}{2}} \tag{7}$$

where a is the mean particle radius, y is a correction factor accounting for interparticle forces, k is the Boltzmann constant, T is temperature, and m is particle mass, here estimated by assuming particle density to be 2 g/cm³.   Experimental y factors, shown in fig. 5, were obtained from eqn (7) using K values calculated as described above from line slopes in fig. 3 and a gas velocity of 3 m/s at 2000 K.   Values for all flame positions studied are presented for completeness, but the only values sufficiently free of nucleation effects so as to reflect coagulation behaviour alone are those in the regions described above as yielding coagulation rate constants.   In these regions, y appears approximately constant, indicating little or no net particle size and temperature influences.   The y values from this study are approximately 29 and very similar to those of the absorption study, which are around 21.

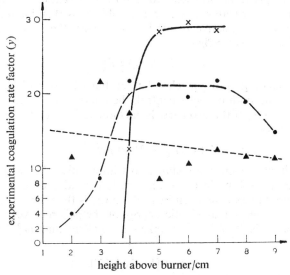

FIG. 5.—Experimental coagulation rate factor (y) [electron microscope data of this study ($\times$); calculation from electron microscope data of Homann and Wagner (▲); calculation from absorption data of Bonne and Wagner (●)].

In an attempt to explain why the observed coagulation rate is much larger than the kinetic theory collision rate, the contributions of Van der Waals and electrostatic forces were examined by calculating theoretical y values for simplified cases described presently.   Cloud shielding and diffusional effects are negligible under the experimental conditions and the particles are again assumed to be uniform in size.   The effects of gas-particle collisions on the energy and monentum of two interacting particles are neglected. The contribution of Van der Waals forces to the potential of two spherical particles of radius a with distance r between centres is [15]

$$E_v = -(H/12)[z^{-1}+(z-1)^{-1}+2 \ln (1-z^{-1})] \tag{8}$$

where H is the Hamaker constant related to the London-Van der Waals constant α by $H = \pi^2 g^2\alpha$, g being the number of atoms per unit volume in the particles, and $z = (r/2a)^2$. The electrostatic contribution to the potential, using Maxwell's [16] method of electric images, is

$$E_e = (k_e e^2/2a)[(S_{11}\psi^{-1}-1)(Q_1^2+Q_2^2)+2(a/r)S_{12}\psi^{-1}Q_1Q_2] \tag{9}$$

where

$$k_e = 9\times10^9 \, J \, m \, C^{-2}, \quad e = 1.6\times10^{-19}C, \quad \psi = S_{11}^2-(a/r)^2S_{12}^2,$$

$$S_{11} = (1-\beta)\sum_{m=0}^{\infty} \theta^m/(1-\beta\theta^{2m})$$

$$S_{12} = (1-\theta^2)\sum_{m=0}^{\infty} \theta^m/(1-\theta^{2m+2})$$

$\beta=[(1+\theta)a/r]^2$, $\theta=\gamma-(\gamma^2-1)^{\frac{1}{2}}$, $\gamma=r^2/2a^2-1$, and eQ_1 and eQ_2 are the particle charges. The equivalent equations for unequal particle radii are given elsewhere.[6]

If both particles are charged with the same polarity, opposing electrostatic repulsion and Van der Waals attraction lead to a positive maximum in the potential $E(r_m) = E_v+E_e$ at $r = r_m$, where $r_m > 2a$. Since collision is then limited to particles whose initial kinetic energy relative to axes moving with the mass centre exceeds $E(r_m)$, it is reasonable to assume that

$$y = \exp [-E(r_m)/kT]. \tag{10}$$

In all other cases, including both particles charged but with opposite polarity, only one particle charged, and both particles neutral, the interparticle forces are attractive and, from classical analysis of the two particle encounter,[17] the collision cross section is increased by the factor

$$y = (1+\varepsilon/a)^2[1-2E(\varepsilon)/\mu v_r^2] \tag{11}$$

where 2ε is the minimum separation distance to within which the particles' surfaces may approach without resulting in collision, $E(\varepsilon)$ is the value of E_v+E_e when $r = 2a+2\varepsilon$, μ is the reduced mass here given by $m/2$, and v_r is the relative velocity of the particles. Since the average initial kinetic energy of the pair relative to axes moving with their mass centre is $2 kT$,[18] v_r^2 is taken as $4 kT/m$ and μv_r^2 becomes $2kT$. Therefore

$$y = (1+\varepsilon/a)^2[1-E(\varepsilon)/kT]. \tag{12}$$

The proper value of ε is that value for which y is minimum.[19] If neither particle is charged, eqn (8) and (12) give

$$y = z_m[1+(H/12kT)\{z_m^{-1}+(z_m-1)^{-1}+2 \ln (1-z_m^{-1})\}] \tag{13}$$

where z_m, which is the value of z at $r = 2a+2\varepsilon$, is the root of the equation

$$(3-2z_m)/(z_m-1)^2-2 \ln (1-z_m^{-1}) = 12kT/H. \tag{14}$$

If one particle is charged, or if both particles are charged but of opposite polarity, ε is found by numerical or graphical minimization of y in eqn (12) using eqn (8) and (9).

Values of y calculated as described above for different particle sizes, states of charging, and H values are shown in fig. 6. The value of H for carbon particles in flames is not known but it should be within the range 10^{-20}–10^{-18} J. If neither particle is charged, y is independent of particle size and equal to 2.75 for the largest H here considered. If one particle carries one charge, y is increased by image forces

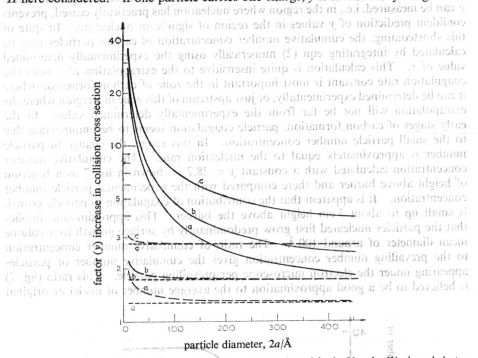

FIG. 6.—Increase in collision cross section of two equal sized particles by Van der Waals and electrostatic attraction $[Q_1 = -Q_2 = 1$ (solid); $Q_1 = 0$, $Q_2 = \pm 1$ (broken); $Q_1 = Q_2 = 0$ (dashed); Hamaker constant $= 10^{-20}(a)$, $10^{-19}(b)$, $10^{-18}(c)$ J; $T = 1800$ K].

but this effect compared with that of Van der Waals forces alone is substantial only for small particles and small values of H. It appears that the y resulting from image forces cannot be substantially larger than 3 if the particles have predominantly only one charge. If both particles carry one charge of opposite polarity, y is of order 10 for small particles. However, if ambipolar charging predominates, repulsion between particles of the same polarity must also be considered and the net effect on coagulation rate may be small.

In view of the above calculations and the observed condition of 0 or 1 positive charge per particle, it appears that Van der Waals and electrostatic forces together may account for a factor of only 2 or 3 increase in the coagulation rate constant under the conditions studied. The situation may however, be quite different for other flame conditions in which particle ionization is more pronounced, and even under the present conditions the detected charge must be regarded as one cause for the chained appearance of the final carbon particles. Nevertheless, a factor of order 10 increase in y remains to be explained. Other possible causes meriting study include polydispersity and deviations from the assumed spherical shape.[20] Our calculations, not reported here, show that polydispersity exerts less than a 20 % increase if the particles are assumed to be neutral, but the actual effect undoubtedly exceeds this prediction since y for small charged particles colliding with large neutral particles can be significant. The possibility that substantial numbers of particles could be decomposed or burnt out seems unlikely for the fuel rich conditions employed.

The inability to predict the coagulation rate constant in the flame region in which it can be measured, i.e., in the region where nucleation has practically ceased, prevents confident prediction of y values in the region of significant nucleation. In spite of this shortcoming, the cumulative number concentration of carbon particles may be calculated by integrating eqn (2) numerically using the experimentally determined value of y. This calculation is quite insensitive to the extrapolation of y since the coagulation rate constant is most important in the zone of carbon formation where it can be determined experimentally, or just upstream of this zone in a region where the extrapolation will not be far from the experimentally determined value. In the early stages of carbon formation, particle coagulation seems to be unimportant due to the small particle number concentration. In this range, the change in particle number is approximately equal to the nucleation rate.[7] The cumulative number concentration calculated with a constant $y = 28.7$ is shown in fig. 7 as a function of height above burner and there compared with the experimental particle number concentration. It is apparent that the contribution of coagulation to particle growth is small up to about 3 cm height above the burner. This approximation implies that the particles nucleated first grow predominantly by surface growth to a volume mean diameter of around 100 Å. The ratio of cumulative number concentration to the prevailing number concentration gives the cumulative number of particles appearing under the electron microscope per prevailing particle. This ratio (fig. 7) is believed to be a good approximation to the average number of nuclei or original

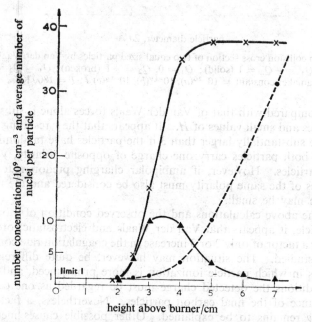

FIG. 7.—Instantaneous and accumulative particle number concentration and average number of nuclei per particle at different growth stages [accumulative particle number concentration ($\times$); instantaneous particle number concentration ($\blacktriangle$); ratio of accumulative to instantaneous particle number concentration ($\bullet$)].

particles in each prevailing particle because the concentration of unobservable particles should be small owing to the good lower limit of visibility (15 Å) and the rapid growth of young particles by surface reaction. Surface growth of carbon particles becomes quite small after 4 cm height above the burner, which position coincides with the onset of predominant chain formation.[7] Thus, the number of nuclei per spherical unit in a chainlike particle is about equal to that calculated between 4 and 5 cm height above the burner. This ratio is of order 10 and is substantially smaller than the number of crystallites per spherical unit, which is of order 10^3. According to this result, crystallites in carbon particles do not represent former particles. Thus the structure of these particle domains may be used to locate zones of predominant surface growth which in turn identify nuclei within spherical units.

We are grateful to Project SQUID whose support under contract N00014–67–A–0226–0005, NR–098–039 made this work possible.

[1] K. H. Homann, *Angew. Chem. Int. Ed.*, 1968, **7**, 414.

[2] E. Bartholomé and H. Sachsse, *Z. Elektrochem.*, 1949, **53**, 326.

[3] C. P. Fenimore and G. W. Jones, *Combustion Flame*, 1969, **13**, 303.

[4] E. R. Place and F. J. Weinberg, *Eleventh Symp. (Int.) on Combustion*, (The Combustion Inst., Pittsburgh, 1967), p. 245.

[5] J. B. Howard, *Twelfth Symp. (Int.) on Combustion*, (The Combustion Inst., Pittsburgh, 1969), p. 877.

[6] R. T. Ball and J. B. Howard, *Thirteenth Symp. (Int.) on Combustion* (The Combustion Inst., Pittsburgh, 1971), p. 353.

[7] B. L. Wersborg, J. B. Howard and G. C. Williams, *Fourteenth Symp. (Int.) on Combustion* (The Combustion Inst., Pittsburgh, 1973, p. 929).

[8] L. Fox, *S.M. thesis* (1972, Massachusetts Inst. Tech., Cambridge, Massachusetts).

[9] F. A. Heckman, personal communication, 1971, Cabot Corp., Billerica, Massachusetts.

[10] U. Bonne, K. H. Homann and H. Gg. Wagner, *Tenth Symp. (Int.) on Combustion* (The Combustion Inst., Pittsburgh, 1965), p. 503.

[11] M. von Smoluchowski, *Z. phys. Chem.*, 1917, **92**, 129.

[12] K. H. Homann and H. Gg. Wagner, *Ber. Bunsenges. phys. Chem.*, 1965, **69**, 20.

[13] U. Bonne and H. Gg. Wagner, *Ber. Bunsenges. phys. Chem.*, 1965, **69**, 35.

[14] B. L. Wersborg, *Sc.D. thesis* (1972, Massachusetts Inst. Tech., Cambridge, Massachusetts).

[15] H. C. Hamaker, *Physica*, 1937, **4**, 1058.

[16] J. C. Maxwell, *A Treatise on Electricity and Magnetism* (Dover Publications, Inc., New York, 1954, republication of 3rd ed. of 1891), vol. 1, chap. 11, pp. 244-283.

[17] J. O. Hirschfelder, C. F. Curtiss and R. B. Bird, *Molecular Theory of Gases and Liquids* (John Wiley and Sons, Inc., New York, 1954), chap. 1, pp. 45-51.

[18] S. Chapman and T. G. Cowling, *The Mathematical Theory of Non-Uniform Gases* (Cambridge University Press, Cambridge, 2nd ed., 1962), chap. 5, p. 93.

[19] N. A. Fuchs and A. G. Sutugin, *J. Colloid Sci.*, 1965, **20**, 492.

[20] G. Zebel, *Aerosol Science*, ed. C. N. Davis (Academic Press, New York, 1966), chap. 2, p. 31.

Smokes, Droplets, Flames and Electric Fields

By F. J. Weinberg

Imperial College, London, S.W.7

Received 23rd November, 1972

The paper summarises recent results on the influence of electric fields on carbon, silica and lead oxide smokes, as well as on suspensions of fuel droplets, in flame systems. The object, in each case, is to cause the particles to acquire charge for their subsequent manipulation by fields. Examples of using this as a method of controlling the trajectories of particles—either to remove them or to affect the process of their growth or consumption in the reaction zone—are discussed. The latter includes a measure of control over the reaction, by varying particle sizes and concentrations and by transposing charged nuclei. Mechanisms of charge acquisition are considered theoretically and it is shown that, in the absence of other charging mechanisms (such as thermionic emission or electrical breakdown of the gas), chemi-ionization in the flame may be used for this purpose. On the supposition that diminishing resources of fossil fuels and increasing concern about pollution will allow consideration of more complex combustion systems in future, a theoretical assessment of the maximum effects attainable in practice is carried out for the variety of effects observable in the laboratory.

A great variety of smokes—e.g., of soot, ash, metal oxides from additives—are produced in flames. On the input side, suspensions or sprays of fuel droplets are frequently involved. Particulate suspensions associated with flames acquire charge, if for no other reason than because flames produce a plentiful supply of ions and, in the presence of electric fields, these attach to particles. Charged particulates can be manipulated by electric fields, not only when they are already fully grown, but also during the process of their formation or burning up. It is for this reason that the association of electric fields with flames involving smokes or droplets is of practical, as well as of fundamental, interest.

A series of studies [1-6] of these phenomena has been carried out, yielding many interesting results showing the large effects which can be exercised by applied fields, but perhaps not enough by way of clear distinction between what is of purely academic interest and what methods of electrical control may have practical potential. It is to be expected, as one consequence of diminishing resources of fossil fuels and increasing concern about pollution, that the use of more elaborate combustion systems—including, perhaps, the application of electric fields—will come to seem less far-fetched and become more generally accepted. The object of this paper is to bring together the theoretical mechanisms and practical consequences of these effects in order to make suggestions as to the practicability of the various possible schemes.

EFFECTS OF MOVING CHARGED PARTICLES BY FIELDS

A charged particle will respond to a local field intensity E by acquiring a local velocity,

$$v = kE \tag{1}$$

in the direction of E, where k is its mobility. The manner in which k depends on particle size and on the charge acquired will be considered in the next section. This drift velocity of the particle is superimposed upon any flow-induced velocity and may be used to produce a variety of different effects.

The first and most obvious application is to modify the trajectories of fully-formed particles or of non-reacting droplets. They can be induced to deposit in specified places (the electrodes), prevented from depositing on other surfaces, caused to deviate from their normal trajectories along flow lines, even made to proceed in sine-waves by the application of an alternating field. As regards control of deposition, the best known example is probably that of " electrostatic " precipitators. In these devices, however, much energy is expended in maintaining a corona discharge for generating the charges which will attach to particles. In the applications discussed in this paper, the charges used are, in the main, formed spontaneously—for example, by chemi-ionization in the reaction zone. In the absence of the field they would merely recombine uselessly. Accordingly, the power dissipation is entirely due to the drift of charge and is exceedingly small (see later).

An example of using the principle of guiding fully-formed particles is the prevention of deposition on a particular surface. In the case illustrated by fig. 1, positively

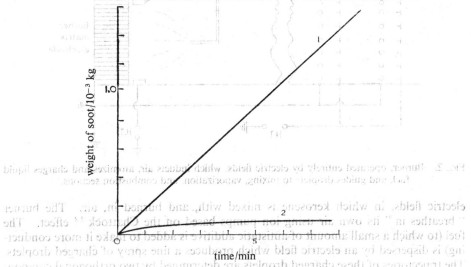

Fig. 1.—Weight of soot deposited on collector plate, against time. Curve 1, no field ; curve 2, plate positive with respect to burner.

charged soot particles [1] from a flame are prevented from collecting on a cooled plate immediately above it. The upper curve shows the continuously growing mass deposition in the absence of a field, the lower that when the collector plate is charged positively with respect to a matrix-electrode in the burner mouth. Under the latter conditions, carbon deposits copiously on the matrix and all around the burner mouth, although it has to travel downward to reach these sites. It has been shown [2] that all the carbon particles become charged, at least when a suitable field is applied, and can be made to drift to an electrode even against the direction of the gas flow.

Incidentally, in addition to its site, the form of the deposit is altered when deposition is influenced by an electric field. Since field lines converge on the protuberances formed by deposits, the growth on electrodes tends to occur in tree-like structures and at a much reduced density.

This principle can be applied to precipitate any particulate pollutant.[6] A somewhat modified procedure must be used for substances whose boiling point lies below the final flame temperature and which are at the same time not sufficiently active thermionically to emit electrons at temperatures below which they condense from their vapour phase. Lead oxide falls into this category. In that case we should have to depend on charging by flame ions over fairly large distances determined by the condensation process (unless the species happens to have a low ionization potential in the vapour phase). However, because of limitations due to space charge (see later), it is unprofitable to maintain fields over large distances and it has been shown [6] that very effective precipitators can be constructed based on small secondary flames used purely as ion sources, or even just on special surfaces maintained hot by flame products.

An entirely different example is provided by using a field to produce charged fuel droplets and guide them into a flame.[5] Fig. 2 shows a burner, operated entirely by

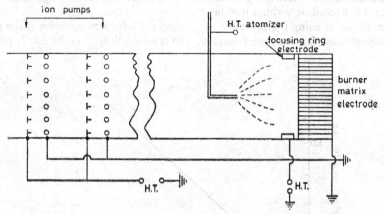

FIG. 2.—Burner, operated entirely by electric fields, which inducts air, atomizes and charges liquid fuel, and guides droplets to mixing, vaporization, and combustion sections.

electric fields, in which kerosene is mixed with, and burned in, air. The burner " breathes in " its own air using ion pumps based on the Chattock [12] effect. The fuel (to which a small amount of antistatic additive is added to make it more conducting) is dispersed by an electric field which produces a fine spray of charged droplets. The trajectories of these charged droplets are determined by two orthogonal components of the electric field : that between the jet and the matrix which guides them into the flame and that applied by the circumferential ring electrode which serves to vary the cross-sectional area of the spray and to focus it on a part of the matrix. In this manner a highly controllable, high-intensity flame has been produced [5] without the use of any fuel pump or air compressor, the process being controlled entirely by the potentials applied to the various electrodes.

Alternating fields may be used, for example, to cause droplets to evaporate in shorter distances by lengthening their trajectories in a given distance downstream. Thus, trajectories in the form of sine waves with excursion amplitudes of the order of centimetres have been recorded [3] for electrically sprayed liquids subjected to transverse a.c. fields.

A second group of applications arises when charged particles or droplets are manipulated by fields during the process in which they are formed or burned up. This makes it possible to vary their residence time in the reaction zone and, for example, exercise control over the size of particles which are formed in flames. Fig. 3 shows an example taken from two different studies.[4, 6] The carbon particles derive from a

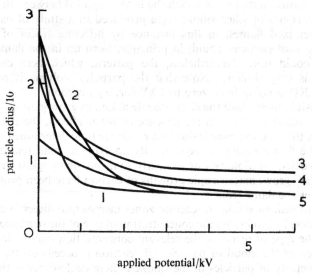

FIG. 3.—Particles grown in applied fields; variation of radius with applied potential. Curves 1 and 2, carbon particles in positive and negative charge flux; curves 3, 4 and 5, silica particles in positive flux at electrode separations of 0.35, 0.09 and 0.02 m,

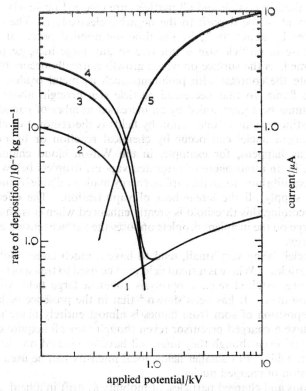

FIG. 4.—Collection rate of carbon from counter-flow diffusion flame as a function of applied potential in flux of positive charge. Curves 1, 2, 3 and 4 respectively on negative electrode, exhaust system, burner flange and total; curve 5, current.

flat counterflow diffusion flame [8] in which the field is applied between the two burner mouths. The particles of silica smoke were produced in a study of oxide particles generated in premixed flames, in this instance by injecting traces of hexamethyl disiloxane. The soot particles could, in principle, burn up in the flame zone; the silica particles could not. Nevertheless, the pattern, which here depends upon residence time, is very similar. Note that the particles' volume is reduced by a factor of about 200 in going from zero to 1 kV for, e.g., carbon.

It is also possible to produce the converse effect, i.e., to grow giant particles by the application of a suitable field. In the absence of other effects, the size to which a particle grows in the reaction zone is due to a residence time determined by the zone's thickness and the flow velocity through it. By applying a small retarding field, so as to hold the particles stationary (or as nearly so as possible) aginst the flow in the zone in which they grow, macroscopic growths of carbon have been produced simultaneously all over the flame front.[2]

The control of residence time in reaction zones merges into direct interaction with the reaction process by modifying the concentration of one of the participating species. Depending on the type of reaction, the relevant concentration may be in the form of total surface area of the cloud of particles (if reaction proceeds on the surface), or of the number density of particles in the smoke (where coalescence is the important process). Again, an example from studies on flame carbon [2] is taken. Fig. 4 shows rates of mass deposition on various parts of a counterflow diffusion flame system when the ion flux through the pyrolysis zone is positive (so that attachment charging reinforces thermionic emission and all particles are charged positively—as evidenced by the confinement of the deposit to the negative electrodes). The total mass deposited decreases by about 98 % by the time the applied potential reaches 1 kV. Thus, the decrease in particle size is not due to any large increase in the number of particles formed, as the surface on which growth normally occurs is being rapidly removed. (Note the contrast with pollutants such as metal oxides, which cannot burn up in the flame, so that decreased particle size brought about by decreased residence time must be accompanied by an increased number of particles.)

A fourth distinct means of interaction by fields is the removal of charged nuclei. Growth on charged nuclei can occur by chemical reaction or by purely physical condensation—as happens, for example, in the Wilson cloud chamber.[9-11] This occurs because, in an atmosphere of saturated vapour, droplets below a certain size cannot exist in equilibrium, when the surface energy made available by their contraction is sufficient to supply all the latent heat of vaporization. The effectiveness of a nucleus in overcoming this threshold is greatly enhanced when it is charged, for then the surface charge on the incipient droplets opposes the surface tension and diminishes the surface energy.

Charged nuclei, being very small, tend to have a much larger mobility than the fully-formed particles. Whereas a small field may be used to transport them to a zone in which they are required (e.g., a pyrolysis zone), a large field will very greatly diminish their number. It has been shown [4] that in the presence of large fields the mass rate of deposition of soot from flames is almost entirely made up of particles which do not have a charged precursor (even though they all acquire charge later in their existence and even though they might all have originated on charged nuclei in the absence of a field). For smaller fields, local intensity can be used to control the local concentration of charged nuclei.

Whenever ions and charged particles, of mobility k, drift in a field, a body force F per unit volume, acts on the gas, i.e.,

$$F = j/k,\qquad(2)$$

where j is the local current density. This induces a gas flow (the " Chattock wind effect "[12]) the precise nature and magnitude of which [13, 14] depends on the geometry of the field and the surrounding surfaces. Although this is incidental to the subject of controlling particulate suspensions by fields, it is inevitably present, and usually quite large, because of the low k values. It also has several uses in its own right. These range from modifying heat transfer from flame gases, to mixing, flame stabilisation, and other situations where control over the fluid mechanics without the use of solid walls is beneficial [14, 15] to combustion.

Two such processes are particularly relevant here. One is the impingement, due to fluid mechanical forces, which contributes to causing particulates to deposit on electrodes in any kind of electrical precipitator. The other is the application of ionic winds to gas pumping, as in the air induction states of fig. 2. The velocity obtainable per ion pump stage is of the order of several 100 cm/s,[13, 14] so that, for fuels burning in air, one or two stages are generally adequate.

SIZE, CHARGE AND MOBILITY

The manner in which the field modifies the trajectory of a charged particle is defined, in terms of the particle mobility k by eqn (1). The mobility, in turn, depends on the particle radius r and its charge Ne (e being the electronic charge, positive or negative). These quantities vary with time according to the history of the particle's growth, or burning up, the rate of charge acquisition being itself a function of r. These histories become modified by the application of a field from the moment the first charge has been acquired.

The mobility is calculable at any instant, depending on the regime, which is determined largely by the particle radius r. Starting from the very smallest, at molecular diameters, the theory of small ions (see, e.g., ref. (16)) applies. Here the mobility is

$$k = \frac{0.235[(M+M_i)/M_i]^{0.5}\rho_0}{[(D-1)_0 M]^{0.5}\rho},\tag{3}$$

where ρ is density, M is the molecular weight and D is the dielectric constant; the suffixes i and 0 denote ion and carrier gas respectively. For larger ions the effects of divergence of the field induced around them by their own charge becomes negligible and the classical Langevin [11] equation,

$$k = 0.815\,(e\lambda_i/Mc)[(M_i+M)/M_i]^{0.5}\tag{4}$$

becomes relevant. When particles become large in comparison with the mean free path λ and no longer " sense the gas as individual collisions ", the viscosity η and density, ρ become the relevant gas properties. In the Stokes regime the mobility then is

$$k = eN/6\pi\eta r,\tag{5}$$

and in the Newton regime, at a field strength E,

$$k = (eN/0.22\pi\rho E)^{0.5}/r.\tag{6}$$

Which of these is applicable depends on the Reynolds number attained. Using eqn (5) for $Re < 3$ and (6) for $Re > 700$, keeps error to below 20 %. The equation,

$$k = 0.12(Ne)^{0.71}/r(E\rho)^{0.29}\eta^{0.43},\tag{7}$$

has been proposed for the intermediate region.[18]

The case of particles continuously acquiring charge along their trajectories has also been considered. For bombardment charging (see later) the equations become

$$k = Er/2\pi\eta\tag{8}$$

in the Stokes regime, and

$$k = 2.08/\rho^{0.5} \qquad (9)$$

in that covered by Newton's law.   These values are too large by about 20 % because the particles never quite attain their equilibrium charge under bombardment.[18]   The numerical values are in fact very high, exceeding 1/20th of the mobility of a molecular ion, in some cases.

As regards the mechanisms by which particles or droplets acquire charge, there is much variety, ranging from the spontaneous processes of thermionic emission to those which are entirely contrived by the application of a field.   When the object is to produce a charged dispersion of liquid or solid fuel,[5] dispersion in a field (but in the absence of breakdown) is ideally efficient in terms of minimizing the wastage of charge deliberately provided.   In this, the particulate phase may be treated as the fragments of an initially continuous charged capacitor,[19] resulting in high levels of specific charge and of mobility.   Fig. 5 shows results for droplets of kerosene, with some

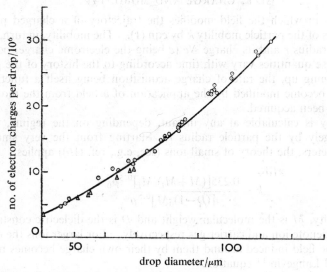

FIG. 5.—Electrically sprayed droplets;   charge against diameter.   Circles, horizontal; triangles, vertical sprays.   Curve from theory, see eqn (10).

anti-static additive, dispersed by an electric field, the solid line being calculated on the theory of a disintegrating charged condenser which yields

$$Ne = 9\sqrt{2}\varepsilon\pi r^2 E. \qquad (10)$$

In this way, many millions of electronic charges can be impressed upon a small droplet;   the experimental points obtained for a range of horizontal and vertical sprays conform well to the theory.   For solid fuel dusts, the dispersing field is applied to a fluidized bed of the powder.[5]   These methods give rise to suspensions which are highly controllable by fields right up to the point of burning.

In flame zones, other methods of charging become useful, particularly thermionic emission, and the attachment of chemi-ions produced in the reaction zone.   Thermionic emission is specific to materials of low work function and depends on local temperature as well as on the nature of the material.   Since it always leaves the particles with a positive charge, it is important to apply fields in such a way as to subject the smoke to a flux of positive ions so as to reinforce, rather than to oppose, thermionic charging. In the absence of an applied field, the thermionic emission current density is

$$j = BT^2 \exp(-e\phi/kT) \tag{11}$$

where B, like ϕ, the work function, is characteristic of the material; e is the electronic charge, k the Boltzmann constant and T the temperature, which determines the number of electrons with sufficient energy to escape. When the emitter is a positively charged particle of small radius r, two additional terms arise in the work function [20]; (Ne/r) due to the surface charge (Ne), and $(e/2r)$ due to the dipole induced by the departing electron. The current then becomes

$$j = BT^2 \exp\{(-e/kT)[\phi + (N + \tfrac{1}{2})(e/r)]\}. \tag{12}$$

If an electric field E is applied so as to assist the removal of electrons, the effective work function of the material is decreased (the Schottky effect) and the emission current density then becomes

$$j = BT^2 \exp[-(e/kT)\{\phi - (eE)^{\frac{1}{2}}\}]. \tag{13}$$

This theory has been further elaborated for very small particles, for clouds of reacting particles, and for the simultaneous presence of ions in fields.[14]

The use of fields to induce chemi-ions from the reaction zone to attach to any particles generated in flames is based on two mechanisms: " diffusion " charging and " bombardment " charging. The former refers to the attachment of charge as the result of ion particle collisions due to random thermal motion of the ions and occurs irrespective of the local field intensity, except insofar as this determines local ion concentration. The rate of charge acquisition by this mechanism is given by

$$d(Ne)/dt = \pi r^2 c n_i \exp[-e^2(N - \tfrac{1}{2})/r\, kT], \tag{14}$$

where c and n_i are the root mean square velocity and the concentration of the ions, respectively. Bombardment charging is due to ions drifting along lines of field intensity which terminate on the particle due to the dipole induced on it by the applied field. The ions drift at a very much higher velocity than the particles do, so much so that the velocity of the latter can generally be ignored by comparison. The rate of charging then is

$$d(Ne)/dt = 3\pi r^2 j_i[1 - (Ne/3Er^2)]^2. \tag{15}$$

For a non-conducting particle the right-hand side is multiplied by $D/(D+2)$ which is of the order 1. In this case there is an equilibrium charge

$$Ne = 3Er^2, \tag{16}$$

which is due to the formation of an electrostatic stagnation point upstream when the effect of the dipole is neutralized.

However, it turns out [6] that when large fields are applied to flames, the equilibrium conditions—indeed all the retardation effects due to appreciable particle charge in bombardment, diffusion and thermionic charging—are often irrelevant. This is because the field tends to remove the particle from the charging zone in a time too short for its charge to become appreciable. There are obvious exceptions to this— for example, see above for the case of using a small field to hold particles stationary against the gas flow in order to produce large agglomerates—but, when it applies, a unified and greatly simplified theory may be used for calculating the charge acquired by particles.[6]

Thus, in principle, particle charge, mobility, and hence trajectories in fields are calculable. However, the physics of the subject is rather in advance of the chemical kinetics (not perhaps an unusual state of affairs, at least in the field of combustion) and the kinetics of the growth of carbon particles, for example, is not sufficiently well understood to allow fully predictive calculations. It is much simpler to measure the mobility of particles withdrawn from flames by electric fields experimentally, measure their size and deduce their charge. The values used in the next section were so obtained.

PRACTICAL EFFECTS AND THEIR LIMITATIONS

The largest mobilities occur for droplets (or particles) charged during their dispersion. Fig. 6 shows velocities of charged kerosene droplets (corresponding to those shown in fig. 5) in applied fields. These velocities were measured by photographing tracks by interrupted illumination for the lower range and by laser Doppler

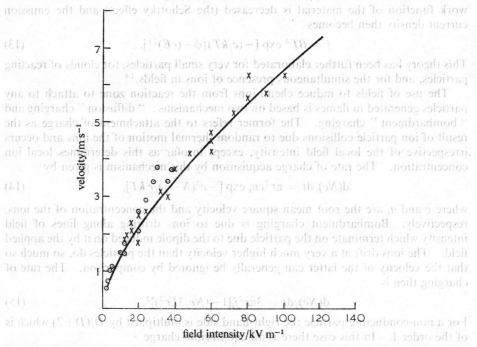

FIG. 6.—Electrically sprayed droplets; velocity against applied field. Circles and crosses show results obtained by photographing particles by interrupted illumination and by laser Doppler velocimetry, respectively. Curve from theory, see text.

velocimetry for the higher range, the solid curve being based on the mobility theory discussed above. Velocities of many m/s are attainable at quite modest fields. The lowest mobilities occur when large fields are applied to flames producing smokes. The large fields may be useful for controlling the trajectories of charged particles but, where they are simultaneously used for particle charging, they decrease ion concentration and tend to remove particles from the zone of charge acquisition as soon as the first charge has been acquired.

This has been shown, for carbon [4] and silica [6] to result in mobilities of the order of 10^{-3} m^2 s^{-1} kV^{-1}, as compared to 10^{-1} m^2 s^{-1} kV^{-1} for electrically sprayed droplets.[5] The latter is an appreciable fraction of the mobility of unattached flame ions, owing to the many millions of electronic charges carried by sprays produced in this manner.

In order to assess the practicability of various applications, we need to know not only mobilities but also field intensities attainable in practice. Now the maximum field to which these charge-carriers can be subjected is limited, for unipolar space charges between the ion source and each electrode, by the onset of breakdown at the electrode at which the field intensity reaches a maximum. This limits the maximum current density which can be drawn in a uni-dimensional system to

$$j = E_b^2 k/8\pi X, \tag{17}$$

where E_b is the breakdown field at the electrode and X is the distance between the electrode and the ion source.[7] This applies for an unlimited source of charge; for weak sources there is the obvious limitation

$$j_{max} = j_s, \tag{18}$$

where j_s represents the saturation current density for which charges are removed as fast as they are generated, there being no time for recombination. For flames of hydrocarbons burning in air, however, the former restriction (eqn (17)) is generally limiting. This is because j_s is relatively large, at least for near stoichiometric mixtures, and because the strength of an ion source can always be made greater, the simplest method being by increasing the area of flame surface per unit area of electrode.

Using these theoretical concepts [14] the absolute maximum effects obtainable by fields have been predicted. Thus, for a system of minimum separation between cold electrodes (taken as 1 cm) in which only flame ions (taken as mostly H_3O^+ and negative ions of about the same mobility produced by attachment of electrons in the cold electrode space) drift along, the maximum current density is 2.5 A m^{-2} providing, at the absolute maximum, one charge for each of 1.6×10^{19} particles. The corresponding expenditure of power is

$$W = kE_b^3/6\pi, \tag{19}$$

which predicts 920 W m^{-2} (the SI system of units tends to disguise the fact that this is a negligible quantity; the value is for hot gas and should be compared with the power generated per square metre of flame!)

In the presence of particles or droplets, two cases arise; that in which particles drift in the presence of ions and acquire charge from them and that in which the particulate phase is the sole charge carrier (e.g., the electrically dispersed fuel droplets discussed above). In the former case, the current density is almost entirely due to the ions alone and the space charge and consequent field distribution may be treated on this basis.[18] In the latter case, taking electrical dispersion of droplets as an example, the relevant mobility is that of the droplets which, as mentioned above, is exceedingly high. Although it is at the bottom of the droplet size range (fig. 5) that mobilities of the same order as that of ions arise, it is the large droplets that transport most mass. Thus, it follows from eqn (17) that the volume of liquid that can be conveyed in this manner per unit area per unit time is

$$V = (E_b^2 k/8\pi X Ne)(4\pi r^3/3). \tag{20}$$

Substituting the Stokes mobility for this case (eqn 5) gives

$$V = E_b^2 r^2/36\pi X\eta. \tag{21}$$

This is of the order of hundreds of litres m^{-2} s^{-1} for electrode separations of the order of centimetres.

Keeping electrode separations small is indeed the main problem in introducing large field intensities into flames. Here it is important to note that the zone of ion generation (the exceedingly thin chemi-ionization region which accounts for well over 99 % of the free charges) generally does not coincide with the region in which particulates are formed. Even though the pyrolysis zone, in carbon formation, or the region in which metal oxide smokes condense, may be quite a small distance from the chemi-ionization zone, even a fraction of a millimetre makes an important difference to the field intensity, as shown later.

As regards the zone of ion generation, the field intensity in this region of virtually infinitesimal thickness does not become appreciable until the applied potential exceeds that at which a saturation current is drawn. The field distribution is given by

$$E^2 = E_0^2 + 8\pi jx/k \qquad (22)$$

where E_0, the field in the ion source, remains small so long as the ion source can respond to increased potential by yielding more charge. Once saturation is reached, further increases in potential result in a rapid rise of E_0. However, for strong ion sources and large electrode separations, the breakdown condition (eqn (17)) is likely to be exceeded first. Fig. 7 shows the maximum distance between cold electrodes

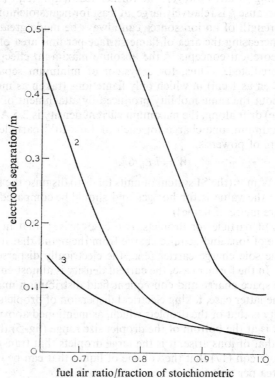

FIG. 7.—Maximum electrode separation for attainment of supersaturation field intensities in ion source as a function of fuel/air ratio. 1, methane; 2, propane; 3, ethylene.

(assumed symmetrical about the flame surface) for achieving appreciable fields in the chemi-ionization zone itself, as a function of fuel/air ratio.

However, even when the field in the ion source is insignificant—perhaps because the electrode spacing has to be considerably larger than the values of fig. 7 so that the saturation condition is unattainable—the field intensity in a closely adjacent zone in which particulates are formed can be appreciable.   This is illustrated in fig. 8 which shows the growth of field intensity with distance from an unsaturated ion source. For example, for an electrode spacing of 20 cm, under conditions just below break-down at a cold electrode (3×10^3 kV m^{-1}) the field is 300 kV m^{-1} at a distance of 1 mm from the ion source and still almost 100 kV m^{-1} at 1/10 mm.   These correspond to velocities of metres per second even for the lowest mobilities mentioned above.

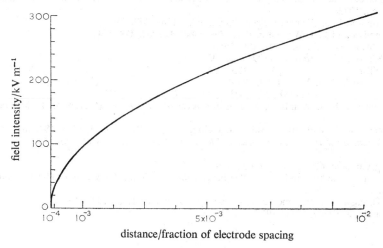

distance/fraction of electrode spacing

FIG. 8.—Field intensity as a function of (small) distance from ion source for conditions of incipient breakdown without attainment of saturation.

We may conclude that this is a subject in which practical applications do not always follow directly from a scaling-up of laboratory experiments—no matter how spectac-ularly successful the latter are—and should not be attempted without a thorough understanding of the theory.   Unsuccessful transposition to large-scale apparatus without taking theory into account have sometimes led to the equally erroneous conclu-sion that the methods are generally not useful.   Thus, there is obviously no prospect of removing all the soot generated in a jet engine flame tube by applying a field right across the duct—the ion source is much too strong in relation to the distance across which the potential is applied—this being a situation in which closely spaced plates are ruled out by the consequent pressure drop.   Yet, even under such conditions, no great difficulty would be expected in attempting to prevent carbon deposition on some particular cold surface which is part of the device.   Again, as regards diminishing carbon formation by removal of the growing particles from the pyrolysis zone, a local field intensity of 100 V/cm will suffice to induce the least mobile of the particles mentioned above to cross a growth zone of 1 mm width in 0.1 s.

For precipitation of particulate clouds, the geometry of closely spaced plates as used in " electrostatic " precipitators is ideal, the difference being that here no power is dissipated in producing a corona discharge.   Under conditions when flame ions cannot be made to survive long enough (because distances are too large to apply a field), a small auxiliary flame or even ion emission from hot plates can provide the necessary charge.   Lastly, as regards droplets or particles deliberately charged during their dispersion, very few of the above limitations apply.   Owing to their high specific charges appreciable mass fluxes can be induced by quite modest fields, linear velocities being 1-2 orders of magnitude greater than normal burning velocities.

I am indebted to Mr. R. J. Bowser for checking the manuscript.

1 K. G. Payne and F. J. Weinberg, *Proc. Roy. Soc. A*, 1959, **250**, 316.
2 E. R. Place and F. J. Weinberg, *Proc. Roy. Soc. A*, 1965, **289**, 192.
3 F. J. Weinberg, *Proc. Roy. Soc. A*, 1968, **307**, 195.
4 P. J. Mayo and F. J. Weinberg, *Proc. Roy. Soc. A*, 1970, **319**, 351.
5 K. C. Thong and F. J. Weinberg, *Proc. Roy. Soc. A*, 1971, **324**, 201.
6 D. R. Hardesty and F. J. Weinberg, *14th Int. Symp. Combustion* (The Combustion Institnte Pittsburgh, 1972).
7 J. Lawton and F. J. Weinberg, *Proc. Roy. Soc. A*, 1964, **277**, 468.
8 T. P. Pandya and F. J. Weinberg, *Proc. Roy. Soc. A*, 1964, **279**, 544.
9 H. A. Wilson, *Phil. Trans.*, 1897, **189**, 265.
10 H. A. Wilson, *Phil. Trans. A*, 1899, **192**, 403.
11 H. A. Wilson, *Phil. Trans. A*, 1899, **193**, 289.
12 A. P. Chattock, *Phil. Mag.*, 1899, **48**, 401.
13 J. Lawton, P. J. Mayo and F. J. Weinberg, *Proc. Roy. Soc. A*, 1968, **303**, 275.
14 J. Lawton and F. J. Weinberg, *Electrical Aspects of Combustion* (Clarendon Press, Oxford 1969)
15 P. J. Mayo, L. A. Watermeier and F. J. Weinberg, *Proc. Roy. Soc. A*, 1965, **284**, 488.
16 L. B. Loeb, *Basic Processes of Gaseous Electronics* (University of California Press, Berkeley 1961.).
17 P. Langevin, *Ann. Chim. Phys.*, 1905, **5**, 245.
18 K. Gugan, J. Lawton and F. J. Weinberg, *10th Int. Symp. Combustion* (The Combustion Institute, 1965), p. 709.
19 K. C. Thong and A. R. Jones, *J. Phys. D: Appl. Phys.*, 1971, **4**, 1159.
20 F. T. Smith, *J. Chem. Phys.*, 1958, **28**, 746.

Brownian Coagulation of Aerosols at Low Knudsen Number †

By Gilbert A. Nicolaon and Milton Kerker *

Dept. of Chemistry and Institute of Colloid and Surface Science, Clarkson College of Technology, Potsdam, New York, 13676, U.S.A.

Received 15th January, 1973

Dibutyl phthalate aerosols of narrow size distribution have been prepared in a falling-film generator using nitrogen rather than helium as the carrier gas. The Knudsen number in nitrogen is considerably lower so that the Cunningham correction is much less. A large number of coagulation experiments give average coagulation times in excellent agreement with theory. However, the spread of the values is much greater than obtained earlier in helium. The spread of the results reported here may be due to the lower thermal conductivity of nitrogen.

Smoluchowski's theory [1] of Brownian coagulation of aerosols in which the motion of the particle is controlled by the Stokes-Einstein diffusivity is valid in the hydrodynamic domain where

$$Kn = \lambda/a \ll 1. \tag{1}$$

The Knudsen number is the ratio of the mean free path λ of the gas molecules to the radius of the particle a. When this becomes as large as unity the empirical Cunningham correction must be utilized, leading to

$$
\frac{-dn_h}{dt} = \frac{kT}{3\eta} \int_{a_0}^{a_h-0} (a_i + a_{h-i}) \left[\frac{1}{a_i}\left(1 + \frac{A_i\lambda}{a_i}\right) + \frac{1}{a_{h-i}}\left(1 + \frac{A_{h-i}\lambda}{a_{h-i}}\right) \right] \times
$$
$$
\left(\frac{a_h}{a_{h-i}}\right)^2 n_i n_{h-i}\, da_i - \frac{2kT}{3\eta} n_h \int_{a_0}^{a_f} (a_h + a_i) \times
$$
$$
\left[\frac{1}{a_h}\left(1 + \frac{A_h\lambda}{a_h}\right) + \frac{1}{a_i}\left(1 + \frac{A_i\lambda}{a_i}\right)\right] n_i\, da_i. \tag{2}
$$

This correction is given by Davies [2] as

$$A = 1.257 + 0.4 \ldots \exp\left(-1.10\, a/\lambda\right). \tag{3}$$

The first integral of eqn (2) describes the rate of formation of particles of radius a_h by coagulation of particles of radius a_i with those of radius a_{h-i}. The second integral gives the rate of disappearance of particles of radius a_h by coagulation with other particles. The smallest and largest classes of particles are given by a_0 and a_f. The particle concentration of class a_h is given by n_h, k is the Boltzmann constant, T is the Kelvin temperature and η is the viscosity of the gas.

When the Knudsen number is large ($Kn > 10$), the particles can be treated as if they were large molecules, and the coagulation can then be described by the kinetic theory of gases. Lai et al. [3] have discussed this case recently. There is a transition regime ($10 > Kn > 0.1$) for which the fluid mechanics of the particles have not yet

† This project has been financed in part with federal funds from the National Science Foundation under grant number GP-33656X.

been reduced to theoretical analysis.[4]   Indeed, it is the lower end of the transition regime $(1.0 > Kn > 0.1)$ which is treated with the aid of the Cunningham correction. For aerosols suspended in air at atmospheric pressure and 20°C, the transition regime corresponds approximately to $1.5\,nm < a < 150\,nm$, and it includes in the atmosphere the important class of so-called Aitken nuclei which probably act as condensation and freezing nuclei.

Although Smoluchowski's theory was published more than 50 years ago, numerical solutions to his non-linear integro-differential equation have been obtained only recently with the advent of electronic digital computers.   Virtually all earlier work had been restricted to the initial rate of coagulation of a monodisperse system for which the process follows second-order reaction kinetics

$$\frac{-dN}{dt} = \tfrac{4}{3}\frac{kT}{\eta}N^2, \tag{4}$$

where N is the total particle concentration.

Experimental studies have lagged even further.[5]   These have mainly utilized eqn (4) and typically have attempted to demonstrate merely that the particle concentration follows the second-order rate law, hopefully with a rate constant close to that predicted by the theory.   Frequently, these aerosols were poorly-defined systems, and the particle sizes, shapes, and concentrations were not determined accurately so that the results can hardly be considered definitive.

We have recently completed [6] an experimental study of the Brownian coagulation of an aerosol for which $Kn = 0.78$.   The results were in agreement with Smoluchowski's theory of Brownian coagulation as modified by the Cunningham correction [i.e., eqn (2)], and we plan to extend this experiment throughout the entire range of Knudsen numbers, viz., the free molecule, the transition, and the hydrodynamic regimes.

This paper reports the next step in this programme.   It is a study of coagulation at a lower Knudsen number $(Kn = 0.20)$.*   This lower value of the Knudsen number was obtained by preparing the dibutyl phthalate (DBP) aerosol in nitrogen rather than in helium, as in the earlier work.   Thus, it was mainly the mean free path of the gaseous medium that was altered rather than the aerosol particle size, and this permitted utilization of our previously developed light-scattering technique for monitoring the particle size distribution [7] as well as an aerosol generator similar to the one which had proved so successful in the earlier work.   A number of modifications were made in the preparation of the aerosol when nitrogen was utilized as the carrier gas in place of helium.

DBP AEROSOLS IN NITROGEN

The aerosol generator has been described earlier.[8-11]   A mixture of the gas and NaCl nuclei flows laminarly down a vertical tube along whose wall flows a film of DBP maintained at an elevated temperature.   Aerosol is formed upon cooling to room temperature by condensation of the DBP upon the nuclei.   The monodispersity of the aerosol can be significantly improved by evaporating and then recondensing the initial DBP aerosol.   This will be termed a regenerated aerosol.   Heat transfer [9] and convective diffusion [11] calculations are in agreement with measurements of the temperature distribution and the extent of saturation of the vapour, respectively.

---

* This value of the Knudsen number corresponds to the modal value in the size distribution.   For the uncoagulated systems the coefficient of variation was about 0.10.   However, for the coagulated systems, the spread of sizes becomes considerably greater.

The influence upon the particle size distribution of parameters such as furnace temperature,[8] DBP boiler temperature,[8] flow rate,[8] number and size of nuclei,[10] and cooling rate,[10] have been discussed.

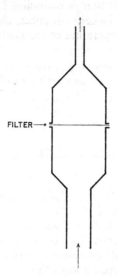

FILTER→

FIG. 1.—Filter for collection of aerosol.

The major procedural change in this work with nitrogen was to collect the aerosol for gravimetric analysis by filtration rather than by thermal precipitation. There was considerable leakage of aerosol through the thermal precipitator when nitrogen was used, presumably because of the lower thermal conductivity of nitrogen compared to helium. Fig. 1 depicts the filter. It utilized millipore filters with pore diameters of either 1.2 or 3.0 μm. The results in table 1 verify that the amount of aerosol collected was independent of pore size over the range 0.8-8.0 μm.

TABLE 1.—AMOUNT OF AEROSOL COLLECTED FOR DIFFERENT PORE SIZES OF THE MILLIPORE FILTER
(CARRIER GAS N_2; FLOW RATE 1 l/min; BOILER TEMPERATURE 110°)

pore diam./ μm	mass/(mg/l) (expt 1)	mass/(mg/l) (expt 2)
0.8	0.76	0.79
1.2	0.78	0.79
3.0	0.75	0.80
8.0	0.74	0.78

We have also noted, even for helium, that the mass concentration of aerosol obtained, when collection was by thermal precipitation, was about 5 % less than that by filtration. This would give higher aerosol number concentrations in the earlier coagulation work with better agreement between theoretical and experimental coagulation times.

The percentage saturation of the DBP vapour at the exit of the boiler was calculated using the earlier convective diffusion theory, and this is compared in table 2 with the experimental results at two flow-rates. Also listed in this table are new results for helium based upon collection by filtration rather than thermal precipitation. The agreement is excellent, particularly since there is significant uncertainty both in values for the diffusion constant of DBP as well as the actual temperature of the DBP at the vapour-liquid interface.

In this connection a comment on the temperature of the DBP is in order. The elevated temperature of the DBP film is maintained by circulating oil at constant temperature through an external jacket. In effect, the gas stream is always slightly cooler than the oil so that the temperature of the DBP at the vapour/liquid interface

TABLE 2.—COMPARISON OF THE PERCENTAGE SATURATION AT THE EXIT OF THE VAPORIZER OBTAINED THEORETICALLY AND EXPERIMENTALLY (DBP TEMPERATURE 108°)

gas	flow rate/ (l/min)	% saturation theoretical	% saturation experimental
He	1.0	96	95
He	2.0	84	88
N_2	1.0	74	82
N_2	2.0	53	51

is also probably cooler. Thus, for the above convective diffusion calculation, we have assumed a DBP temperature of 108° in view of the fact that the oil temperature was 110° and the temperature within the gas stream was 106-107°. Acutally, the measured concentration of DBP provides a better criterion for the effect of the boiler conditions upon the properties of the aerosols than the " boiler temperature ", and the former quantity will be utilized henceforth.

The coagulation experiments to be described in the next section were carried out (as in the earlier work) with a standard aerosol. The conditions were : nitrogen flow rate 1.0 l/min ; furnace temperature 590°C ; DBP flow rate 25 ml/min ; concentration (by filtration) 0.78 mg/l. This aerosol was regenerated in the manner described earlier.

We have prepared and analyzed the particle size distribution of several hundred DBP aerosols in both helium and nitrogen over the past three years, and these results are summarized in table 3. The second column pertains to the standard aerosol in helium, the third column to the regenerated standard aerosol in helium, and the fourth column to the regenerated standard aerosol in nitrogen. The operating conditions for the helium system are : helium flow rate 2.0 l/min ; furnace temperature 590°C ; DBP flow rate 25 ml/min ; concentration (by filtration) 0.84 mg/l. The conditions for the nitrogen system have been given above. The low values of the standard deviation of the modal radius and of the coefficient of variance indicate the high degree of reproducibility obtainable with this aerosol generator.

TABLE 3.—SUMMARY OF PARTICLE SIZE ANALYSES FOR DBP AEROSOLS IN HELIUM AND IN NITROGEN

	DBP in helium	DBP in helium regenerated	DBP in nitrogen regenerated
no. of runs	210	100	125
modal radius/μm	0.235	0.236	0.314
std. deviation	0.005	0.006	0.007
coefficient of variation	0.16	0.10	0.11
std. deviation	0.01	0.01	0.01

Just as in the case with helium, the effect of regeneration in nitrogen was to give a more monodisperse aerosol with the same modal radius. Also, even a narrower size distribution was obtained if only the aerosol near the axis or near the wall is sampled. Indeed, in such a case, the aerosol is about as monodisperse as the well-known Dow polystyrene latexes.

The effects are illustrated in fig. 2 and 3. In fig. 2 the angular distribution of the polarization ratio of the scattered light is plotted against scattering angle for (A) a standard aerosol which has not been regenerated, (B) for a regenerated standard aerosol, and (C) for the latter aerosol which has been sampled from within the axial region. The polarization ratio is the ratio of the polarized radiance whose electric vector is parallel to the scattering plane relative to the polarized radiance whose electric vector is perpendicular. The procedure for inverting these data to obtain the logarithmic particle size distribution is described elsewhere.[7] The corresponding size distributions are plotted in fig. 3. The modal value of the radius is 0.240 μm for each aerosol, but the breadth parameters (which correspond closely to the co-efficient of variation) are 0.16, 0.10 and 0.04, respectively. Although these particular examples were selected from results with helium, similar effects were obtained with nitrogen.

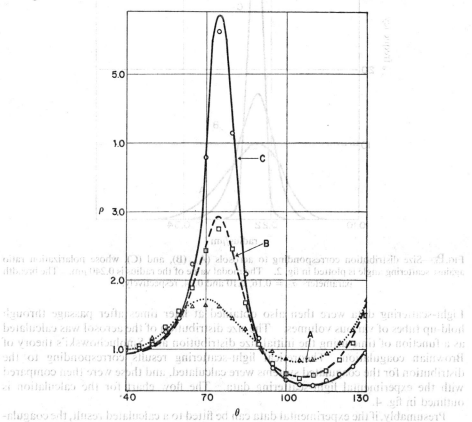

FIG. 2.—Polarization ratio against scattering angle for (A) standard DBP in helium; (B) the same which has undergone evaporation and condensation ; (C) the same as (B) which has been sampled from the axial region.

COAGULATION OF DBP AEROSOLS IN NITROGEN

The coagulation experiment was similar to that described earlier.[6] The initial size distribution of the regenerated standard DBP aerosol in nitrogen was determined by light scattering early in the life history of the aerosol. This must occur prior to appreciable coagulation since inversion of the light-scattering data with the aid of the Mie-Lorenz functions [7] is accurate only if the distribution is narrow and is unimodal.

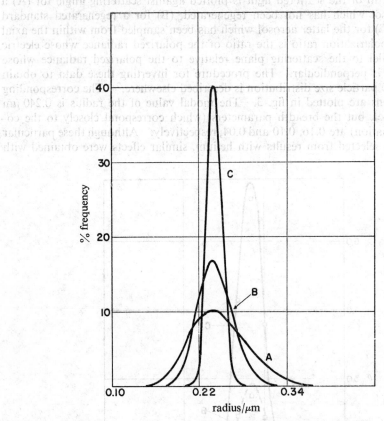

FIG. 3.—Size distribution corresponding to aerosols (A), (B), and (C). whose polarization ratio against scattering angle is plotted in fig. 2. The modal value of the radius is 0.240 μm. The breadth parameters $\sigma_0 = 0.16, 0.10$ and 0.04, respectively.

Light-scattering data were then also obtained at later times after passage through hold-up tubes of various volumes. The size distribution of the aerosol was calculated as a function of time using the initial size distribution and Smoluchowski's theory of Brownian coagulation. Theoretical light-scattering results corresponding to the distribution for the coagulated systems were calculated, and these were then compared with the experimental light-scattering data. The flow chart for the calculation is outlined in fig. 4.

Presumably, if the experimental data can be fitted to a calculated result, the coagulation mechanism proceeds in accordance with Smoluchowski's model. Furthermore, if the experimental and calculated time scales agree, there is no potential barrier to coalescence upon collision. If the experimental time is greater than the calculated time, the collision efficiency is less than unity and the potential barrier can be calculated.[12] If the experimental time is less, the aerosol is coagulating faster than predicted by Brownian diffusion so that other mechanisms must be involved.

One improvement in the procedure used in this work was to make 4 to 6 light-scattering analyses of the aerosol over an extended period of time prior to obtaining any coagulation data and using the average of the values for the size distribution. The values obtained were usually similar, attesting to the stability of the aerosol generator. However, on occasion there would be a small deviation, and, if this transient value had been used to characterize the initial aerosol, the calculated size distribution of the coagulated aerosol would have been significantly different.

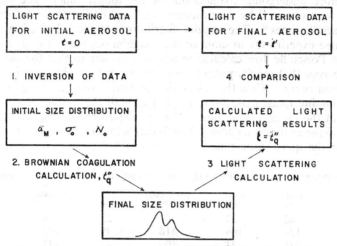

FIG. 4.—Flow chart for coagulation calculation. Average hold-up time is t'; average calculated time is t''.

Another procedural change was to utilize for the aerosol number concentration the value based upon a gravimetric analysis of each particular run. In the earlier work an average value for many runs had been used, and the concentration was not determined for each particular run. The aerosol was collected for weighing by

TABLE 4.—VARIATION OF NUMBER CONCENTRATION OVER A PERIOD OF 12 DAYS

no.	modal value of radius, $a_M/\mu m$	breadth parameter, σ_0	mass concentration/ (mg/l)	number concentration no./$(10^{-6}\,cm^{-3}$
1	0.308	0.10	0.75	5.5
2	0.309	0.11	0.79	5.6
3	0.315	0.12	0.76	5.0
4	0.311	0.11	0.72	5.0
5	0.313	0.11	0.74	5.1
6	0.317	0.12	0.77	5.0
7	0.313	0.12	0.78	5.3
8	0.314	0.11	0.80	5.4
9	0.311	0.10	0.79	5.6
10	0.320	0.12	0.79	5.0
11	0.308	0.10	0.79	5.8
12	0.311	0.11	0.75	5.2

filtration rather than by thermal precipitation. The extent of variation in the number concentration for a series of runs carried out over a period of 12 days is shown in table 4. The day-to-day variation was sufficient to introduce a significant error in the number concentration of the initial aerosol, had the average value been used. On the other hand, the concentration was stable over the course of a day run.

The results are shown in table 5. The experimental times are average residence times obtained from the volume of the hold-up tube and the flow rate. The third column, termed quasi-static time, is the calculated time with the assumption that each fluid particle spends the same amount of time in the hold-up tube. Actually, the aerosol is in Poiseuille flow with a parabolic velocity profile. The aerosol near the wall is moving much more slowly than the aerosol along the axis of the tube and is therefore undergoing coagulation for the longer time. The results in the last column were obtained by the procedure outlined earlier for transforming quasi-static to Poiseuille times [6] The angular distribution of the polarization ratio, which is used in these experiments to monitor the coagulation, goes through a sequence of states for the Poiseuille flow calculation which is similar to that for the quasi-static calculation except that the former proceeds more slowly. This permits preparation of a calibration curve. Then the calculation is carried out according to the scheme of fig. 4, assuming quasi-static flow, varying t_q'' until the calculated light-scattering results best fit the experimental data. Finally, the corresponding Poiseuille time is obtained from the calibration curve. The fourth column in table 5 gives the standard deviation for the quasi-static times.

TABLE 5.—COMPARISON OF EXPERIMENTAL AND CALCULATED COAGULATION TIMES (SECONDS)

exptl time	no. of runs	quasi-static time	s.d.	Poiseuille time
82	32	67	23	84
154	105	116	49	145
235	23	196	41	245
327	24	268	61	340

The criterion for best fit was the minimum value of the deviation measure given by

$$D = \left\{ \sum_{\theta=40°(5°)}^{130°} [\rho(\theta) - \rho'(\theta)]^2 \right\}^{\frac{1}{2}}, \quad [5]$$

where $\rho(\theta)$ and $\rho'(\theta)$ are the measured and calculated values of the polarization ratio at each of the 19 angles obtained between 40° and 130° at 5° intervals.

Fig. 5 illustrates a typical example of the fit of the calculated results to the experimental data which are plotted as points. The curve represents the angular distribution of the polarization rates calculated for that coagulation time for the initial aerosol which minimizes the deviation measure (eqn (5)). For this example the experimental hold-up time is 154 s. The calculated result gives a hold-up time of 169 s with a corresponding deviation measure of 0.10.

Although the average values of the coagulation time in table 5 agree well with the experimental coagulation times, there is a considerable spread in the individual values as indicated by the standard deviations. In order to determine whether this spread arose from the accuracy in fitting the experimental and calculated results, all runs were eliminated for which the deviation measure was greater than 0.25. The results are shown in table 6. The agreement between the experimental and calculated coagulation times is not affected significantly (it is slightly poorer), nor is the spread of the results any narrower. Accordingly, the light-scattering analysis does not appear to be a factor in accounting for the spread of the coagulation time.

There is another factor, which may account for these results. We have observed occasionally sporadic convective " storms " in these aerosols in nitrogen, particularly in the hold-up tubes, in contrast to the quiescent appearance under illumination of the helium system. This tendency may be due to the low heat conductance (and sharper temperature gradients) of nitrogen, and the randomization of the results, which was not encountered in the earlier work with helium, might be caused by this effect. The subsequent mixing would tend to make the system deviate from the condition of Poiseuille flow and more resemble the well-mixed system which we have

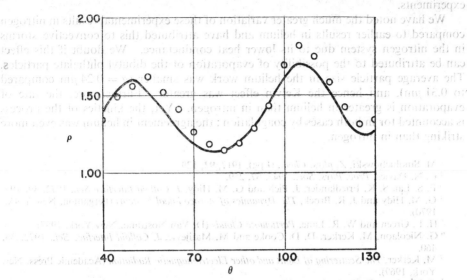

FIG. 5.—Angular distribution of polarization ratio. Points are measured values for experimental time of 154 s. Curve corresponds to calculated time (169 s) which best fits these values (D = 0.10).

called the quasi-static model. One would expect then that the coagulation time calculated according to Poiseuille flow would be an upper limit and that the average values would be lower. Any barrier to coalescence corresponding to a coalescence efficiency of less than unity would lengthen the coagulation time. A combination of these two effects could account for the observed results.

TABLE 6.—COMPARISON OF EXPERIMENTAL AND CALCULATED COAGULATION TIMES (SECONDS). RUNS WITH DEVIATION MEASURES GREATER THAN 0.25 ELIMINATED

exptl time	no. o runs	quasi-static time	s.d.	Poiseuille time
82	20	71	22	89
154	59	127	47	158
235	21	203	35	254
327	24	268	61	340

A question has been raised about the stability of the aerosol to evaporation during its passage through the coagulation tube. There is the possibility because of the Kelvin effect that material might distill to the walls, or from the smaller to the larger particles, or both of these effects might occur. The possibility of distillation to the walls has been checked repeatedly by collecting and weighing the aerosol prior to entrance and upon emergence from the coagulation tube, and we were unable to detect any hold-up. Furthermore, the light-scattering data can only be interpreted by an increase in average particle size which would not be the case were distillation to the walls to occur to a significant extent. Distillation from the smaller to the larger particles—for which the driving force is much less than distillation to the walls—

would have the effect of shifting the size distribution to a greater average size just as coagulation. However, since the effects which we have observed are accounted for by coagulation, which must proceed in any case, it seems highly unlikely that evaporation of these particles occurs to any significant extent in the course of these experiments.

We have noted the much greater variation of these experimental results in nitrogen compared to earlier results in helium and have attributed this to convective storms in the nitrogen system due to its lower heat conductance. We doubt if this effect can be attributed to the possibility of evaporation of the dibutyl phthalate particles. The average particle size in the helium work was smaller ($a = 0.24\ \mu m$ compared to $0.31\ \mu m$), and hence the Kelvin effect was greater. Furthermore, the rate of evaporation is greater in helium than in nitrogen. Yet, the kinetics of the process is accounted for in both cases by coagulation; the agreement in helium was even more striking than in nitrogen.

[1] M. Smoluchowski, *Z. phys. Chem.* (Lpg), 1917, **92**, 129.

[2] C. N. Davies, *Proc. Phys. Soc.*, 1945, **57**, 259.

[3] F. S. Lai, S. K. Friedlander, J. Pich and G. M. Hidy, *J. Colloid Interface Sci.*, 1972, **39**, 395.

[4] G. M. Hidy and J. R. Brock, *The Dynamics of Aerocolloidal Systems* (Pergamon, New York, 1970).

[5] H. L. Green and W. R. Lane, *Particulate Clouds* (D. Van Nostrand, New York, 1957).

[6] G. Nicolaon, M. Kerker, D. D. Cooke and M. Matijevic, *J. Colloid Interface Sci.*, 1972, **38**, 460.

[7] M. Kerker, *The Scattering of Light and other Electromagnetic Radiation* (Academic Press, New York, 1969).

[8] G. Nicolaon, D. D. Cooke, M. Kerker and E. Matijevic, *J. Colloid Interface Sci.*, 1970, **34**, 534.

[9] G. Nicolaon, D. D. Cooke, E. J. Davis, M. Kerker and E. Matijevic, *J. Colloid Interface Sci.*, 1971, **35**, 490.

[10] G. Nicolaon and M. Kerker, *J. Colloid Interface Sci.*, 1973, **42**, to be published.

[11] E. J. Davis and G. Nicolaon, *J. Colloid Interface Sci.*, 1971, **37**, 768.

[12] N. A. Fuchs, *The Mechanics of Aerosols* (Macmillan, New York, 1971).

A Contribution to the Theory of Fibrous Aerosol Filters

By N. A. Fuchs, A. A. Kirsch and I. B. Stechkina

Karpov-Institute of Physical Chemistry, Moscow, 120, Obucha 10

Received 7th November, 1972

Almost all properties of the " parallel " filter model—a system of parallel, cylindrical, staggered and regularly arranged fibres, can be treated theoretically, but these properties differ considerably from those of real filters. On the contrary, the theoretical treatment of the " fan " model, obtained by turning in the parallel model all fibre rows in their planes by an arbitrary angle, is very difficult, but its properties are the same as those of real filters with a perfectly homogeneous structure. The " degree of inhomogeneity " of a real filter is the reverse ratio of its resistance and of the particle capture coefficient on its fibres (in absence of inertial deposition) to those in an equivalent fan model. This makes it possible to calculate the filter efficiency from its resistance.

In the past 30 years, many papers on the theory of fibrous aerosol filters have been published, beginning with the fundamental work of Sell, Albrecht, Kaufmann and Langmuir. However, on the basis of these papers it has been impossible to calculate the main characteristics of these filters (i.e., their hydraulic resistance and their efficiency in respect to aerosols with various particle size and at various flow rates) from measurable filter parameters—the fibre width and the shape of their cross-section, the volume fraction occupied by the fibres (packing density), their orientation, the homogeneity of filter structure, etc.—without resorting to a number of empirical equations and coefficients. For several years we have been working on the development of a theory which would make possible such a quantitative calculation of filter efficiency. So far, we have been able only to approach this goal but not to reach it. However, the results of this work seem to have led to a better understanding of the complex processes of aerosol deposition in fibrous filters.

For the development of the theory we have used filter models approaching real filters, combining in this work, wherever possible, theoretical deductions with experimental studies. At small flow velocities (not exceeding 10-20 cm/s), at which the fibrous filters show a high degree of efficiency, it may be assumed that all particles of size not greater than a few μm coming into contact with a fibre, adhere to it. Besides, at such small flow velocities the flow is automodel, i.e., the pressure drop across the filter is proportional to the flow rate. We have excluded from consideration the effect of electrical forces, i.e., the filtration of aerosols with not very small particle charges, as well as filters charged or polarized by an external field. In modern filters in the shape of papers, cardboard sheets and pads, the fibres are oriented more or less parallel to the same plane and the packing density is usually less than 0.1.

THE "PARALLEL" MODEL. RESISTANCE

In Langmuir's model—an isolated cylindrical fibre, the effect of neighbouring fibres on the flow field is neglected and this model cannot be used for our purpose. The simplest model approaching real filters, called by us the " parallel " model, is a system of straight equal, cylindrical, parallel, staggered, regularly arranged fibres (fig. 1), perpendicular to the flow direction. The flow field near the fibre surface in this model was calculated by Kuwabara.[1] For the flow function he obtained the following expression (in polar coordinates), accurate to the terms of α to the first power :

$$\Psi(\rho, \theta) = -\frac{U_0 a \sin \theta}{(\ln \alpha + 1.5 - 2\alpha)}\left\{\left(1-\frac{\alpha}{2}\right)\left(\frac{\rho}{a}\right)^{-1} - (1-\alpha)\frac{\rho}{a} + 2\frac{\rho}{a}\ln\frac{\rho}{a} - \frac{\alpha}{2}\left(\frac{\rho}{a}\right)^3\right\}, \quad (1)$$

where U_0 is the face value of the flow velocity, a, the fibre radius, and α, the packing density.

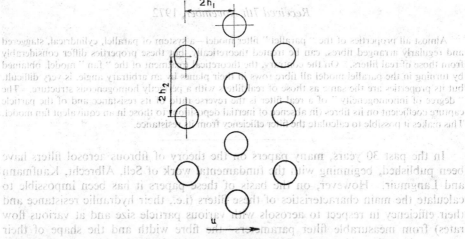

FIG. 1.—The " parallel " model.

Kuwabara assumed the fibres to be arranged parallel, but disorderly. In reality, as shown experimentally by us (see below) and theoretically by Golovin and Lopatin,[2] formula (1) can be used only for a regular staggered fibre arrangement shown in fig. 1.

The accuracy of formula (1) was checked in our model experiments [3] with glycerol flowing in a system of staggered parallel cylinders with diameters of 7 or 14 mm, with a velocity 0.06-0.16 cm/s (Re = 0.01-0.05). The velocity vector in each point was determined by photographing under intermittent illumination the trajectories of metallised spherical polymer beads suspended in glycerol, having the same density as the liquid and therefore moving along the flow lines. The trajectories and velocities of the beads agreed accurately with those calculated by means of (1) at $\rho/a \leqslant 2$ for $\alpha = 0.05$ and at $\rho/a \leqslant 1.5$ for $\alpha = 0.2$.

Another question, important to the filtration theory, was solved in these experiments. It is usually assumed that the centre of a spherical inertia-less particle moves exactly along the flow lines. However, under the action of the flow velocity gradient existing in the vicinity of a cylindrical obstacle, the particle must rotate and we cannot assume a priori that no lateral drag is acting on this particle. In any case, the larger the particle whose centre moves along a given flow line, i.e., the smaller the minimal gap between the particle and the cylinder, the larger must be the lateral drag, In our experiments we found that spherical inertialess particles with diameters of 0.1 and 3.0 mm move around 7 to 14 mm thick cylinders along quite identical trajectories, i.e., along the flow lines. As the hydrodynamical forces in liquids are much larger than in gases, the validity of this conclusion for aerosols cannot be doubted.

From (1) the hydrodynamic drag F_*^P acting on the unit fibre length in the parallel model can be calculated. It is more convenient to use the dimensionless drag $F^P = F_*^P/\mu U_0$, where μ is the viscosity of the medium. The following expression for F^P can be derived:

$$F^P = 4\pi/\kappa; \quad \kappa = -0.5 \ln \alpha - 0.75 + \alpha, \tag{2}$$

(superscript P stands for the " parallel " model).

For a single regular row of parallel cylinders, Mijagi[4] obtained the formula

$$F^P = 4\pi[-\ln(\pi a/h_2) + 0.5 + (\pi a/2h_2)^2/3 + \ldots]^{-1}, \tag{3}$$

where $2h_2$ is the distance between the axes of neighbouring fibres.

The pressure drop across the model is related to F^P by the formula

$$\Delta p = F^P U_0 \mu \alpha H/\pi a^2, \tag{4}$$

where H is the thickness of the filter (or of the model).

For a single row

$$\Delta p = F^P U_0 \mu/2h_2 \tag{5}$$

Formulae (2)-(5) were verified by model experiments[5] with glycerol at very low Reynolds number. The fibres were modelled by wires and capron filaments with diameters 0.15-0.70 mm. A plot of F^P against α drawn in accordance with formula (2) is shown in fig. 2, together with the experimental results obtained on models

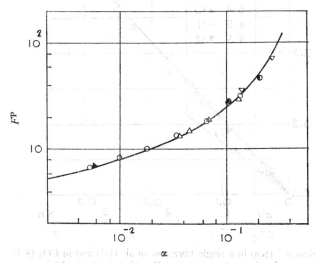

FIG. 2.—The dependence of F^P upon α in the parallel model. Theoretical curve, eqn (2). Experimental points:

	$\triangledown$	$\oplus$	$\triangle$	$\blacktriangledown$
a/h_2	0.41	0.365	0.21	0.074

with $h_1 = h_2$ and $a/h_2 = 0.067$-0.41. Good agreement with the theory was observed up to $\alpha = 0.27$. An equally good agreement was obtained for models with $h_1 < h_2$. Formula (3) for single fibre rows was valid up to $a/h_2 = 0.7$. Approximately at $h_1/h_2 = 1$, the F^P values for a single row and for a system of cylinders become equal, i.e., at $h_1 > h_2$ the hydrodynamic interaction between the fibre rows vanishes, and the resistance of the parallel model is equal to the sum of resistances of separate isolated rows.

In filters made of ultrafine fibres ($a < 1$ μm) or in filtration at reduced pressure, the Knudsen number $Kn = \lambda/a$ (λ is the mean free path of gas molecules) is finite and the gas slip at the fibre surface should be taken account of. In this case, the following formulae can be derived for the parallel model,[6]

$$(F^P)^{-1} = (F_0^P)^{-1} + \tau Kn(1-\alpha)/4\pi, \tag{6}$$

and for a single fibre row [7]

$$(F^P)^{-1} = (F_0^P)^{-1} + \tau Kn[1 - \tfrac{1}{3}(\pi a/2h_2)^2]/4\pi, \tag{7}$$

where F_0^P is the value of F^P at $Kn = 0$, and τ is the ratio of the slip coefficient at the fibre surface to λ. Formula (7) was verified on a model with $a = 4.45$ μm, $2h_2 = 62$ μm, $2h_1 = 1.1$ mm in the air and in CO_2 at pressures $\geqslant 10$ Torr. As follows from above, in such a model the hydrodynamic interaction between fibre rows is absent. The results are shown in fig. 3. Experimental points were obtained at

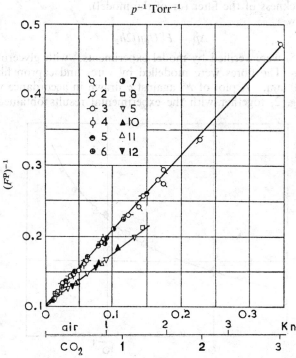

FIG. 3.—$(F^P)^{-1}$ against p^{-1} (Kn) in a single fibre row in air (1-7) and in CO_2 (8-12). The experimental points refer to various Re values up to 6×10^{-2}.

$Re = 1 \times 10^{-3} - 6 \times 10^{-2}$. The lines were drawn in accordance with (7) at $\tau = 1.18$ for air and $\tau = 1.12$ for CO_2. According to the latest data,[8] in air $\tau = 1.15$.

Thus, formula (7) was valid up to large values of Kn (Kn $\approx$ 3), but already at $Re = 0.15$ the relationship between $(F^P)^{-1}$ and Kn begins to deviate from linearity, $(F^P)^{-1}$ increasing faster than Kn.* The absolute value of F^P at $Kn = 0$ found in these measurements agreed exactly with formula (3).

Real filters consist of fibres of different width. In order to estimate the effect of fibre polydispersity on the resistance of the parallel model, a model consisting of a single row of fibres with alternately larger a_1 and smaller a_2 radii and with the distance

* Later experiments did not confirm this conclusion.

between the fibre axes $2h_2$ was studied. The flow field in such a model was calculated [9] and the following formulae were obtained for the drags F_1^P and F_2^P acting on thick and thin fibres, respectively, which are valid for small values of a_1/h_2 and a_2/h_2:

$$F_1^P = 8\pi\xi_1; \quad F_2^P = 8\pi\xi_2; \tag{8}$$

$$\xi_1 = \Omega_2/(\Omega_1\Omega_2 - K^2); \quad K = 2\ln 2 - (\pi a_1/4h_2)^2 - (\pi a_2/4h_2)^2;$$

$$\Omega_1 = \ln(\pi a_1/4h_2)^2 - 1 - 2(\pi a_1/4h_2)^2/3, \tag{9}$$

and similar formulae for ξ_2 and Ω_2. If $\bar{F}^P = (F_1^P + F_2^P)/2$ is the averaged drag and $\bar{a} = (a_1 + a_2)/2$ the mean fibre radius, then, as shown by calculations, for $\bar{a}/h_2 \leqslant 0.4$ and $a_1/a_2 \leqslant 5$ $\bar{F}^P$ differs little (less than by 5 %) from the drag F^P in a mono-disperse grid with the fibre radius equal to $\bar{a}$. This result was corroborated by model experiments with a viscous liquid at $a_2 = 22$ μm, $a_1 = 79$ or 160 μm, $h_2 = 500$ μm,

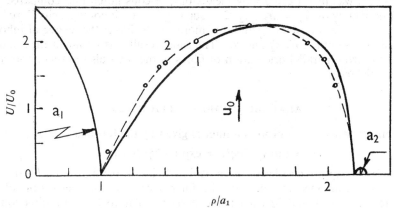

FIG. 4.—Theoretical (1) and experimental (2) flow velocity profiles along the line joining the fibre axes at $\bar{a}/h_2 = 0.238$ and and $a_1/a_2 = 52$.

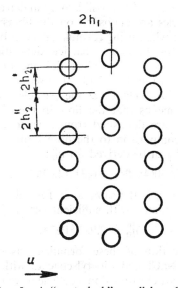

FIG. 5.—A " perturbed " parallel model.

$Re \leqslant 0.05$. The values of $\bar{F}^P$ determined from these experiments agreed within 1-2 % with those calculated for a monodisperse grid. From these results it follows with high probability that the resistance of not very polydisperse filters can be calculated from the mean fibre width.

The validity of the flow field near the fibres calculated for the above model was also corroborated in these experiments. The calculated flow lines coincided with those determined experimentally at $\bar{a}/h_2 = 0.133$ up to $\rho = 2a_2$ near thin fibres and up to $\rho = 1.20a_1$ near thick ones. Even for a very large difference in fibre diameters, the perturbing effect of thin fibres on the flow field is considerable, as can be seen from fig. 4, showing the experimental and calculated flow velocity profiles along the line joining the fibre axes at $\bar{a}/h_2 = 0.238$ and $a_1/a_2 = 52$.

The effect of the irregularity of the model structure on its resistance was also estimated. For that purpose a " perturbed " model (fig. 5) with equal but irregularly arranged fibres was investigated [5] by means of a viscous liquid and compared with a regular model with $h_2 = (h_2' + h_2'')/2$. Such a " microinhomogeneity " reduced the model resistance considerably and, the more so, the larger the degree of inhomogeneity, i.e., the quotient h_2''/h_2' and α. The same result was obtained theoretically. The deviation from parallel orientation of fibres in the rows also lowers appreciably the model resistance.

PARALLEL MODEL.　EFFICIENCY

The aerosol penetration through a filter is given by the formula

$$P = \exp\{-2a\eta l\} = \exp\{-2\eta\alpha H/\pi a\}, \tag{10}$$

in which η is the capture coefficient of aerosol particles on the fibres and l is the total length of fibres contained in 1 cm^2 of the filter sheet. In the derivation of this formula, it is assumed that in each plane perpendicular to the flow direction the aerosol concentration is constant despite particle deposition on the fibres. In the absence of turbulence in the flow through the filter, such equalisation of aerosol concentration in the parallel model is possible only under the influence of Brownian diffusion. When the particles are deposited on the fibres not by diffusion, but by other mechanisms, the error when using formula (10) can be significant.

The capture coefficient for diffusional particle deposition in the parallel model η_D^P can be determined by solving the differential equation of convective particle diffusion towards the fibres in the flow field expressed by formula (1). We assume that $\alpha \ll 1$; $Re < \alpha^{\frac{1}{2}}$; $Pe = 2aU_0/D \gg 1$ (D the particle diffusion coefficient). The second of these conditions means that the flow in the fibre system is automodel, the third, that the particles are deposited from a layer at the fibre surface whose thickness is very small in comparison to the fibre radius. Under these conditions the following formula [10, 11] can be derived for η_D^P:

$$\eta_D^P = [2.30(4\kappa/Pe)^{\frac{2}{3}} + 0.312(4\kappa/Pe) + \ldots]/2\kappa. \tag{11}$$

The hydrodynamic factor κ is the same as in formulae (1) and (2). At $Pe > 10$, formula (11) can be approximated with sufficient accuracy by a simpler expression

$$\eta_D^P = 2.9\kappa^{-\frac{1}{3}}Pe^{-\frac{2}{3}}. \tag{12}$$

The experimental verification of these formulae was performed [12] using fairly monodisperse aerosols of NaCl and dioctylsebacate with the mean particle radii from 1.5 to 9 nm. The particle diffusion coefficient was measured by means of diffusion batteries. The relative particle concentration before and after a battery, etc., was determined by means of a tyndallimeter, after growing the particles by vapour condensation on them. The model filters were made of wires and filaments with a = 0.021-0.25 mm. The experimental results are shown in fig. 6 together with the theoretical lines drawn in accordance with formula (11). This formula is valid already at Pe values of the order of a few units and for α as large as 0.27, i.e., in a much wider range than imposed by the conditions of its derivation.

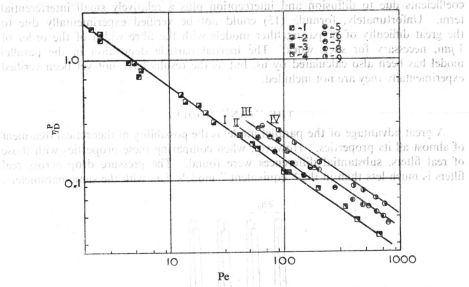

FIG. 6.—The diffusional capture coefficient against Pe in parallel models. Theoretical curves; I. α = 0.01; II. α = 0.05; III, α = 0.135; IV, α = 0.27. Experimental points: (1-4) α = 0.01; 1, r = 15 Å; 2, r = 18 Å; 3, r = 60 Å; 4, r = 83 Å; 5, α = 0.05; r = 70 Å; (6-8) α = 0.135; 6, r = 41 Å; 7, r = 70 Å; 8, r = 55 Å; 9, α = 0.27; r = 55 Å.

The diffusional deposition of aerosols in a polydisperse parallel model was studied by the same method as its resistance. In this case the aerosol penetration is expressed (instead of (10)) by the formula,

$$P = \exp\{-2\eta^P_{1D}a_1l_1 - 2\eta^P_{2D}a_2l_2\} = \exp\{-2\overline{\eta^P_D}al\}, \qquad (13)$$

where $l_1 = l_2$ is the length of fibres with radii a_1 and a_2 contained in a part of the model with 1 cm^2 cross-section, $l = l_1 + l_2$.

As shown [9] by calculation based on the flow field in such a model, at $a_1/a_2 \leqslant 3.5$ and $\bar{a}/h_2 \leqslant 0.2$, the value of $\overline{\eta^P_D a}$ is not more than by 5 % less of that of $\eta^P_D \bar{a}$, calculated for a model with an averaged fibre radius $\bar{a} = (a_1 + a_2)/2$. This conclusion was corroborated by measurements with monodisperse NaCl aerosols with r = 1.5 nm at Pe = 10-48 on two models—with a_1 = 0.79 mm, a_1/a_2 = 3.59, $\bar{a}/h_2$ = 0.101, and with a_1 = 0.16 mm; a_1/a_2 = 7.27; $\bar{a}/h_2$ = 0.182, respectively.

The capture coefficient due to interception in the parallel model η^P_R (the subscript R stands for "interception") is expressed by Langmuir's formula

$$\eta^P_R = [2(1+R)\ln(1+R) - (1+R) + (1+R)^{-1}]/2\kappa, \qquad (14)$$

where $R = r/a$ is the ratio between particle and fibre radii. The deposition due to simultaneous effect of diffusion and interception was calculated by means of a computer [13] for the following conditions: $R \ll 1$; $\delta = (4\kappa/\text{Pe})^{\frac{1}{3}} \ll 1$, where δ is the ratio of the thickness of the layer at the fibre surface from which the particles are deposited, to the fibre radius. The results of these calculations can be expressed (with accuracy 2-3 %) by an interpolation formula

$$\eta_{DR}^{P} = \eta_{D}^{P} + \eta_{R}^{P} + 1.24\kappa^{-\frac{1}{2}}Pe^{-\frac{1}{2}}R^{\frac{2}{3}}. \tag{15}$$

This means that the total capture coefficient η_{DR}^{P} is equal to the sum of the capture coefficients due to diffusion and interception plus a relatively small interferential term. Unfortunately, formula (15) could not be verified experimentally due to the great difficulty of preparing filter models with the fibre width of the order of 1 μm, necessary for such work. The inertial particle deposition in the parallel model has been also calculated by us, but as the results have not yet been verified experimentally they are not included.

THE "FAN" MODEL

A great advantage of the parallel model is the possibility of theoretical treatment of almost all its properties. However, when comparing these properties with those of real filters, substantial differences were found. The pressure drop across real filters is much less than in the " equivalent " models, i.e., with the same parameters.

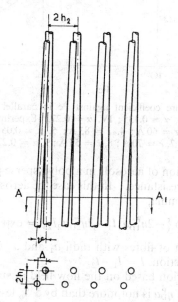

FIG. 8.—A fan model with very small θ.

The diffusional capture coefficient in the model increases considerably with α (see fig. 2), e.g., when the model is compressed, but changes very little, or not at all, on compression of a real filter. After testing a series of models, we found that the best agreement with real filters is shown by the "fan" model [5] obtained from the parallel model by turning each fibre row in its plane by an arbitrary angle θ. The properties of the model proved to be independent of the values of θ, provided they were not zero. In fig. 7, photographs of thin layers of a fan model and of a real filter are given, which show a similarity in their structure.

From measurements with a viscous liquid the following empirical formula was

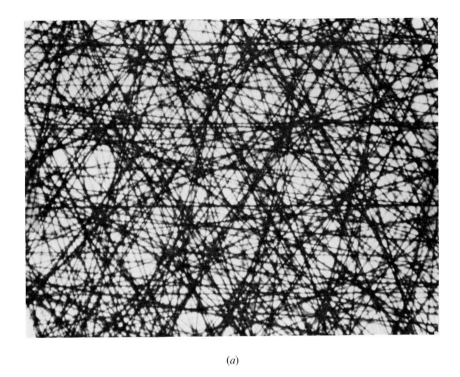

(a)

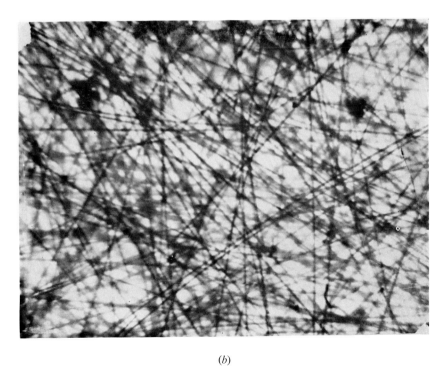

(b)

FIG. 7.—A photograph of a fan model (a) and an electron micrograph of a real filter (b).

[*To face page* 150

obtained for the drag on the fibres in the fan model [12] when the ratio of the distance between the rows to that between neighbouring fibres in a row was less than 0.65:

$$F^f = 4\pi/\kappa', \quad \kappa' = -0.5 \ln \alpha - 0.52 + 0.64\alpha, \tag{16}$$

(f stands for the "fan" model). When this ratio exceed 0.65, the hydrodynamical interaction between the rows vanishes and the drag is given by formula (3).

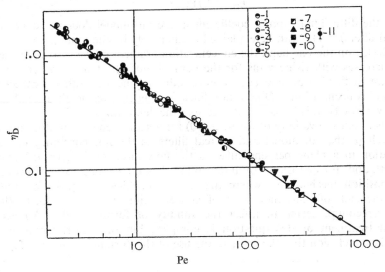

FIG. 9.—The diffusional capture coefficient in the fan model (1-6) and in real filters, corrected for their inhomogeneity (7-11). The full curve is plotted according to formula (18). Experimental points:

	1	2	3	4	5	6
$2a$/(mm)	0.25	0.5	0.1	0.052	0.043	0.043
$2h_2$/(mm)	1.0	2.5	1.0	2.0	1.0	2.0
α	0.187	0.157	0.079	0.02	0.034	0.017

	7	8	9	10	11
$2a$/(μm)	7.14	18.1	13.4	32	3.6
ε	1.05	1.8	1.3	1.1	2.0

A theoretical analysis of the flow field in a fan model is extremely difficult, but we were able to make an approximate theoretical evaluation of F^f making use of the fact that F^f remains constant even at very small values of θ. We consider several adjoining fibre rows divided into short sections (in fig. 8, for clarity, only two rows are shown). At very small θ each section can be approximated by a system of parallel grids shifted with respect to one another by various distances Δ. Calculation of the drag F^f as a function of Δ, based on superposition of the flow fields generated by each separate grid and averaging this drag for all Δ values from 0 to h_2, leads to the formula,

$$F^f = 4\pi/(-0.5 \ln \alpha - 0.44), \tag{17}$$

which is similar to (16). Thus, we obtained an explanation of the fact that the resistance of the fan model is less than that of the parallel model, but we could not explain why F^f is independent of θ. The conclusions made above for the effect of fibre poly-dispersity and gas slip on the model resistance proved to be applicable to the fan model as well, but in the second term of formula (6) a numerical factor 1.22 had to be introduced.[6]

An especially sharp difference between the two models was observed for diffusional particle deposition. As shown by measurements,[12] the diffusional capture coefficient in the fan model at $\alpha = 0.01\text{-}0.15$ and $Pe = 1\text{-}1000$ is expressed by the simple formula (see fig. 9):

$$\eta_D^f = 2.7Pe^{-\frac{2}{3}}. \tag{18}$$

Thus, the diffusional capture coefficient in the fan model does not depend on α (as in real filters). This can be explained qualitatively by the mutual compensation of two effects: on the one hand the concentration gradient of the aerosol at the fibre surface increases with rising α (as for the parallel model). On the other hand, the aerosol stream flowing around each fibre is inhomogeneous, both in respect to its velocity and concentration. Due to non-linear dependence of the diffusional capture on the flow velocity, this leads to a decrease of the deposition.

Doubts about the validity of formula (10) for aerosol penetration does not apply equally well to the fan model and to real filters as the non-constancy of aerosol concentration in a plane perpendicular to the flow direction is averaged over the fibre length and, for deposition by interception, has no significance. However, for other deposition mechanisms, where the capture coefficient depends on the flow velocity, the lack of constancy both of concentration and flow velocity (hydrodynamic screening), seems to affect the validity of formula (10). An accurate theoretical treatment of this question is complex, but the experimental evidence tends to the conclusion that the error in the use of this formula is small. The effect

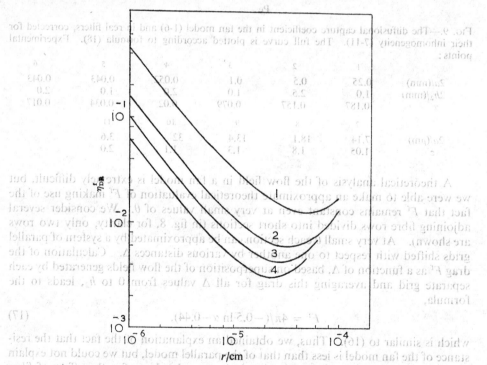

FIG. 10.—The total capture coefficient against particle radius in a fan model with $a = 10^{-3}$ cm, $\alpha \approx 0.05$. 1, $u_0 = 1$ cm/s; 2, $u_0 = 5$ cm/s; 3, $u_0 = 10$ cm/s; 4, $u_0 = 20$ cm/s.

of fibre polydispersity on the diffusional deposition in the fan model is the same as in the parallel model.

The capture coefficient by interception in the fan model can be expressed by a formula similar to (14), but because of the pecularity of the flow field in this model, it is necessary to introduce the hydrodynamic factor k' (see formula (16)) into it instead of κ. Thus,

$$\eta_R^f = [2(1+R)\ln(1+R)-(1+R)+(1+R)^{-1}]/2\kappa'. \tag{19}$$

The last term in (15) is small and depends relatively slightly on κ. We may therefore retain it for the fan model, substituting k' for k in it, and obtain the formula for the combined capture coefficient [14]:

$$\eta_{DR}^f = \eta_D^f + \eta_R^f + 1.24(\kappa')^{-\frac{1}{2}}Pe^{-\frac{1}{2}}R^{\frac{2}{3}}. \tag{20}$$

For practical purpose, the most important question in the theory of aerosol filtration is the filter efficiency in the range of maximum penetration. The values of η_{DR}^f plotted against the particle radii calculated by means of formula (20) for the fan model with $\alpha \approx 0.05$ and $a = 10\ \mu m$ at $U_0 = 5$, 10 and 20 cm/s are given in fig. 10. As shown by our calculations, the inertial deposition in the range of particle size corresponding to maximum penetration is relatively small (Langmuir came to this conclusion intuitively 30 years ago) and the minima on the curves are due to increase of η_R^f and decrease of η_D^f with rising particle size at constant flow velocity. However, in the curves η_{DR}^f against U_0 the minima are caused by the increase of inertial deposition and decrease of η_D^f with rising U_0.

REAL FILTERS.   DEGREE OF INHOMOGENEITY

For real filters, notwithstanding a large number of published experimental data, very few of these could be used in this work, chiefly due to incomplete characterisation of the filters used.

In all filters with cylindrical fibres, as shown below, the resistance is less than in the fan model with the same parameters. This is caused mainly by the inhomogeneity of the structure of real filters. As already pointed out, the filter resistance decreases considerably in the presence of structural micro-inhomogeneities (on a scale of the mean distance between the fibres). A similar effect is produced by macro-inhomogeneities, such as fluctuations of the thickness and packing density of the filter, by any deviation from the parallel fibre orientation, and from the perpendicularity of the fibres to the flow direction. The presence of doubled, trebled etc., fibres caused by incomplete dispersion of the fibres in the fabrication of filters must be regarded also as a kind of inhomogeneity. As shown by calculation and by experiments with fan models, when all the fibres in the filter are doubled, the resistance decreases almost two-fold.

Various types of inhomogeneity affect the values of the drag F in the formula (4) differently. As the determination of the magnitude of fluctuations of H and α in real filters is very difficult, it is expedient to assume formally that the effect of inhomogeneity of any kind on the filter resistance, expressed by formula (4), consists in reducing the drag F. In fig. 11 the values of F^r (the superscript r stands for " real ") calculated by means of (4) (the mean values of a were used) are plotted against α for a number of real filters with cylindrical fibres, together with the curve (F^f, α) for the fan model plotted according to (16). For all filters with cylindrical fibres tested by us or described in the literature, together with necessary data for calculating F^r in the function of α, the F values were lower than in the " equivalent " (i.e., with the same H, α and α) fan model. Therefore, we used for the ratio $F^f/F^r = \varepsilon > 1$ the term " degree of inhomogeneity " of a real filter. The work " inhomogeneity " is taken in the broad sense mentioned above.

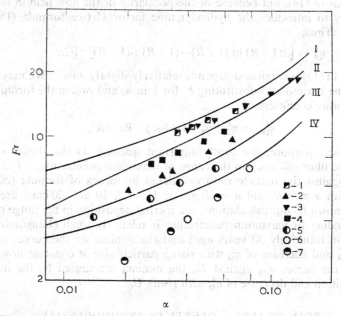

FIG. 11.—The hydrodynamic drag against α. Fan model, formula (16), (curve I). Real filters: according to Chen [15] (curve II), Davies [16] (curve III), Langmuir [17] (curve IV). Our data for filters with $2a = 7.14$; 18.1; 32 and 13.4 μm respectively (1-4). Data of First [18] (5), Wong [19] (6) and Blasewitz [20] (7).

The effect of gas slip on the resistance of real filters was studied [6] on monodisperse filters with $a = 1.5\text{-}9\ \mu$m, $\alpha = 0.03\text{-}0.14$ and $\varepsilon = 1.08\text{-}2.2$ at pressures $\geqslant 10$ Torr. As shown by these measurements, $(F^r)^{-1}$ increases linearly with Kn (as in models) in accordance with the experimentally found formula,

$$(F^r)^{-1} = (F_0^r)^{-1} + 1.21\tau\beta(1-\alpha)\text{Kn}/4\pi, \qquad (21)$$

in which $\tau = 1.18$ (in air), 1.21 is an empirical coefficient corresponding to the transition from parallel to fan model and β a coefficient related to the inhomogeneity of filter structure. To the first approximation, $\beta = \varepsilon^{\frac{1}{2}}$.

In the efficiency of real filters, we must take into account that in the expressions for F^r (formula (16)) and for η_R^f (formula (19)) the same hydrodynamical factor κ' is included. It follows that the effect of inhomogeneity of the filters on both these quantities should be the same, i.e., in real filters η_R^f should be ε times less than in the fan model.

By investigating a large number of commercial filters as well as those prepared in our laboratory, we found [12] that the diffusional capture coefficient in real filters, as in the fan model, does not depend on α, i.e., does not change during compression of the filter. Moreover, η_D in real filters, as a rule, is less than in the fan model with the same parameters. There can be no doubt that the main reason of these differences is the inhomogeneity of real filters, because any kind of deviation from homogeneity leads to increase in the aerosol penetration through the filter. We made the simplest assumption that the effect of the inhomogeneity on the drag F and on the diffusional capture coefficient η_D is equal (as for interception), i.e., that $\eta_D^f = \varepsilon\eta_D^r$. In order to prove this hypothesis, the diffusional deposition of an aerosol with $r = 27$ nm in the fan model and in the filters prepared in our laboratory from isodisperse glass fibres was measured.[12] The values of η_D^f for these filters as well as for filters described by Chen,[15] multiplied by ε (determined from the filter resistance) together with the values of η_D^f for the fan model are plotted against Pe in fig. 9. All experimental points lie on one straight line corresponding to formula (18) in compliance with our hypothesis.

Due to the smallness of the last term in (20) we can generalize this result and assume that

$$\eta_{DR}^f = \varepsilon\eta_{DR}^r. \tag{22}$$

An experimental check of these deductions was made [21] with monodisperse aerosols and a filter prepared from isodisperse terylene fibres in the laboratory (no. 1-14 in table 1) and on the basis of Whitby's [22] data obtained with glass-fibre filters (no. 14-16), in the range of maximum penetration. The change of α in our filter was achieved by compression. The table lists the following parameters: fibre diameter $2a$, filter thickness H, packing density α, degree of inhomogeneity ε, determined by comparing the drag F^r calculated from filter resistance (formula 4) with the drag F^f in an equivalent fan model. U_0 is the face velocity of flow, r the particle radius, $P\uparrow$ and $P\downarrow$, aerosol penetration for upward and downward flows, respectively.

TABLE 1.—CALCULATED AND EXPERIMENTAL VALUES OF THE CAPTURE COEFFICIENT IN REAL FILTERS

no.	$2a/\mu$m	H/cm	α	ε	U_0/(cm/s)	r/μm	$P\uparrow$	$P\downarrow$	η_{DR}/ε	η_{DR}
1	23.1	3.7	0.042	1.53	5.2	0.67	0.73	0.65	0.0043	0.0045
2	23.1	3.7	0.042	1.53	3.8	0.72	0.73	0.63	0.0045	0.0047
3	23.1	3.7	0.042	1.53	2.6	0.63	0.73	0.61	0.0047	0.0048
4	23.1	3.7	0.042	1.53	4.1	0.85	0.62	0.53	0.0065	0.0056
5	23.1	3.7	0.042	1.53	5.4	0.88	0.65	0.53	0.0061	0.0057
6	23.1	3.7	0.042	1.53	2.7	0.73	0.65	0.50	0.0065	0.0052
7	23.1	3.7	0.042	1.53	3.8	0.55	0.72	0.65	0.0044	0.0039
8	23.1	2.0	0.077	1.53	1.7	0.70	0.65	0.45	0.0072	0.0065
9	23.1	2.0	0.077	1.53	1.6	0.70	0.62	0.54	0.0063	0.0060
10	23.1	2.0	0.077	1.53	0.53	0.35	0.38	0.26	0.013	0.011
11	23.1	2.0	0.077	1.53	0.92	0.35	0.55	0.43	0.0085	0.0082
12	23.1	2.0	0.077	1.53	1.4	0.35	0.55	0.50	0.0072	0.0065
13	23.1	2.0	0.077	1.53	2.3	0.35	0.66	0.60	0.0054	0.0050
14	10.0	2.0	0.03	1.4	2.1	0.04	0.835		0.014	0.013
15	10.0	2.0	0.03	1.4	2.1	0.3	0.937		0.0051	0.0054
16	10.0	2.0	0.03	1.4	2.1	0.55	0.855		0.013	0.010

The difference between $P\uparrow$ and $P\downarrow$ is caused by gravitational particle deposition. We excluded this effect by taking the mean penetration $\bar{P} = (P\uparrow + P\downarrow)/2$. In the next column the values of η_{DR}^f/ε evaluated by means of (20) are given, i.e., the theoretical values of the total capture coefficient, and in the last column are the experimental values of this coefficient, determined from $\bar{P}$ by means of (10). The fact that the experimental values are somewhat larger than the calculated ones is evidently due to the neglect of inertial deposition.

It follows that when the geometrical parameters a, α and H of the filter and its resistance are known, we can calculate with an accuracy sufficient for practical purposes its efficiency when inertial deposition can be neglected, i.e., in the particle size range corresponding to maximum penetration and to the left of it, i.e., for still smaller particles.

We realize that there are still many gaps in our work. The most significant is the lack of model experimental data on the inertial particle deposition and the too-small number of filters on which all conclusions were tested. We hope to be able to fill up these gaps in the near future.

[1] S. Kuwabara, *J. Phys. Soc. Japan*, 1959, **14**, 527.

[2] A. M. Golovin and V. A. Lopatin, *Prikladnaya Mekhanika i Tekhnicheskaya Fizika*, 1969, no. 2, 99.

[3] A. A. Kirsch and N. A. Fuchs, *J. Phys. Soc. Japan*, 1967, **22**, 125.

[4] T. Mijagi, *J. Phys. Soc. Japan*, 1958, **13**, 493.

[5] A. A. Kirsch and N. A. Fuchs, *Ann. Occup. Hyg.*, 1967, **10**, 23.

[6] A. A. Kirsch, I. B. Stechkina and N. A. Fuchs, *Kolloid Zhur.*, 1973, **35**, 34.

[7] A. A. Kirsch, I. B. Stechkina and N. A. Fuchs, *J. Colloid Interface Sci.*, 1971, **37**, 458.

[8] S. Albertoni, C. Cercignani and L. Gotusso, *Phys. Fluids*, 1963, **11**, 217.

[9] A. A. Kirsch and I. B. Stechkina, *J. Colloid Interface Sci.*, 1973, **43**, 10.

[10] N. A. Fuchs and I. B. Stechkina, *Ann. Occup. Hyg.*, 1963, **6**, 27.

[11] I. B. Stechkina, *Doklady Akad. Nauk. USSR*, 1966, **167**, 1372.

[12] A. A. Kirsch and N. A. Fuchs, *Ann. Occup. Hyg.*, 1968, **11**, 299.

[13] I. B. Stechkina and N. A. Fuchs, *Ann. Occup. Hyg.*, 1966, **9**, 59.

[14] I. B. Stechkina, A. A. Kirsch and N. A. Fuchs, *Ann. Occup. Hyg.*, 1969, **12**, 1.

[15] C. Y. Chen, *Chem. Rev.*, 1955, **55**, 595.

[16] C. N. Davies, *Proc. Inst. Mech. Eng. B*, 1952, **1**, 185.

[17] I. Langmuir, OSRD, 1942, report no. 865.

[18] M. W. First *et al.*, Harvard University, Boston, 1951, NYO-1581.

[19] J. B. Wong, W. E. Ranz and H. F. Johnstone, *J. Appl. Phys.*, 1956, **27**, 161.

[20] A. G. Blasewitz *et al.*, U.S. AEC, Hanford Works, 1951, HW-20847.

[21] A. A. Kirsch, I. B. Stechkina and N. A. Fuchs, *Kolloid Zhur.*, 1969, **31**, 227.

[22] K. T. Whitby *et al.*, *J. Air. Poll. Contr. Ass.*, 1961, **11**, 503.

GENERAL DISCUSSION

Prof. M. Kerker (*Clarkson Coll. Techn., Potsdam*) said: The measurement of the extinction cross section of a particle by attenuation measurements of a sample collected on a glass slide is quite precarious. Among the difficulties are reflection effects due to the glass slide, interference effects among the assembled particles, and, if the collection is somewhat dense, multiple scattering effects. Also, there is the purely optical problem of eliminating the forward scattered light from the detection system. What precautions did Howard take to assess these? And did he calculate the refractive index that would correspond to his measured extinction cross-section for comparison with the literature values? Alternatively, did he compare calculated values of the extinction cross-section for particles of the size he had with his measured values of the extinction cross-section?

Prof. J. B. Howard and **Dr. B. L. Wersborg** (*Dept. Chem. Eng., M.I.T.*) said: In reply to Kerker, attenuation by reflection from the glass slide was adequately eliminated by directing the laser beam first at a clean spot adjacent to the particle deposit and then at the deposit. The recorded signal, which was the difference between the second and first attenuation signals, measured the attenuation by soot particles. Interference among particles was trivial, a conclusion based on the fact that attenuation by the different deposits, which ranged from less than a monolayer to only a few particle layers, was a linear function of deposit depth. Calculations, employing the ranges of possible values of the optical coefficients of the particles studied, show that scattering is negligible compared with absorption for all values of the diameter/wavelength ratio encountered in the experiment. The optical measurements will be described more fully in a forthcoming publication.

The extinction cross-sections cannot be calculated since data on the refractive index of young, growing soot particles are not available. However, data are available on the refractive index of aged soot, and the values give extinction cross sections larger than those measured in this work. According to Dalzell and Sarofim,[1] the complex refractive index of aged acetylene soot for the wavelength in question (6328 Å) is $m = 1.57 - 0.44i$, which gives an extinction cross-section larger, by a factor of 2.8-3.8, than the values found in this study. This difference is qualitatively reasonable since young soot particles contain more hydrogen and have less crystal stucture than aged soot.

Dr. C. N. Davies (*University of Essex*) said: I think that aerosols of dibutyl phthalate are too volatile for use in the experiments of Nicolaon and Kerker. Since the aerosols were undiluted the gas phase must have been saturated with the vapour of dibutyl phthalate and eqn (2.9) and (3.1) of my paper are then suitable for calculating rates of evaporation.

Coagulation times from 82-327 s are shown in table 5; it will be supposed that the temperature of the aerosol in the ageing vessel was 20°C. Calculations of evaporation have been carried out for particles of radii as shown in table 3.

---

[1] W. H. Dalzell and A. F. Sarofim, *J. Heat Transfer*, 1969, **91**, 100.

It is evident that during the coagulation period vapour must be distilling isothermally from the smaller particles to the larger ones so that the ascribing of change in size

aerosol	particle radius/ μm	lifetime/s	loss of weight in	
			320 s	160 s
DBP in helium	0.235	940	39 %	19 %
DBP in nitrogen	0.314	1210	27.6 %	12.8 %

distribution to coagulation alone is incorrect. Some of the vapour would also condense on the walls of the vessel, which have an area much exceeding that of the aerosol particles; the authors state that they were unable to detect any hold-up on this account but an assessment of the amount of vapour concerned in relation to the accuracy of analysis is lacking. An assessment, also, of the accuracy of the rather indirect optical measurement of size distribution would be of interest.

The mass concentration of aerosol measured by thermal precipitator sampling was 5 % less than the figure obtained with millipore filters. A thermal precipitator can be a very accurate instrument for sampling aerosols but it is possible for vapour to condense in the small cavities of filters, due to the Kelvin effect.

Prof. M. Kerker (*Clarkson Coll. Techn., N.Y.*) said: In reply to Davies, we have checked repeatedly for hold-up of dibutylphthalate in the coagulation chamber and have always found this to be negligible. Some recent results are presented here for three different flow rates. In this case the dibutylphthalate aerosol is in helium at a pressure of 0.50 ± 0.01 atm so that any distillation to the walls would be expected to be more pronounced than for the aerosol in the paper which is for nitrogen at atmospheric pressure. The modal radius was 0.25 μm. The aerosol was collected on millipore filters (pore 1.2 μm) just prior to entrance into and after exit from the coagulation chamber (volume 2570 ml; wall area 1800 cm²). Residence time in the chamber varied from 1.28-2.57 min. As is apparent from the table, the loss appeared to be about 2 %. The error in weighing the samples is about 1 % so that hold-up in the coagulation chamber is negligible.

TABLE 1.—HOLD-UP OF DIBUTYLPHTHALATE AEROSOL IN THE COAGULATION CHAMBER

	aerosol concentration/(mg/l)		
	flow 1.0 l/m	flow 1.5 l/m	flow 2.0 l/m
initial aerosol	1.70	1.62	1.57
coagulated aerosols	1.68	1.59	1.55

One would expect that isothermal distillation from smaller particles to larger ones would occur even more slowly than distillation to the walls both because the wall area is larger than the surface area of the aerosol particles, but more especially because these aerosols are quite monodisperse (even those which have coagulated for some time) so that the driving force, which is derived from the range of Kelvin vapour pressures, is much smaller. Accordingly, we do not believe that distillation either to the walls or from particle to particle plays a significant role in the processes occurring in the hold-up tube.

More direct evidence that the mechanism by which the aerosol ages is coagulation rather than distillation is contained in the two electron micrographs, fig. 1 and 2. These depict a linolenic acid aerosol (modal radius $a_M = 0.248$ μm) prior to entry into the coagulation chamber and after exit (hold-up time 5.26 min). The aerosol was "fixed" prior to collection for electron microscope observation by treatment with OsO_4. (The apparent spots in the centre of each particle are due to penetration of the glossy photographic print in the process of obtaining the particle size distri-

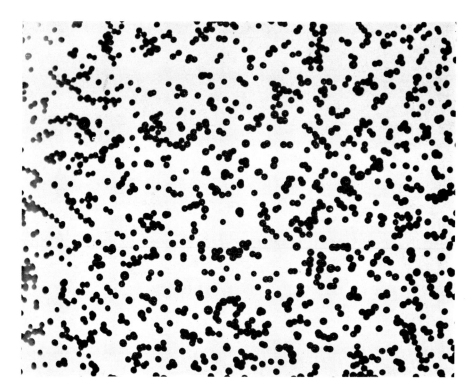

FIG. 1.—Electron micrograph of linolenic acid aerosol prior to coagulation; see table 2 for size distribution.

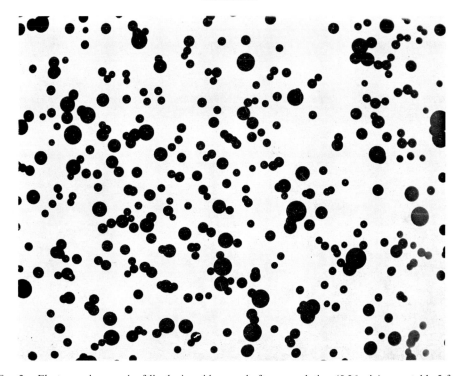

FIG. 2.—Electron micrograph of linolenic acid aerosol after coagulation (5.26 min); see table 2 for size distribution.

[*To face page* 158

bution with a Karl Zeiss particle counter.) The size distributions for each of these electron micrographs is given in table 2.

It is significant that although the average particle size increases, the smallest particles in the population are neither completely scavenged nor reduced to a smaller size as would be expected were the principal mechanism distillation from small to

TABLE 2.—PARTICLE SIZE DISTRIBUTION OF INITIAL AND COAGULATED LINOLENIC ACID AEROSOL

radius/μm	0.18	0.21	0.25	0.28	0.32	0.35	0.38	0.41
initial (%)	—	13.9	58.1	23.3	3.8	0.6	—	—
coagulate (%)	0.5	8.3	24.9	19.1	13.8	9.6	5.3	5.4

radius/μm	0.44	0.47	0.51	0.54	0.57	0.60	0.63	0.67
initial (%)	—	0.2	—	—	—	—	—	—
coagulated (%)	3.7	2.7	3.0	1.0	1.1	0.6	0.9	0.2

large particles rather than coagulation. Also, examination of the distribution of sizes in table 2 shows that the frequency of the modal size decreases as would be expected for coagulation and does not shift to a smaller size category of the same frequency as would be expected for the distillation mechanism.

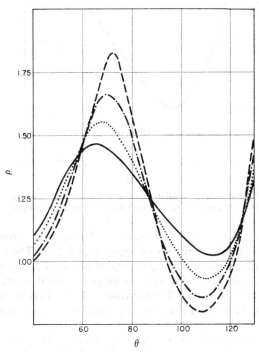

FIG. 3.—Polarization ratio against scattering angle for initial aerosol ($a_M = 0.24$ μm, $\sigma_0 = 0.10$, $N = 1.2 \times 10^7$ cm^{-3}) for coagulation times 41 (– – –), 56 (– · – ·), 78 (. . . . .) and 110 (——) s.

Davies is surely mistaken when he characterizes the optical measurements as " rather indirect." They are most direct since they occur *in situ* without perturbing the system and can be interpreted in a straightforward method. The sensitivity of the light scattering to the evolution of the particle size distribution in the course of coagulation is illustrated in fig. 3 which represents the curves of polarization ratio against scattering angle for an initial aerosol $a_M = 0.24$ μm, $\sigma_0 = 0.10$, $N = 1.2 \times 10^7$ cm^{-3} for coagulation times 41, 56, 78 and 110 s. The separation of these curves indicates that the light scattering can clearly resolve differences of 2-3 s in coagulation time.

Fig. 4 depicts graphically the resolution in coagulation time attainable for a particular experimental run. In this case, the initial particle size distribution was $a_M = 0.31$ μm, $\sigma_0 = 0.10$, $N = 5.6 \times 10^6$ cm^{-3}. The experimental coagulation time was 82 s. The figure is a plot of the deviation measure (eqn (5)) against the

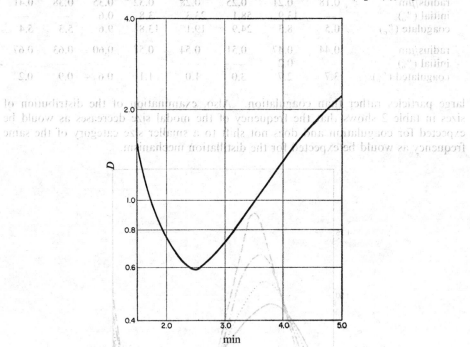

FIG. 4.—Deviation measure against coagulation time for initial aerosol $a_M = 0.31$ μm, $\sigma_0 = 0.10$ $N = 5.6 \times 10^6$ cm^{-3} after 82 s in hold-up tube. The minimum is at 2.50 min.

calculated coagulation time. The minimum at 2.50 min is certainly well resolved by these light scattering data to within no more than 1-2 s. The resolution becomes less at longer coagulation times when the aerosol becomes polydisperse and it is for that reason that the light scattering can no longer be used to monitor the process beyond about one-third to one-half a life-time. The criterion becomes the depth of the minimum in the curves of the deviation measure against time.

Dr. C. N. Davies (*University of Essex*) (*communicated*): I am grateful to Kerker for the details of his experiments but must admit that I am puzzled by the results. His fig. 1 and 2, which claim to show the coagulation of 0.25 μm radius aerosol of linolenic acid during 326 s, which may be due to incorrect sampling,[1] and many circular particles of about the same volume as the chain, in the sample of coagulated aerosol. His table 2 shows that some 3 % of the final number of particles has twice the initial radius. I cannot see how so many multiplet particles could have formed

[1] J. O. Irwin, P. Armitage and C. N. Davies, *Nature*, 1949, **163**, 809; S. A. Roach, *The Theory of Random Clumping* (Methuen, 1968).

by coagulation while airborne. A rough calculation, based on the half-life of the aerosol being 250 s, indicates that there are about 20 times too many eightfold multiplets. The effect of evaporation might therefore have been obscured.

Dr. G. H. Walker (*Clark College, Atlanta, Ga.*) said: The techniques of light beating spectroscopy have been developed to the point where they offer a valuable supplement to the more traditional approaches. Recently, Hinds and Reist [1] have applied these techniques successfully to aerosol measurements. Does Kerker think that light beating spectroscopy can be applied profitably to the problems of aerosol growth and coagulation?

Prof. M. Kerker (*Clarkson Coll. Techn., Potsdam*) said: The use of *in situ* light scattering measurements to study dynamical processes of aerosols, such as coagulation, appears to have many advantages. Would Brock please comment on the possibility of relaxing some of the present constraints on his method, i.e., the restrictions of narrow size distributions and unimodality. On the same subject, some of the people at Clarkson are working on the problem of investigating diffusion battery measurements. Brock and his colleagues have done quite a lot on the related light scattering problem. We would be interested to learn about his numerical inversion techniques. Any information would be appreciated.

Prof. J. R. Brock (*University of Texas at Austin*) said: The problem is that conventional light scattering may be quite inadequate to resolve unimodality versus bimodality for a narrow distribution. In fig. (7.35) of ref. (2) we have shown that if light scattering data corresponding to a bimodal distribution is *assumed* to be unimodal, one will obtain quite a good fit to the data. Accordingly, it is necessary to know *a priori* whether the system is or is not unimodal. The same applies to the skewness of the distribution. Also, we generally find that a unique fit to the data cannot be obtained for 0.1 μm particles when the standard deviation is greater than 20-30 %. For larger particles the conditions are even more stringent. Of course, our techniques do not involve absolute intensity measurements which are often difficult to obtain. These might relax matters somewhat.

Our numerical inversion technique is : experimental and calculated measurements (for a two parameter distribution) are compared at each of 19 scattering angles. A deviation measure is obtained by summing the square of the differences between these quantities and plotting contours of equal deviation measures in a two dimensional domain of the two size distribution parameters. If there is a " well ", the bottom of the " well " is selected as the solution. If the distribution is too broad, one will obtain open valleys which means there is no unique solution.

It is my view that light scattering can be a sensitive tool for particle size study but that it must be based upon observation of single particles such as we have carried out recently.[3] Then one takes advantage of the high sensitivity of light scattering to particle size. Thus we were able [4] to determine the size and refractive index of single glass fibres to 0.25 % and 0.01 R.I. units, respectively. I believe the instrumentation recently developed by the late Prof. Gucker of Indiana University offers a great opportunity in this regard.

[1] *Aerosol Sci.*, 1972, **3**, 000.
[2] M. Kerker, *The Scattering of Light and Other Electromagnetic Radiation* (Academic Press, New York, 1969), pp. 359-373.
[3] D. D. Cooke and M. Kerker, *J. Colloid Interface Sci.*, 1973, **42**, 150.
[4] W. A. Farone and M. Kerker, *J. Opt. Soc. Amer.*, 1966, **56**, 481.

Deposition of Aerosols from Turbulent Pipe Flow

By I. Williams and A. B. Hedley

Dept. of Chemical Engineering, University of Sheffield, Mappin Street, Sheffield, Yorkshire

Received 11th January, 1973

Several approaches to the calculation of the rate of deposition of particles from a turbulent fluid stream on to the boundary walls are discussed. In a turbulent flow system containing suspended particles, the need to consider the relationship between the particle eddy diffusivity and the fluid eddy diffusivity in calculating the deposition rate, has been indicated. A quantitative estimation is made of the effect of temperature gradients between the fluid and the wall surface in inducing a radially-directed thermophoretic velocity on the particles.

A flow system is described in which a turbulent air stream passes through a cylindrical duct. The flow was assumed to be two-dimensional and was characterized by measuring the mean velocities and the fluctuating turbulent velocities of the fluid in the axial and radial directions, and also the shear stress profile in the radial direction. From the latter measurement the eddy diffusivity of the fluid was determined. The measurements were carried out at Reynolds numbers of 1.27×10^5 and 2.67×10^4 and at several duct wall temperatures between 279 and 317 K. Droplets of approximately 1 μm diam. were injected into the turbulent fluid and the results indicate the effect of the flow conditions and wall temperatures on the particle deposition rates.

The prediction of the rate of deposition of particles from a turbulent fluid on to boundary surfaces has many important applications. Examples include deposition in atomic reactors, spray dryers, particle sampling lines and in any flow system where suspended particles are transported from a generating source to the place of application.

A straight, smooth walled, cylindrical duct offers the most convenient means for studying the rate of particle deposition in turbulent flow systems. The processes by which particles deposit on a pipe wall include,[1] eddy diffusion, gravity settling, thermophoresis, diffusiophoresis, electrostatic effects and inertial effects such as impaction and interception. The parameter K, which describes the deposition rate, has been defined as [2]

$$K = \frac{\text{amount of particulate deposited per cm}^2 \text{ of surface s}^{-1}}{\text{the airborne particulate concentration above the surface}}.$$

The approach to the problem has usually been to evolve methods of predicting K for different systems and to correlate the predictions experimentally.

In previous investigations the following assumptions were often made. The structure of the turbulent fluid in pipe flow consisted of a laminated boundary layer and a turbulent core. The boundary layer was characterized by three regions [3]:

(i) laminar sub layer, $y+ < 5$;
(ii) buffer layer, $5 < y+ < 30$;
(iii) main boundary layer $y+ > 30$,

where, $y+$ is the dimensionless variable, yu/v, y is the distance normal to the surface measured outwards, and u_τ is the fluid friction velocity defined as

$$u_\tau = \sqrt{(\tau_0/\rho)}. \tag{1}$$

162

τ_0 is the tangential shearing stress on the surface over which the fluid flows, ρ is the fluid density, and v is the fluid kinematic viscosity.

The equation used to describe the rate R of transport of particles from the turbulent core to the wall is

$$R = (D+\varepsilon_p)\mathrm{d}C/\mathrm{d}y, \tag{2}$$

where D is the molecular diffusivity and ε_p is the particle eddy diffusion coefficient due to the turbulence; C is the concentration of the diffusing substance at a distance y from the surface. The particles were usually assumed to diffuse by eddy diffusion from a constant particle concentration in the turbulent core of the pipe up to, and in some theories, into, the boundary layer. In the diffusion process the eddy diffusivities of the particle and fluid were assumed equal. At the point where the eddy diffusion process was assumed to end, the particle was associated with a free flight velocity v, and a stop distance [3] $\mathrm{d}s$, where $\mathrm{d}s = v_f + \tau$ and τ is the particle relaxation time. For particles obeying Stokes law of resistance,

$$\tau = \frac{m}{6\pi r_p \eta} = \frac{2}{9}\frac{r_p^2 \rho_p}{\eta}, \tag{3}$$

where r_p is the particle radius, m the particle mass, ρ_p its density and η is the viscosity of the fluid. The value of v was usually equated to a function of the root-mean-square radial resolute of the fluid fluctuation velocity $v_f +$.

Friedlander and Johnson [4] derived deposition velocities on the basis of the above postulate. They assumed that $v = 0.9\,u_\tau$. This figure seemed unreasonably high and according to the fundamental turbulence measurements made by Laufer [5] this velocity existed at a distance $y^+ = 80$ which was within the turbulent core and not within the boundary layer. Even using such a high initial velocity, the particle stopping distance was often less than the thickness of the laminar sublayer. This led Friedlander and Johnson [4] to use the hypothesis of Lin et al.[6] who determined the following empirical expression for ε_f, the fluid eddy diffusivity, within the laminar sublayer:

$$\varepsilon_f/v = (y^+/14.5)^3. \tag{4}$$

According to this model, eddies from the turbulent core at a distance $y^+ = 80$, penetrated the boundary layer and retained their momentum until they were within a distance S^+, from the wall, where $S^+ = 0.9\tau^+$ and τ^+, the dimensionless particle relaxation time was equal to $\tau u_\tau^2/v$. A finite eddy diffusivity within the laminar layer was assumed. When S^+ was calculated using the actual values of v' at $y^+ = S^+$, transport coefficients were obtained which were four orders of magnitude lower than those found experimentally by Friedlander and Johnson.[4]

Davies [7] derived a deposition scheme in which he considered both inertial deposition and deposition by Brownian diffusion. The particle radius was taken as the distance of closest approach to the deposition surface. The main difference between this theory and that mentioned previously for inertial deposition [4] was that Davies calculated his free-flight particle velocity from an analytical expression derived from the measured turbulent velocity data in fully-developed turbulent pipe flow derived by Laufer.[5] He determined the free-flight velocity at a distance from the wall where he considered free flight began, not as previously,[4] in the turbulent core. Lawrence and Huang [8] adapted this theory and obtained solutions valid for a cylindrical coordinate system rather than the rectangular coordinate system used by Davies.[7] In all the above work, re-entrainment of particles from the boundary walls was assumed to be absent. Reviews of these theories and of others [10-12] differing little from the above have been given by Montgomery and Corn [13] and Sehmel.[14]

In a recent theory, Lawrence and Huang [8] considered that the size of the particles relative to the scale of the turbulence was of importance and they defined a relative entrainment factor, as

$$\alpha = ds/l, \tag{5}$$

where l is the fluid mixing length [15] at a point within the fluid. If this ratio was greater than unity the concept of a particle stop distance was used; however, if the quantity, α was less than unity then the mixing length was used as a measure of the particle free flight distance. On the basis of work by Tchen [16] and Soo and Tien [17] the authors assumed equality of particle and fluid diffusivities but included a specification of the particle root-mean-square turbulent fluctuation velocity, $v_p'^+$, with respect to the r.m.s. fluid fluctuation velocity, $v_f'^+$, in the form of a non-linear differential equation relating the latter two quantities and the particle relaxation time in the following manner:

$$\frac{dv_p'^+}{dy^+} = \frac{1}{\tau^+}1 + \frac{v_f'^+}{v_p'^+}. \tag{6}$$

The authors calculated the discrete particle deposition flux for fully-developed turbulent pipe flow. The results deviated widely, as did those in all the previous work reviewed, from the small amount of experimentally obtained aerosol deposition data available from other sources.

Rouhiainen and Stachiewicz [18] used the concept of frequency response developed by Hjelmfelt and Mockros [19] to obtain a quantitative evaluation of $\varepsilon_p/\varepsilon_F$. They showed that for 30 μm diam. particles of lycopodium spore, a fourfold increase in Reynolds number Re of the suspending fluid which caused a more than fourfold increase in ε_F, only resulted in a twofold increase in ε_p. A more important result of their work for small particles was their quantitative evaluation of the shear flow induced transverse lift force on a particle in the laminar sublayer. They considered that for a vertical flow system, if the particle radial velocity was sufficient to carry the particle to such a distance from the wall, that the particle velocity in the x coordinate direction was higher than the local stream velocity in this direction, then the lift force was directed towards the wall. For lycopodeum spheres of 2 μm diam. they calculated that for Re $> 1 \times 10^4$, the particle velocity at the edge of the sublayer such that deposition on the wall took place, was three orders of magnitude lower when considering the lift force effect than when a purely inertial mechanism was considered. Further work was needed to apply this mechanism to horizontal pipe flow to determine the distance from the wall at which the lift reversal takes place and to clarify the mechanisms which propel the particles to within the latter distance from the wall.

Sehmel [1] examined the effect of removing the assumptions of regarding an equality of diffusivity of the particle and fluid and an equality of particle and fluid root-mean-square turbulent fluctuation velocities. He determined what dependence these variables had upon other parameters of the problem in order that theoretical calculations agreed with the experimental data, i.e. he described the combined effect of the two parameters as an " effective eddy diffusion coefficient " and gave empirical correlations for predicting this quantity for various flow conditions. He also made deposition measurements on all surfaces of a duct and introduced a gravitational factor into the correlations. Finally, an effect was investigated by Byers and Calvert [20] which had been subject to few previous investigations. They determined the particle deposition from turbulent streams by means of a thermal force. Experimental work carried out measured the deposition rate of 0.3-1.3 μm diam. particles from pipe flows at Re $= 1.376 \times 10^4$ when the gas temperature was several hundred degrees above the pipe wall temperature. High particle collection efficiencies were measured and compared with negligible particle collection efficiencies under similar experimental conditions with the temperature gradient removed. Unfortunately, there seems to be few experimental data relating to the thermal deposition of micron size aerosols from fully-developed turbulent pipe flow incorporating small temperature gradients.

It was apparent from the current state of aerosol deposition studies in turbulent flow, that certain aspects of the problem warranted further investigation; these were (1) more experimental results of particle deposition rates from turbulent pipe flow under closely controlled conditions were needed. (2) The relationship between the particle diffusivity and the fluid diffusivity $\varepsilon_P/\varepsilon_F$ needed clarification. (3) The relative importance of thermal, electrostatic, and diffusive forces should be investigated. (4) The reverse lift force [18] warranted further theoretical investigation along the previously suggested lines.

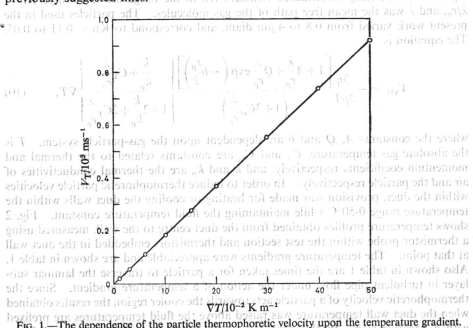

FIG. 1.—The dependence of the particle thermophoretic velocity upon the temperature gradient.

It was decided to construct a variable flow system in which fully-developed turbulent pipe flow was achieved. An initial investigation was designed to characterize the flow in terms of the mean and fluctuating velocities U, u', V, v' in the axial and radial directions respectively, and to allow the determination of the shear stress, $-\overline{uv}$ as a function of y and hence the eddy diffusivity of the fluid from the relationship

$$\varepsilon/\nu = \frac{\overline{uv}/u_\tau^2}{du^+/dy^+},$$

where

$$\frac{du^+}{dy^+} = \frac{d(U/U_0)}{d(y/a)} \cdot \frac{U_0 \nu}{U_\tau a U_\tau},$$

and a is the pipe radius, U is the mean axial velocity at a point, and U_0 is the maximum mainstream velocity at the centre line.

The measurement of the above quantities was carried out using hot-wire anemometry. Non-volatile droplets were chosen as the disperse phase since in the deposition measurements particle evapouration would be minimized. By carrying out concentration traverses of the aerosol injected into the turbulent flow, the diffusivity of the particles in the fluid was determined.[23] The measurement of the aerosol concentration was carried out by sampling the aerosol isokinetically and using a multi-channel light-scattering counter which was developed for the purpose.[24]

For the purpose of this experiment the effect of charge was minimized by generating a condensation aerosol, examining it for charge using a charge analyzer and if necessary neutralizing the aerosol using a charge generator designed to produce equal numbers of $+$ve and $-$ve ions. Fig. 1 indicates the magnitude of the thermophoretic velocity V_{TH}, induced in a particle by a temperature gradient ∇T. The quantities were calculated from the equation of Brock[12] derived from the slip-flow region, corresponding to Knudsen numbers Kn in the range 0.1-0.01 where Kn $= \lambda/r_p$, and λ was the mean free path of the gas molecules. The particles used in the present work varied from 0.8 to 4 μm diam. and correspond to Kn $= 0.11$ to 0.05. The equation is

$$V_{TH} = -\frac{3\eta}{2\rho T} \frac{\left[1 + A\frac{\lambda}{r_p} + Q\frac{\lambda}{r_p}\exp\left(-b\frac{r_p}{\lambda}\right)\right]}{\left(1 + 3C_m\frac{\lambda}{r_p}\right)} \left\{\frac{\frac{k}{k_p} + C_T\frac{\lambda}{r_p}}{1 + 2\frac{k}{k_p} + 2C_T\frac{\lambda}{r_p}}\right\} \nabla T, \qquad (10)$$

where the constants A, Q and b are dependent upon the gas-particle system. T is the absolute gas temperature, C_T and C_m are constants related to the thermal and momentum coefficients respectively, and k and k_p are the thermal conductivities of air and the particle respectively. In order to induce thermophoretic particle velocities within the duct, provision was made for heating or cooling the duct walls within the temperature range 0-50°C while maintaining the fluid temperature constant. Fig. 2 shows temperature profiles obtained from the duct centre to the wall, measured using a thermistor probe within the test section and thermistors embedded in the duct wall at that point. The temperature gradients were appreciable and are shown in table 1. Also shown in table 1 are the times taken for a particle to traverse the laminar sublayer in turbulent pipe flow under the action of a temperature gradient. Since the thermophoretic velocity of a particle acts towards the cooler region the results obtained when the duct wall temperature was raised above the fluid temperatures are prefixed with a negative sign. In this case any particles within a distance, $r'/a \leqslant 0.05$ or 0.25 cm from the wall were subjected to a thermophoretic velocity moving away from the wall. Appreciable thermophoretic velocities were induced when the duct wall and the fluid flow were ostensibly at room temperature.

The velocity referred to acted on a particle from some distance into the flow although the maximum value occurred over a distance, $r'/a \sim 0.05$ as shown, where r' is equal to $a-r$, and r is the coordinate in the radial direction, $r = 0$ is the pipe centre. This velocity was maintained through the laminar sublayer so no question of a stop distance arose. It was considered that the magnitude of the approximate velocities calculated were sufficient to warrant an experimental investigation of this additional driving force acting on the particles.

The experimental unit is shown diagrammatically in fig. 3 and consisted of three units, the flow system, the aerodynamic analysis system and the aerosol generation and analysis unit.   A general view of the duct assembly is shown in fig. 4.   The duct assembly consisted of a valve regulated blower which passed up to 0.4 m³ s⁻¹ of cooled air through an absolute filter unit, a 0.6 cm mesh screen and a 35-cm-long section of paper honeycomb into the first of six interlocking sections of 10.16 cm i.d. 154.2 cm long stainless steel tubes each of which was mirror polished internally.

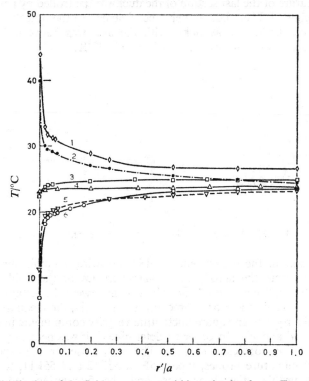

Fig. 2.—The distribution of the fluid temperature within a circular duct.   For curve 1 wall temperature was 317.0 K and $Re = 2.67 \times 10^4$; curve 2, 313.0 K and $Re = 1.27 \times 10^5$; curve 3, 295.2 K and $Re = 1.27 \times 10^5$; curve 4, 296.0 K and $Re = 2.67 \times 10^4$; curve 5, 284.0 K and $Re = 1.27 \times 10^5$; curve 6, 279.8 K and $Re = 2.67 \times 10^4$.

TABLE 1.—THERMOPHORETIC VELOCITY OF PARTICLES IN TURBULENT FLOW UNDER THE INFLU-ENCE OF A TEMPERATURE GRADIENT

Reynolds number	laminar sublayer thickness at $y^+ = 5.0$ cm	duct wall temp./K	fluid temp./K at $r' = 0.25$ cm	∇T/ K cm⁻¹	V_{TH}/cm s⁻¹	time/s taken to traverse laminar sublayer
2.67×10^4	4.18×10^{-2}	296.0	296.6	2.6	4.5×10^{-3}	9.29
2.67×10^4	4.18×10^{-2}	279.8	292.6	51.2	9.2×10^{-2}	0.45
2.67×10^4	4.18×10^{-2}	317.0	304.2	51.2	-9.2×10^{-2}	0.45
1.27×10^5	1.23×10^{-2}	295.2	297.3	8.4	1.6×10^{-2}	0.79
1.27×10^5	1.23×10^{-2}	284.0	293.2	36.8	6.8×10^{-2}	0.18
1.27×10^5	1.23×10^{-2}	313.0	302.2	43.2	-8.0×10^{-2}	0.15

The turbulent boundary layer was instigated by an annular protuberance of 1.5 mm depth in the first section.   Each tube was fitted with the facility to accommodate an aerosol injection point in the form of an airfoil wedge section across the duct.   The last two sections of the duct acted as test sections and were fitted with 20 equispaced pressure tappings and each section had facilities for fitting a probe scanning unit shown in fig. 5. Around the periphery of the duct at the corresponding axial position to the internal probe tip, eight thermistors recorded the internal wall temperature and eight adjacent, removable plugs were fitted flush with the inside tube wall to act as droplet sample holders which were subsequently examined microscopically. The wall temperature of the last section of the duct was controlled by passing ethylene glycol through eight, 1.27 cm i.d. copper tubes fastened to the outer tube wall. The flow Reynolds number range available with the unit was between 2.67×10^4 and 1.27×10^5 with wall temperatures between 279 and 317 K.

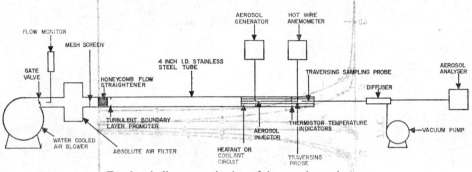

FIG. 3.—A diagrammatic view of the experimental system.

The second unit in the experiment a DISA hot-wire anemometer type 55D01 was used to determine the aerodynamic characteristics of the fluid flow. These quantities were the fluid shear stress $-\overline{uv}$, where u and v were the instantaneous values of velocity fluctuations in the x or y directions respectively, the mean axial velocities, U and U_0, and the root mean square fluctuating velocity components in the axial and radial directions, u' and v'. In order to determine v', it was necessary to determine the double correlation coefficient $\overline{uv}/u'v'$. The probes used in the experiment were Disa gold-plated miniature probes, types 55F14, 55F12 and 55F11, to measure the average velocity profiles, the shear stress and the fluctuating root-mean-square velocities respectively. The correlation coefficient was measured at several points during a traverse in the test section, using a DISA cross-wire probe. In the aerodynamic measurements two dimensional duct flow was assumed.

The effect of the fluid temperature variation on the hot-wire results was taken into account by calibrating the probes at several temperatures within the range of interest. A plot of the calibration constants against the temperature was then made. For calibration purposes the DISA calibration wind tunnel was used with a modification. The air was heated or cooled by passing through an automobile radiator at the inlet to the tunnel. Ethylene glycol acted as heatant or coolant and the temperature of the air in the wind tunnel was monitored using a thermistor.

The third part of the experimental apparatus was the aerosol generation, sampling and analysis unit. The aerosol was generated from two materials, dioctyl phthalate and di-2-ethyl hexyl sebacate respectively. The generator is shown in fig. 6. This was a condensation generator a description of which had been given previously.[25] Some modifications to the generator described [25] have been made. The two most important were the provision of additional flow controllers at the outlet of each gas supply and a more sophisticated temperature control system. The temperature controller incorporated an electronic proportional control circuit with a fine differential control applied. The sensor units were negative temperature coefficient

Fig. 4.—A view of the duct, showing the diffuser/sampling unit.

Fig. 5.—The end of the duct test section showing the scanning unit and thermistor and sampling plug positions.

[*To face page* 168

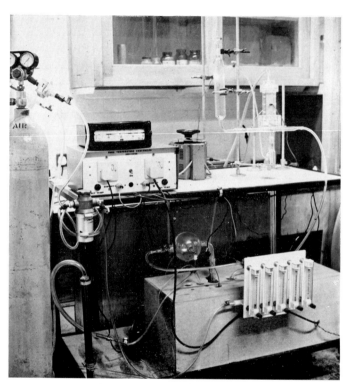

FIG. 6.—The aerosol generator.

thermistors which were fitted into the boiler and reheater flasks respectively. This unit enabled temperature control within $\pm 0.5°C$ to be maintained. Two different nucleii sources were used in the condensation generator. Incoming air was passed over a heated wire coated with Apiezon W wax and an alternative method of introducing anthracene into the boiler flask was also used. The use of a condensation generator precluded the formation of charged droplets. That this condition was satisfied was tested by passing the aerosol in a laminar air stream between two plates with a potential of $\sim 5\,kV$ between them. The plates were examined for deposited droplets using photo-micrography. The aerosol could be neutralized by passing through a charge apparatus designed to generate equal numbers of $+ve$ and $-ve$ ions, both the charge analyzer and charger were designed after Langer and Radnik.[26]

Particles were pumped through the sampling probe and then through a conical diffuser, the included angle of which was 5°. The diffuser reduced the velocity to a level acceptable to the sensing system. The particles were classified into ten size-ranges and total counts in each range were indicated digitally. The anemometer hot-wire data was processed using a statistical approach to the signal analysis developed by Dvorak and Syred.[27]

The spacial resolution of the velocity vectors acting on a hot-wire probe in each of three 45° mutually differing positions, provided a set of three non-linear equations whose analytical solutions represented the three velocity components as functions of three random variables. The random functions were processed to obtain the mean velocities and the various turbulent components. This method was applied to the two-dimensional system under discussion and necessitated measurements from a straight wire probe in two 45° mutually differing positions. The equations were solved for the mean and fluctuating velocities in the axial and radial direction at a number of points on a traverse across the duct test-section.

The correlation coefficient was measured at several points across the duct using a cross-wire probe. The shear stress component was evaluated from measurements

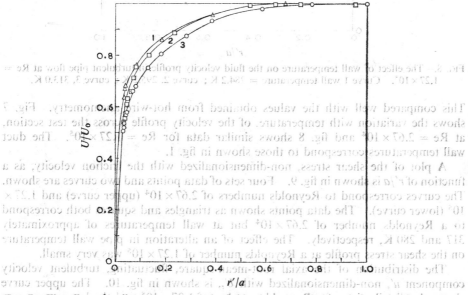

FIG. 7.—The effect of wall temperature on the fluid velocity profile in turbulent pipe flow at Re = 2.67×10^4. Curve 1 wall temperature = 279.8 K; curve 2, 296.0 K; curve 3, 317.0 K.

made with a 45°-slant wire probe [28] rotated through 180°, assuming that the heat transfer from the wire depended only upon the flow velocity normal to the wire.

In a fully-developed pipe flow the velocity distribution across a pipe is independent of the stream wise position. Under these conditions the pressure drop along a pipe is balanced by the shear stress

$$\tau_0 = a\mathrm{d}P/2\mathrm{d}x \qquad (9)$$

$$\tau_0 = \text{laminar stress} - \rho\overline{uv}, \qquad (10)$$

where $-\rho\overline{uv}$ is the apparent turbulent stress. Except very close to the pipe wall τ_0 is composed entirely of the turbulent stress. In this experiment the static pressure tapping along the last two pipe sections enabled a measurement of $\mathrm{d}P/\mathrm{d}x$, the pressure drop, to be made and so a direct determination of the shear stress was possible.

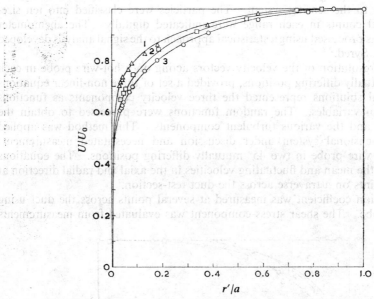

FIG. 8.—The effect of wall temperature on the fluid velocity profile in turbulent pipe flow at Re = 1.27×10^5. Curve 1 wall temperature = 284.2 K; curve 2, 295.2 K; curve 3, 313.0 K.

This compared well with the values obtained from hot-wire anemometry. Fig. 7 shows the variation with temperature, of the velocity profile across the test section, at Re = 2.67×10^4 and fig. 8 shows similar data for Re = 1.27×10^5. The duct wall temperatures correspond to those shown in fig. 1.

A plot of the shear stress, non-dimensionalized with the friction velocity, as a function of r'/a is shown in fig. 9. Four sets of data points and two curves are shown. The curves correspond to Reynolds numbers of 2.67×10^4 (upper curve) and 1.27×10^5 (lower curve). The data points shown as triangles and squares both correspond to a Reynolds number of 2.67×10^4 but at wall temperatures of approximately 317 and 280 K, respectively. The effect of an alteration in pipe wall temperature on the shear stress profile at a Reynolds number of 1.27×10^5 was very small.

The distribution of the axial root-mean-square, fluctuating, turbulent velocity component u', non-dimensionalized with U_τ, is shown in fig. 10. The upper curve shows the distribution of a Reynolds number of 1.27×10^5 and the lower curve was determined for a Reynolds number of 2.67×10^4.

The last of the turbulent quantities, the distribution of the radial root-mean-square turbulent fluctuating velocity component, v', is shown in fig. 11. This quantity is again non-dimensionalized with the friction velocity. The upper curve corresponds to a Reynolds number of 1.27×10^5 and the lower curve to one of 2.67×10^4.

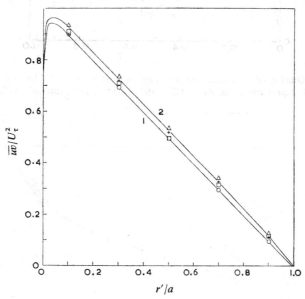

FIG. 9.—The effect of wall temperature on the shear stress profile of turbulent pipe flow. Curve 1, Re = 1.27×10^5 at a wall temperature = 295.2 K. Points designated $+$, Re = 2.67×10^4 at a wall temperature = 296.0 K. Curve 2, Re = 2.67×10^4 at a wall temperature of 317.0 K. Points designated by $\square$, Re = 2.67×10^4 at a wall temperature of 280.0 K.

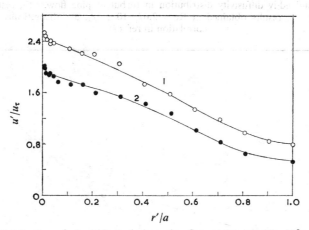

FIG. 10.—The distribution of u' within turbulent pipe flow at Re = 1.27×10^5 and 2.67×10^4 respectively. Curve 1, represents u'/u_τ at Re = 1.27×10^5, curve 2 represents u'/u_τ at Re = 2.67×10^4.

Finally, fig. 12, 13 and 14, show the eddy diffusivity of the fluid in the turbulent pipe flow, non-dimensionalized with the kinematic viscosity of air, plotted against the non-dimensional parameter y^+. Each figure shows the results at Reynolds numbers of 1.27×10^5 and 2.67×10^4 and also the theoretical points derived from

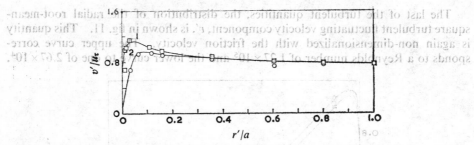

FIG. 11.—The distribution of v' within turbulent pipe flow at $Re = 1.27 \times 10^5$ and 2.67×10^4 respectively. Curve 1 represents v' at $Re = 1.27 \times 10^5$, curve 2 represents v' at $Re = 2.67 \times 10^4$.

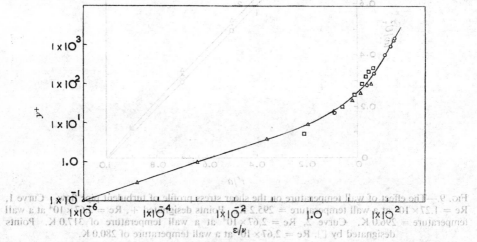

FIG. 12.—The fluid eddy diffusivity distribution in turbulent pipe flow. ○, results obtained at $Re = 1.27 \times 10^5$; □, results obtained at $Re = 2.67 \times 10^4$; △, are theoretically derived from a correlation in ref. (7).

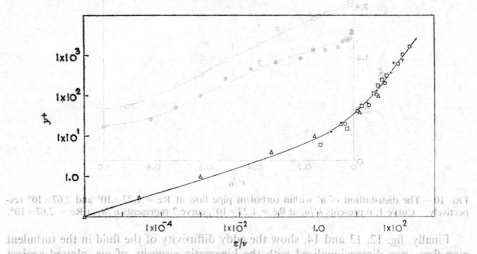

FIG. 13.—The fluid eddy diffusivity distribution in turbulent pipe flow. ○, Results obtained at $Re = 1.27 \times 10^5$; +, results obtained at $Re = 7.03 \times 10^4$; □, results obtained at $Re = 2.67 \times 10^4$; △, theoretically derived results from ref. (7).

Finally, fig. 12, 13 and 14, show the eddy diffusivity of the fluid in the turbulent pipe flow, non-dimensionalized with the kinematic viscosity of air, plotted against numbers of 1.27×10^5 . . . all points derived from ref. (7). Fig. 12 shows the results at the elevated pipe wall temperatures shown in fig. 1 ; fig. 13 gives the results with the pipe wall at nominal room temperature again shown in fig. 1, and fig. 14 shows the results obtained at the low pipe wall temperature, and again the numerical wall temperature can be obtained from fig. 1.

Due to the finite residence time of the fluid in the test section of the duct, it was necessary to derive an approximate particle trajectory in order to evaluate the distance a particle travelled down the duct before deposition on the wall occurred due to its radial thermophoretic velocity. The trajectory of the particle has been considered in the following case to be a function of the axial velocity at the edge of the boundary layer denoted by the directional coordinate x and the thermophoretic velocity in the radial direction denoted by the directional coordinate r ; other diffusive forces were neglected.

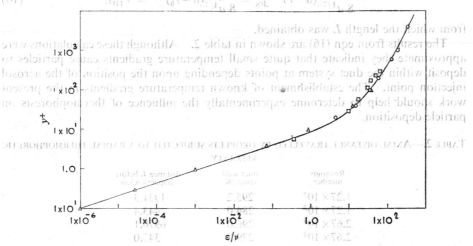

FIG. 14.—The fluid eddy diffusivity distribution in turbulent pipe flow. $\bigcirc$, Results obtained at Re = 1.27×10^5 ; $\square$, results obtained at Re = 2.67×10^4 ; $\triangle$, theoretically derived results from ref. (7).

The axial velocity of the air equalized

$$V_x(r) = dx/dt = f(r), \qquad (11)$$

where $f(r)$ described the fluid velocity profile across the duct. It was assumed that the particle was completely entrained by the fluid and that the axial velocity of the particle was equal to the axial velocity of the fluid.

The radial velocity of the particle dr/dt equals the thermophoretic velocity, V_{TH}; hence

$$\left(\frac{dr}{dt}\right)\left(\frac{dt}{dx}\right) = \frac{dr}{dx} = \frac{V_{TH}}{f(r)} \qquad (12)$$

On integration we obtain

$$\int_{r=r_b}^{r=a} f(r)\,dr = \int_{x=0}^{x=L} V_{TH}\,dx, \qquad (13)$$

where a is the distance from the duct centre line to the wall and r_b is the distance from the duct centre line to the edge of the laminar sublayer. L is the distance a particle moving under the axial velocity would travel from the time it was subjected to the thermophoretic velocity to time of deposition on the tube wall. The expression chosen for $f(r)$ to represent the velocity profile across the duct was the empirically obtained expression,[29]

$$U/U_0 = [(a-r)/a]^{1/n}.$$ (14)

According to Schlichting [29] the exponent has values of 7.0 and 6.6 at Reynolds numbers of 1.1×10^5 and 2.3×10^4 respectively. Substituting for $f(r)$ in eqn (13) for a Reynolds number value of 1.1×10^5,

$$\int_{r=r_b}^{r=a} U^{1/7} \, dr = \int_{x=0}^{x=L} V_{TH} \, dx,$$ (15)

which on integration gives

$$-\frac{7}{8} \frac{U_0}{a^{1/7}}[(a-r)^{8/7}]_{r_b}^{a} = \frac{7}{8} \frac{U_0}{a^{1/7}}(a-r_b)^{8/7} = V_{TH}L$$ (16)

from which the length L was obtained.

The results from eqn (16) are shown in table 2. Although these calculations were approximate they indicate that quite small temperature gradients cause particles to deposit within the duct system at points depending upon the position of the aerosol injection point. The establishment of known temperature gradients in the present work should help to determine experimentally the influence of thermophoresis on particle deposition.

TABLE 2.—AXIAL DISTANCE TRAVELLED BY DROPLETS SUBJECTED TO A RADIAL THERMOPHORETIC VELOCITY

Reynolds number	duct wall temp./K	distance L before impaction/cm
1.27×10^5	295.2	1931.3
1.27×10^5	284.0	443.4
2.67×10^4	296.0	6970.1
2.67×10^4	279.8	342.0

With regard to the determination of the fluid dynamic characteristics of the flow in the duct, it was necessary to determine how closely the present system approached fully-developed turbulent flow and also the effect of the boundary wall temperature on the fluid turbulent characteristics in particular the fluid eddy diffusivity. That the fluid flow in this experiment did closely approach fully developed turbulent flow was indicated by several features. For both values of Reynolds number, the velocity profiles were typical, flat, turbulent profiles as opposed to the parabolic profile expected from laminar flow. The effect of a decrease in the wall temperature in each case resulted in a " flatter " profile. The shear stress profiles shown in fig. 9. showed little dependence on Reynolds number and varied linearly across the duct cross-section. The dependence of the profiles on the wall temperature was only significant for the lower Reynolds number, when an increase in the dimensionless shear stress corresponded to an increase in wall temperature. The dimensionless fluid eddy diffusivity profile was correspondingly affected by temperature, ε/ν increasing with decrease in temperature. Fig. 10 indicated a significant decrease in the axial root-mean-square turbulent component with a decrease in Reynolds number although the radial component profiles were of a similar magnitude for both values of Reynolds number.

The turbulent intensities, u'/U_0 were calculated for $r'/a = 0.1$ and 1.0 for Reynolds number of 1.27×10^5 and 2.67×10^4. The intensities were compared with those calculated by Laufer [5] for Reynolds numbers of 5×10^5 and 5×10^4 and the comparison is shown in table 3. The similarity of the magnitude of the turbulent intensities in the present system and those measured by Laufer [5] at higher Reynolds numbers indicated that fully-developed turbulent flow was achieved in our system.

TABLE 3.—COMPARISON OF RELATIVE TURBULENT INTENSITIES

Reynolds number	r'/a	u'/U_0	
1.27×10^5	0.1	0.079	
1.27×10^5	1.0	0.029	
2.67×10^4	0.1	0.069	
2.67×10^4	1.0	0.021	
5×10^5	0.1	0.070	
5×10^5	1.0	0.027	(after
5×10^4	0.1	0.081	Laufer)
5×10^4	1.0	0.027	

The work so far has established reasons for, and provided a system within which, the relationship between the diffusivity of the fluid and of the particles can be determined. Furthermore, the dependence of particle deposition on a thermophoretic force due to temperature gradients existing between the duct wall and the fluid is clarified.

The authors wish to acknowledge the financial assistance of Shell Research Ltd., and in particular, the help of Prof. T. M. Sugden, F.R.S., which enabled this work to be carried out.

[1] G. A. Sehmel, *Meeting Soc. Eng. Sci.* (Tel Aviv, June, 1972).

[2] A. C. Chamberlain, *Proc. Roy. Soc. A*, 1966, **290**, 236.

[3] C. N. Davies, *Aerosol Sci.*, 1966, **1**, 418.

[4] S. K. Friedlander and H. F. Johnstone, *Ind. Eng. Chem.*, 1957, **49**, 1151.

[5] J. Laufer, *The Structure of Turbulence in Fully Developed Pipe Flow*, N.A.C.A. Report 1147, 1954.

[6] C. S. Lin, R. W. Moulton and G. L. Putnam, *Ind. Eng. Chem.*, 1954, **45**, 636.

[7] C. N. Davies, *Aerosol Sci.*, 1966, **1**, 393.

[8] W. R. Lawrence and A. B. Huang, *A.I.A.A. 10th Aerospace Sci. Meeting* (San Diego, California, January, 1972), A.I.A.A. paper no. 72-81.

[9] S. K. Beal, *Nucl. Sci. Eng.*, 1970, **40**, .

[10] V. E. Levich, *Physiochemical Hydrodynamics* (Prentice Hall, New Jersey, 1962), p. 155.

[11] A. C. Wells and A. C. Chamberlain, *Brit. J. Appl. Phys.*, 1967, **18**, 1793.

[12] P. R. Owen, *Int. J. Air-Water Pollution*, 1960, **3**, 8, 50.

[13] T. L. Montgomery and M. Corn, *Aerosol. Sci.*, 1970, **1**, 185.

[14] G. A. Sehmel, *J. Geophys. Res.*, 1970, **75**, 1766.

[15] L. Prandtl, *Z. angew. Math. Mach*, 1925, **5**, 136.

[16] C. M. Tchen, *Ph.D. Thesis* (Delft, 1947).

[17] S. L. Soo and C. L. Tien, *J. Appl. Mech.*, 1960, **27**, 5.

[18] P. O. Rouhiainen and J. W. Stachiewicz, *J. Heat Transfer*, 1970, **29 C**, 169.

[19] A. T. Hjelmfelt and L. F. Mockros, *Appl. Sci. Res.*, 1900, **16**, 149.

[20] R. L. Byers and S. Calvert, *Ind. Eng. Chem. Fund.*, 1969, **8**, 646.

[21] N. A. Fuchs, *The Mechanics of Aerosols* (Pergamon, London, 1964), p. 56.

[22] G. M. Hidy and J. R. Brock, *The Dynamics of Aerocolloidal Systems* (Pergamon, Oxford, 1970).

[23] W. L. Towle and T. K. Sherwood, *Ind. Eng. Chem.*, 1939, **31**, 457.

[24] I. Williams and A. B. Hedley, *Aerosol Mech.*, 1972, **3**, 363.

[25] I. Williams, *M.Sc. Thesis* (Sheffield, 1970).

[26] G. Langer and J. L. Radnik, *J. Appl. Phys.*, 1961, **32**, 955.

[27] K. Dvorak and N. Syred, *DISA Conference* (Leicester, 1972); also *Internal Report* (Dept. of Chem. Eng., University of Sheffield).

[28] J. O. Hinze, *Turbulence* (McGraw Hill, London, 1959), chap. 2.

[29] H. Schlichting, *Boundary Layer Theory* (McGraw Hill, London, 1, 1968), p. 563.

Light-Scattering Instrument for Kinetic Measurements in Aerosols with Changing Particle Size Distributions

By M. D. Carabine and A. P. Moore

Department of Chemical Engineering and Chemical Technology,
Imperial College, Prince Consort Road, London S.W.7.

Received 13*th December*, 1972

The construction and use are described of a laser light-scattering instrument for kinetic measurements of the particle size distribution in a developing aerosol. In the present stage of development, the time resolution (of the order of seconds) is adequate for the study of aerosols which are developing by growth and by coagulation. Such an *in situ* measurement is preferable for particles, and for kinetic studies. The systems investigated are of importance in atmospheric pollution, namely, the formation of solid particles by interaction of ammonia and sulphur dioxide, and the hygroscopic growth of sulphuric acid droplets in humid atmospheres. The precision of the data-analyzing procedure is such that it yields modal particle sizes and distribution spread parameters accurate to within 4 and 10 % respectively, even with about 5 % random fluctuations in the measurements of the angular distribution of scattered intensity.

The size distribution of particles or droplets in an aerosol suspension can be deduced from the variation of intensity of scattered light with either the angle of scattering, the polarisation, or the wavelength. The method of sizing has the advantage that the particles need not be disturbed by, e.g., deposition before electron microscopic examination, or by electrification prior to sizing.[1] Minimal interference with the aerosol is essential if it is required to observe the changes of particle-size distribution with time which can often be important in practical cases, both in manufacturing of particulate products, and in atmospheric pollution.[2] Instantaneous measurement of light intensity is a further feature which makes the technique particularly suitable for monitoring rate processes, provided that the input parameters, such as scattering angle or wavelength, can be varied quickly enough.

This paper describes a light-scattering instrument designed for kinetic measurements of size distribution in an aerosol with a time resolution, in its present initial stage of development, which is adequate for the study of aerosols which are developing growth and by coagulation of particles. Our particular interest is in systems in which a vapour from the suspending medium is being transferred to the condensed phase, e.g., a suspension of hygroscopic acid droplets which are growing in a humid atmosphere, or a suspension of solid particles being formed by interaction of gases such as ammonia and hydrogen chloride or ammonia and sulphur dioxide.

The size distribution of the aerosol thus formed, and its variation with time, depend on such processes as condensation, coagulation, diffusion, and sedimentation. In the range of conditions which are relevant to atmospheric pollution, significant size change by condensation growth occurs in general on a time scale of tens of seconds.[3, 4] Coagulation in a given aerosol causes time variation in both the number and the size of the particles. The number concentration varies predominantly according to second-order kinetics, and at a moderately high atmospheric concentration of, say, 10^{13} m^{-3} the half-life would be of the order 100 s.

176

The times involved in changes in size due to Brownian coagulation are illustrated in fig. 1, in which the successive distributions have been computed for intervals of 110 s.

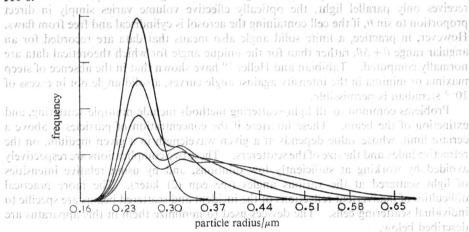

FIG. 1.—The particle size distribution at time intervals of 110 s resulting from the Brownian coagulation of a dispersion initially having a modal radius 0.25 μm and a zeroth-order logarithmic breadth parameter $\sigma_0 = 0.10$.

In the aerosol referred to above which is produced by interaction of ammonia and sulphur dioxide, it has been shown by sampling on filters (with consequent uncertainties), followed by electron microscopy that the particles undergo growth typically from 0.03 μm to 0.2 μm in about 10^3 s, and then to about 0.5 μm in further 5×10^3 s. The aggregates in the 0.2-0.5 μm range are formed of primary particles predominantly of size less than 0.1 μm. The proportion of small particles is augmented when traces of moisture or oxygen are added to the carrier gas.

CRITERIA FOR THE CHOICE OF METHOD

A time interval of about 1-10 s is considered short enough for meaningful size distribution measurements in the systems referred to above, and if angular distribution of intensity is the chosen method, a scan of the angles must be achieved within this time.

To obtain sufficient intensity of scattered light from a dilute suspension of sub-micrometre particles, a high-intensity light-source such as a continuous laser is required. Besides the high intensity, it has the advantages for light scattering of monochromaticity and linear polarisation—and Harris et al.[5] have shown experimentally that there is no difference in scattering behaviour between conventional incoherent light sources and coherent laser sources.

The scanning-speed requirement rules out the use of several techniques, reviewed, e.g., by Kerker[6] which have been developed to study essentially time-invariant dispersions using conventional light sources. Thus the " polarisation ratio " method [7] would require rotating the plane of polarisation of the beam through 90° at each observation angle; while the methods using " scattering ratio " or " turbidity spectra "[8,9] at different wavelengths would necessitate repeated retuning of the laser. Hence the only technique compatible with the required scanning speed and the laser source is one using the angular variation of intensity. Angular scanning introduces its own problems which must be carefully considered in the design. The optically-effective volume is defined by the geometry of the light-receiver system and the incident beam, and contains all the scattering particles which contribute to the measured intensity for a particular angle of scattering θ. Ideally, if the detector receives only parallel light, the optically effective volume varies simply in direct proportion to $\sin \theta$, if the cell containing the aerosol is cylindrical and free from flaws. However, in practice, a finite solid angle also means that data are recorded for an angular range $\theta \pm \Delta\theta$, rather than for the unique angle for which theoretical data are normally computed. Tabibian and Heller [10] have shown that in the absence of steep maxima or minima in the intensity against angle curves, a solid angle not in excess of 10^{-3} steradian is permissible.

Problems common to all light-scattering methods include multiple scattering, and extinction of the beam. These interfere if the concentration of particles is above a certain limit, whose value depends at a given wavelength in a given medium, on the refractive index and the size of the scatterers. These two complications are respectively avoided by working at sufficiently low dilutions, and by using relative intensities of light scattered at the various angles (see eqn (2) later). The more practical difficulties of inadvertent reflections of the incident and scattered beams are specific to individual scattering cells. The devices used to minimize them in this apparatus are described below.

The essence of achieving precision in the size-distribution measurement is to record light intensity for a large number of scattering angles. Before considering the present design, we examine the possible arrangements which are compatible with rapid scanning, a laser source, and a photo-multiplier detector. These alternatives are: (a) to use a stationary light source and a single detector which is moved rapidly through a series of angular positions; (b) to use a stationary source and a separate photomultiplier stationed at each angle; and (c) to hold both source and detector static and to deflect the incident beam itself through the series of angles.

Alternative (a) has been previously adopted [11] but mechanical movement of the detector must be relatively slow in a low-cost instrument. Alternative (b) is also unsuitable as it demands a number of photomultipliers of known relative sensitivities together with a complex and costly multichannel data-acquisition system.

THE INSTRUMENT

The present instrument, based on alternative (c), achieves the measurement economically with one source, one detector, and several inexpensive mirrors. The arrangement is shown schematically in fig. 2. The plane mirror at position R, rotated by a stepper motor about an axis perpendicular to the scattering plane (the plane of the diagram), reflects the source beam sequentially on to a series of static plane mirrors M, at the positions marked. From each of the latter mirrors the beam is directed back to the centre of the scattering system at A, and the photomultiplier detects the light scattered by the optically effective volume of aerosol. There is a slight divergence of the beam over the optical path (less than 1 mradian) and to keep it constant for all the beams, the stationary mirrors are positioned on an ellipse with the principal foci at A and R. The laser beam and the line PM-A define the horizontal scattering plane of the instrument. The scattering angles which range from 8 to 172° have a precision of $\pm 0.33°$, determined by the stepper motor.

A helium–neon laser with a 15 mW output at 632.8 nm is used as the light source. The photomultiplier has a " modified S-20 " spectral response yielding a high quantum efficiency at this wavelength compared with other photocathodes. Plane-front-surface mirrors are used throughout, and precise adjustment of the stationary ones is effected by three-point spring mountings. A special light trap has been constructed from black, glass-fibre-reinforced resin, to minimize back reflections from the transmitted light beams. Based on the conventional Rayleigh horn, but having a wide curving aperture, it traps any light entering within an angular range of 174°. In this apparatus it is attached directly to the gas-tight scattering cell, opposite to a thin semi-circular glass window which admits the incident beams with negligible distortion.

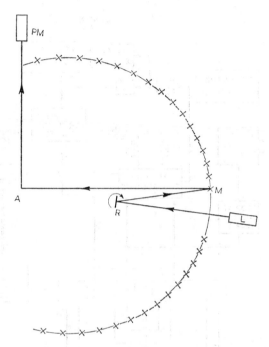

FIG. 2.—Schematic plan view of the optical system. The positions × are locations of stationary mirrors M; R is the rotating mirror; A is the scattering centre; L and PM are the laser source and photomultiplier detector.

ANGULAR SCANNING CONTROL AND DATA ACQUISITION

Initial adjustment of the rotating mirror is made to a start position defined by an infra-red position detector situated under the main baseplate of the instrument. Thereafter, the rotating mirror scans through the predetermined stepping pattern. A count of the number of steps taken determines the end of each scan, whereupon the mirror is rapidly brought around to the start position and the sequence repeated. The mirror can be advanced in single steps to enable alignment of each stationary mirror, and determination of the corresponding scattering angle.

A block diagram of the control circuitry which governs the stepper motor is shown in fig. 3. The motor moves through 3.75°. at each step. When a full scan is required to have readings at eight angular stations, four steps are necessary between each, and for sixteen positions, two steps. Provision is made for half scans and for the peripheral mirrors to be used in " odd " as well as " even " numbered positions.

The control logic is performed by standard integrated circuit techniques, the stepping rate and timing being derived throughout from the mains frequency with basic clock pulses at 100 Hz. The " start " command releases the clock inhibiting gate to enable the motor to step at this rate until the infra-red detector halts it at the start position. A delay of 300 ms follows before the first reading, and thereafter after each change of position, giving time for internal resets.

The time interval between readings of intensity is 200 ms, derived, like the delay, by division of the clock rate. The motor is stepped to a new position each time the required number of readings is satisfied, and this can be up to eight at each position.

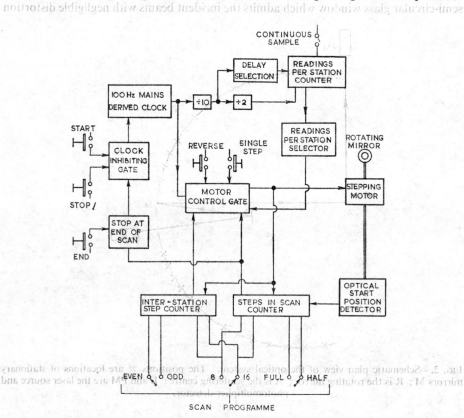

FIG. 3.—Schematic diagram of the electronic system controlling the angular scanning. " Even-Odd " selects which set of mirrors is to be scanned, " 8-16 " selects the number of mirrors to be scanned, " Full-Half " selects full (*ca.* 180 deg.) scan or half (*ca.* 90 deg.) scan.

Selection of " End " inhibits the clock when the current scan is complete. The number of completed scans and angular position are visually displayed on serial counters, and the intensity readings are recorded on paper tape for subsequent analysis.

ANALYSIS OF DATA

The theory of Mie [12] is used to compute the angular intensity functions (i_1 and i_2 for perpendicular- and parallel-polarised incident light respectively) for spherical particles of known size and refractive index. For a system of heterodisperse particles the scattered intensity at a particular angle is given, for the perpendicular polarised case, by

$$I_1(\theta) = \int i_1(\alpha, \theta) p(\alpha) \, d\alpha, \quad (1)$$

where $p(\alpha)$ is the normalised size-distribution function. The experimentally-determined scattering signals are related to $I_1(\theta)$ as follows

$$I_1(\theta) = c \sin \theta [s_\theta/s_0 - s'_\theta/s'_0], \quad (2)$$

where the symbols are: c, a constant proportional to the number concentration; $\sin \theta$ factor for the change in observed volume at different angles; s_θ photomultiplier signal from aerosol at angle θ; s'_θ correction term for background light e.g. stray light, scattering from edges of stops etc.; s_0, s'_0 incident beam intensities at time of measuring s_θ, s'_θ.

For convenience the two-parameter zeroth order logarithmic distribution (ZOLD) of Espenscheid et al.[13] has been adopted in this work, after experimental checks that such a distribution does describe the aerosols under study.[14]

Typical theoretical curves of intensity against the scattering angle are shown in fig. 4, for spherical particles of refractive index 1.52. Readings at suitably chosen angles discriminate well between the different distributions of sizes in this sub-micrometre range. The method is inapplicable if the greater part of the distribution is in the Rayleigh scattering regime, i.e., with diameter $<0.06 \mu m$. A computer programme has been devised to solve the complex problem of inverting the light scattering data to give the corresponding size distributions. First, the theoretical intensities are computed for an assumed distribution (using eqn (1) and producing curves such as those in fig. 4), and the percentage differences for all angles found between these values and the recorded experimental data. The parameters of this "first-guess" distribution are then adjusted in successive steps to minimize the sum of squares of these differences according to the method developed by Powell,[15] until a final estimate for the aerosol is reached.

In order to evaluate the accuracy of the light-scattering inversion programme, theoretical intensity values for a set of eight angles were computed for several chosen

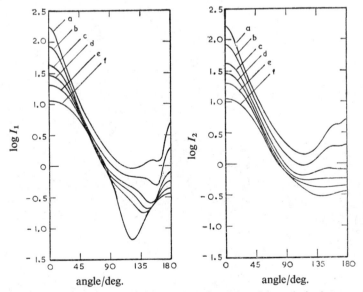

FIG. 4.—Theoretical intensity against scattering angle for light plane-polarised perpendicular (I_1) and parallel (I_2) to the scattering plane. Curves (a-f) are for distributions having a modal diameter 0.40 μm and the following ZOLD spread parameters (a) $\sigma_0 = 0.50$; (b) $\sigma_0 = 0.40$; (c) $\sigma_0 = 0.30$; (d) $\sigma_0 = 0.25$; (e) $\sigma_0 = 0.20$; (f) $\sigma_0 = 0.10$.

distributions.   These were then used as experimental input data on which to perform the routine search analysis.   The resulting " best fit " distributions were within 4 % of the modal diameter and 10 % of σ_0, even when the input intensity data were subjected to 4 % random fluctuations.

The authors acknowledge generous provision by Courtauld's Educational Trust Fund of equipment and a maintenance bursary, and assistance from L. Tyley and T. Hunt in the design of the electronic control system.

[1] B.Y. H. Liu and A. C. Verma, *Analyt. Chem.*, 1968, **40**, 843 ; B. Y. H. Liu, V. A. Marple and H. Yazdani, *Environmental Sci. Tech.*, 1969, **3**, 381.

[2] M. D. Carabine, *Chem. Soc. Rev.*, 1972, **1**, 411.

[3] B. J. Mason, *Discuss. Faraday Soc.*, 1960, **30**, 20.

[4] L. Coutarel, E. Matijevic, M. Kerker and Chao-Ming Huang, *J. Colloid Interface Sci.*, 1967, **24**, 338.

[5] F. Harris, G. Sherman and F. Morse, *I.E.E.E. Trans. Antenna Propagation* AP-15, 1967, p. 141.

[6] M. Kerker, *The Scattering of Light and Other Electromagnetic Radiation* (Academic Press, N.Y. and London, 1969).

[7] M. Kerker, E. Matijevic, W. Espenscheid, W. Farone and S. Kitani, *J. Colloid Interface Sci.*, 1964, **19**, 213.

[8] W. Heller and M. Wallach, *J. Phys. Chem.*, 1963, **67**, 2577.

[9] W. Heller and M. Wallach, *J. Phys. Chem.*, 1964, **68**, 931.

[10] R. Tabibian and W. Heller, *J. Colloid Interface Sci.*, 1958, **13**, 6.

[11] J. E. L. Maddock, *M.Sc. Thesis* (Univ. London, 1970).

[12] G. Mie, *Ann. Phys.*, 1908, **25**, 377.

[13] W. Espenscheid, M. Kerker and E. Matijevic, *J. Phys. Chem.*, 1964, **68**, 3093.

[14] M. D. Carabine, J. E. L. Maddock and A. P. Moore, *Nature, Phys. Sci.*, 1971, **231**, 18.

[15] M. Powell, *Computer J.*, 1965, **7**, 303.

Particle Sizing by Interference Fringes and Signal Coherence in Doppler Velocimetry

By R. M. Fristrom,* A. R. Jones, M. J. R. Schwar † and F. J. Weinberg

Imperial College, London, S.W.7.

Received 15th January, 1973

To supplement another paper‡ presented at this Symposium (which deals with sizing suspended particles by light scattering), a new optical method is proposed for sizes larger than a few wavelengths. To this end, conditions under which the alternating light signal generated by a particle traversing a fringe pattern falls to zero are examined with a view to measuring such particle sizes by varying fringe spacing. The a.c. frequency is a measure of the particle velocity and can be expressed, with identical results, either as a beat note caused by Doppler shift or in terms of the varying illumination of the particle due to its movement across the light grid. The theory, giving the a.c. amplitude for two infinitesimal particles moving with a common velocity as a function of their separation, is extended to a variable number of particles moving together. This provides the basis not only for an assessment of how the signal legibility in Doppler velocimetry falls off as the number of scatterers increases but also for the integration which treats particles of finite size as the sum of their infinitesimal elements.

A variety of optical systems are proposed for measuring the size of particles, droplets, fibres, etc. under different conditions. For some purposes, fringe systems of non-uniform spacing may be advantageous and the use of a dark field schlieren image which shows the particle as a thin circumferential line—in place of the illuminated area produced by normal imaging—is often valuable. Such a schlieren system is used in a simple experimental test of the method; the results accurately conform to the theoretical predictions.

This study was initiated as a potential method for sizing droplets and particles appreciably larger than the wavelength of light during Prof. Weinberg's visit to the Applied Physics Laboratory of the Johns Hopkins University, and pursued further in a wider context at Imperial College.

The light scattered by a particle depends on the local illumination and, when this is in the form of a field of interference fringes which the particle is traversing, an a.c. signal will result, except under certain conditions which are the subject of this paper. When there are two small particles travelling with a common velocity the signal produced by a photodetector receiving light from both will depend on their separation. For certain separations, the amplitude of the a.c. signal falls to zero. A similar succession of zeros occurs as the size of one particle increases in relation to the fringe separation or, more practically, when the fringe separation is decreased in relation to the size of the particle.

All this applies to any field of stratified illumination whether produced interferometrically or, e.g., by projecting the image of a grid. The convenience of interference fringes lies in the ease and precision of varying their separation by changing the angle between the interfering beams. This becomes particularly easy when the light source

* Applied Physics Lab., The Johns Hopkins Univ., Silver Spring, Maryland, U.S.A.

† now at Paint Research Association, Teddington, Middx.

‡ M. D. Carabine and A. P. Moore, " A light scattering instrument for kinetic measurements in aerosols with changing particle size distributions ".

is a laser, which is especially suitable for producing, interferometrically, a fine light grid over a small test area at a very high level of illumination.

The frequency of the a.c. signal is a direct measure of the particle velocity, which can be described either in terms of traversing a fringe pattern or of the beat note between two frequencies which have experienced a differential Doppler shift due to the interaction of one, or both of them, with the moving particle. The two descriptions are mathematically equivalent both where a fringe pattern moves across a point detector in the image plane [1] and for a fringe pattern in the test space (" fringe anemometry ").[2]

The concept is thus relevant to two quite different practical applications. One is a new method of particle sizing based on the disappearance of the a.c. signal at given fringe spacings. The other is the limitation to Doppler velocimetry due to multiple scatterers in the test space.

GENERAL PRINCIPLES

A wide range of optical systems suitable for implementing the various applications of this principle will be discussed. However, it will be convenient to consider general properties in terms of the simplest underlying scheme, as shown in fig. 1, in which two plane waves are incident at symmetric angles θ with respect to the x-axis and form a set of interference fringes in the y-z plane. Observation is made of the light scattered into the direction ϕ by a particle moving with velocity u at an angle α to the y-axis. We shall not concern ourselves with the polar distribution of the scattered light, but deal in terms of a constant fraction f of the illumination of the particle. The a.c. frequency is independent of angle, at least so long as velocities do not approach the speed of light, and for small particles f is almost independent of angle. This means that light can be collected over a range of angles without affecting the result.

The distribution of illumination in the y, z plane is given by

$$I = 2I_0\{1 + \cos(2ky\sin\theta)\}.$$

With $k^* = 2\pi/\lambda^*$, where $\lambda^* = \lambda/2\sin\theta$ is the fringe spacing,

$$I = 2I_0\{1 + \cos k^* y\},$$

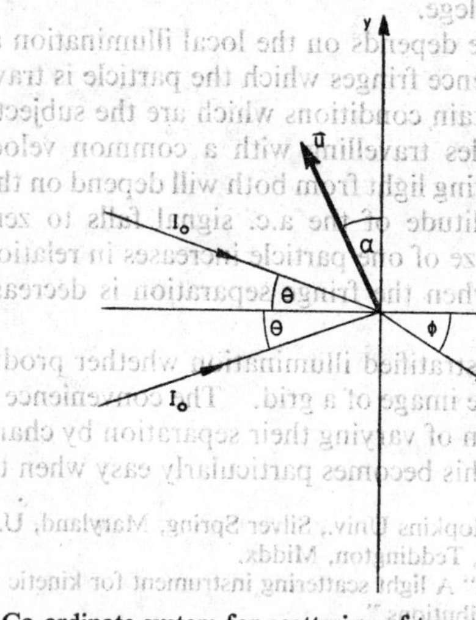

Fig. 1.—Co-ordinate system for scattering of two plane waves by a moving particle.

Thus, the light scattered at the angle ϕ by a point particle situated at Y may be represented by

$$I_{sca} = 2I_0 f(\phi)\{1 + \cos k^* Y\}. \tag{1}$$

Now the particle is moving along the y-axis with speed

$$u_y = dY/dt = u \cos \alpha$$

Thus, as the particle moves, the scattered intensity fluctuates with a frequency ν_b given by

$$\nu_b = (u \cos \alpha)/\lambda^*. \tag{2}$$

An alternative approach is based on the Doppler shift. The apparent frequencies of the two waves as seen by the particle are

$$\nu_{P,1} = \nu\left[1 + \frac{u}{c}\cos\left(\frac{\pi}{2} - \alpha - \theta\right)\right],$$

$$\nu_{P,2} = \nu\left[1 + \frac{u}{c}\cos\left(\frac{\pi}{2} - \alpha + \theta\right)\right],$$

Likewise, the frequency scattered by the particle as seen by an observer looking along ϕ is

$$\nu_0 = \nu_P\left[1 - \frac{u}{c}\cos\left(\frac{\pi}{2} - \alpha - \phi\right)\right]$$

for both waves. The observer sees a beat frequency

$$\nu_b' = |\nu_{0,2} - \nu_{0,1}|,$$

or

$$\nu_b' = \frac{2u\nu}{c}\cos\alpha \sin\theta\left[1 - \frac{u}{c}\cos\left(\frac{\pi}{2} - \alpha - \phi\right)\right]$$

$$= \frac{u\cos\alpha}{\lambda^*}\left[1 - \frac{u}{c}\sin(\alpha + \phi)\right]. \tag{3}$$

If u/c is small then eqn (3) reduces to eqn (2). Alternatively, since the particle is considered as a source emitting at frequency ν_b in the derivation of eqn (2), if the motion of the particle relative to the observer is taken into account the result is

$$\nu_b' = \nu_b\left[1 - \frac{u}{c}\sin(\alpha + \phi)\right]$$

which is identical to eqn (3). So both approaches give the same answer.

To find the scattered intensity, the incident amplitudes of the light wave may be set out as follows:

$$E_{0,1} = E_0 \exp(ikY\sin\theta); \qquad E_{0,2} = E_0 \exp(-ikY\sin\theta).$$

The scattered waves are then

$$E_{s,1} = E_{0,1}\sqrt{f}\exp(-ik_1Y\sin\phi); \qquad E_{s,2} = E_{0,2}\sqrt{f}\exp(-ik_2Y\sin\phi),$$

where k_1 and k_2 are the Doppler shifted wave numbers. We have assumed that $f(\theta + \phi) \simeq f(\theta - \phi)$ which is reasonable for small particles. Adding the amplitudes, the scattered intensity is

$$I_{sca} = 2I_0 f\{1 + \cos[2kY\sin\theta + (k_2 - k_1)Y\sin\phi]\}.$$

Now

$$k_2 - k_1 \simeq (2ku_y/c) \sin \theta,$$

so that

$$I_{sca} \simeq 2I_0 f\{1 + \cos [2k Y \sin \theta (1 + u_y/c \sin \phi)]\}. \qquad (4)$$

For $(u_y/c) \ll 1$ this equation is identical with eqn (1). Thus, the two approaches yield identical results for small u/c. This approximation is inherent in the Doppler equation used, i.e., the full relativistic treatment has not been considered.

Inclusion of a second particle separated from the first by a distance d gives the scattered intensity as

$$I_{sca} = 2I_0 f\{2 + \cos k^* Y + \cos k^*(Y + d)\}, \qquad (5)$$

provided that the detector aperture is sufficiently large for incoherent addition to be used.[3] A large aperture integrating over a range of angles can be used since f for small particles and v_b are almost independent of ϕ. Eqn (5) can be derived either from eqn (1) or (4) with small u_y/c, i.e., either by adding illuminations in two parts of the fringe system, or by combining two beat frequencies with a phase difference between them. The beat frequency observed is the same as for one particle and since

$$I_{sca} = 4I_0 f\{1 + \cos k^*(Y + d/2) \cos (k^* d/2)\}$$

the signal falls to zero whenever

$$d = (2n + 1)\lambda^*/2.$$

In the most general case, we may consider N particles having the same velocity $\bar{u}$ so that their respective separations are constant in time, but randomly distributed. If the jth particle is at a distance y_j from the first, which is situated at Y, one may expand eqn (5) into the form:

$$I_{sca} = 2I_0 f\left\{N + \cos k^* Y + \sum_{j=2}^{N} \cos k^*(Y + y_j)\right\}$$

since $y_1 = 0$. The probable intensity $\langle I_{sca} \rangle$ is the ensemble average over the cloud of N particles. Since the particles are randomly distributed, the probability of y_j having any particular value is a constant. Further, if the width of the particle cloud is w (less than, or equal to, the beam width), then

$$-w \leqslant y_j \leqslant w.$$

Consequently,

$$\langle I_{sca} \rangle = \frac{\int_{-w}^{w} \int_{-w}^{w} \cdots \int_{-w}^{w} I_{sca} \, dy_2 \, dy_3 \ldots dy_N}{\int_{-w}^{w} \int_{-w}^{w} \cdots \int_{-w}^{w} dy_2 \, dy_3 \ldots dy_N},$$

or

$$\langle I_{sca} \rangle = 2I_0 f\{N + \cos k^* Y[1 + (N - 1)(\sin k^* w)/k^* w]\}.$$

This is the probable intensity observed at any one time or value of Y. As Y varies the signal varies and the visibility of the observed a.c. signal is

$$V = \frac{\langle I_{sca} \rangle_{max} - \langle I_{sca} \rangle_{min}}{\langle I_{sca} \rangle_{max} + \langle I_{sca} \rangle_{min}},$$

which gives finally

$$V = \frac{1}{N} + \frac{N - 1}{N} \frac{\sin k^* w}{k^* w}. \qquad (6)$$

We note some of the properties of this function. Clearly, for $N = 1$, $V = 1$, as expected. Also where $\sin k^*w = 0$ (i.e., the width of the cloud is a whole number of fringes), or for an infinitely wide cloud, $V = 1/N$. However, in general for a large number of particles as $N \to \infty$, $V \to (\sin k^*w)/k^*w$. That this is not zero is explained by the fact that the fringe pattern is repetitive. For every whole fringe the scattered intensity integrates to zero. If there is a fraction of a fringe left over, only the effect due to those particles in this section is seen, as over a fraction of a fringe the scattered intensity does not integrate to zero.

The physical implication is that legibility of the a.c. signal can be assured only in the case of a single scatterer. For any greater number it is always possible that zero a.c. signal will result if the particle distribution is unfavourable. On the other hand, it is quite likely that a residual a.c. signal will be obtained for the reasons discussed above, even for a large cloud of particles—a result which explains observations in many practical studies when naturally occurring scatterers are used. This applies purely to the a.c. component, i.e., under conditions where the detector is not saturated by the d.c. signal which increases with number of scatterers.

So far, we have considered particles much smaller than the fringe spacing. The relevance to size measurement, for which the fringe spacing must be made at least equal to the particle dimensions, is by way of regarding infinitesimal particles as elements of a larger particle. We may then take the next step on a model of integrating across all the elements illuminated by a sinusoidal fringe pattern, or of adding those locating the periphery, depending on the optical system used.

Consider first a strip of length $2l$ and width dZ situated with its centre at Y, as seen in fig. 2. Taking an elementary area of length dY, the element of the scattered intensity from the strip is

$$dI_{sca} = 2I_0 f \int_{Y-l}^{Y+l} (1 + \cos k^*Y)\, dY\, dZ,$$

or

$$dI_{sca} = 2I_0 f \left(l + \frac{1}{k^*} \cos k^*Y \sin k^*l \right) dZ,$$

where f is now the scattering efficiency factor. It remains to integrate over Z. We

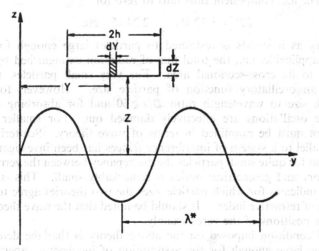

FIG. 2.—Scheme for integration of illumination across a strip situated in an interference pattern.

first note that for a long strip, e.g., a fibre or wire parallel to the fringes, l is independent of Z and

$$I_{sca} = 4I_0 fLl(1 + \cos k^* Y(\sin k^*l)/k^*l), \qquad (7)$$

where L is the length of the strip and $2l$ its width. The a.c. component is zero whenever

$$2l = n\lambda^*,$$

i.e., no beat frequency will be observed if the strip has a width exactly equal to a whole number of fringes. This is obvious physically, since the test object is then exposed to a total illumination which does not vary with change in position and it was this concept which first suggested the method.

For a particle with a circular cross-section

$$l = l(R^2 - Z^2)^{\frac{1}{2}}$$

where R is the radius of the particle. Thus

$$I_{sca} = 8I_0 f \int_0^R \left\{ (R^2 - Z^2)^{\frac{1}{2}} + \frac{1}{k^*} \cos k^* Y \sin (k^* \sqrt{R^2 - Z^2}) \right\} dZ.$$

Substituting $Z = R \cos \phi$ yields

$$I_{sca} = 8R^2 I_0 f \int_0^{\pi/2} \left\{ \sin^2\phi + \frac{1}{k^*R} \cos k^* Y \sin (k^*R \sin \phi) \sin \phi \right\} d\phi.$$

Using [4]

$$\pi J_1(Z) = 2 \int_0^{\pi/2} \sin (Z \sin \phi) \sin \phi \, d\phi$$

gives

$$I_{sca} = 2\pi R^2 I_0 f \left\{ 1 + \frac{2J_1(k^*R)}{k^*R} \cos k^* Y \right\}, \qquad (8)$$

where $J_1(k^*R)$ is a Bessel function of order one which has zeros at $k^*R = 3.832$, 7.016, etc. The a.c. component thus falls to zero for

$$2R = 1.22 \, \lambda^*, \qquad 2.24 \, \lambda^* \quad \text{etc.}$$

The theory as it stands is restricted to particles large enough for geometrical optics to be applicable, i.e., the total flux of radiation extinguished by a particle is proportional to its cross-sectional area. For very small particles, the scattering efficiency is an oscillatory function of particle size.[5] However, for transparent particles with size to wavelength ratio $D/\lambda \gtrsim 60$ and for absorbing particles with $D/\lambda \gtrsim 15$, the oscillations are effectively damped out. For smaller particles the above concept must be examined in terms of wave theory. Scattering by infinite cylinders parallel to a system of interference fringes has been investigated by Jones.[6] It is found that for quite small particles the discrepancy between the zeros as predicted by wave theory and geometrical optics is remarkably small. This is illustrated in fig. 3, which indicates for which particle sizes the two theories agree to within 10 % as a function of refractive index. It should be noted that the wave theory is rigorous and gives the positions of the zeros exactly.

A second condition imposed on the above theory is that the detector aperture must be made large enough for the assumption of incoherent superposition to be applicable. In fact, since large transparent objects scatter very strongly forward it would be advisable to collect as much forward scattered light as possible. The resulting variation would then be expected to be similar to that for the total scattering. The wave theory has shown good agreement between the zeros in the total scattering and in the total forward scattering efficiencies for sizes as low as

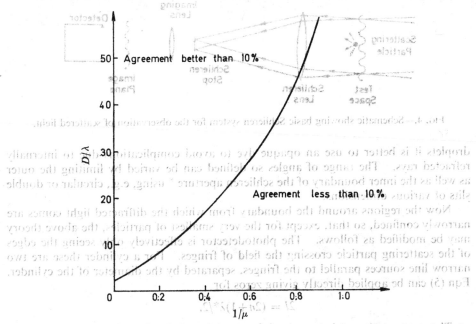

FIG. 3.—Curve approximately indicating particle sizes (D/λ) as a function of refractive index μ for rigorous wave theory and geometrical optics to agree within 10 % in predicting the position of the first zero of the a.c. amplitude $(D/\lambda^* \sim 1)$ for cylinders. $\mu = \infty$ corresponds to a perfectly conducting cylinder.

$D/\lambda \sim 2$. For small metal particles the scattering is mainly backward which suggests obvious modifications to the optical systems discussed in the next section, e.g., a mirror to collect and reflect the backward scattered light.

With the exception of fibres and droplets, particles are not generally cylindrical or spherical. It is therefore of interest to compare the width deduced with that of the area-mean (since this particular optical system is based on illumination of the entire area—but see below). The correspondence is exact for any shape whose width varies linearly with height. For circular discs, the area-mean width is $\pi R^2/2R$ which for the first zero differs from the above value by approximately 5 %. The discrepancy increases for higher-order zeros and, though it is calculated easily, it may be simplest to use only the first zero in circumstances when mixed shapes are likely to occur.

In practice, it is convenient to collect only a fraction of the light scattered by the particle into a certain range of solid angles. Moreover, the circumstance that the direct light from the source must be cut-off, if the photodetector is not to be saturated by an overwhelming d.c. contribution, makes any light scattered about the optic axis unavailable. The use of a schlieren system to select a suitable range of scattering angles is not only simple (see fig. 4) but also allows a simpler and more convenient form of the theory to be used.

The principle is obvious if we consider the image. Here the luminous regions correspond to those parts of the test objects in which the particular deflections originate which are selected by the schlieren aperture used and which, in the absence of refraction, are occasioned by diffraction alone.[7] When this system is applied to transparent

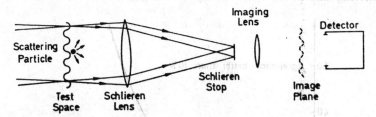

FIG. 4.—Schematic showing basic Schlieren system for the observation of scattered light.

droplets it is better to use an opaque dye to avoid complications due to internally refracted rays. The range of angles so defined can be varied by limiting the outer as well as the inner boundary of the schlieren aperture [8] using, e.g., circular or double slits of various dimensions.

Now the regions around the boundary from which the diffracted light comes are narrowly confined, so that, except for the very smallest of particles, the above theory may be modified as follows. The photodetector is effectively only seeing the edges of the scattering particle crossing the field of fringes. For a cylinder these are two narrow line sources parallel to the fringes, separated by the diameter of the cylinder. Eqn (5) can be applied directly giving zeros for

$$2l = (2n+1)\lambda^*/2.$$

The same result can be arranged for particles of circular cross-section if a strip schlieren stop is used of a width just sufficient to give an image consisting of two points coming from the ends of a diameter. This is the simplest and most direct measurement of width, providing enough light is available.

For a large number of particles in such a system one has effectively N pairs of particles of fixed separation d. Then, eqn (6) takes the form

$$V = \left\{ \frac{1}{N} + \frac{N-1}{N} \frac{\sin k^*w}{k^*w} \right\} \cos k^* \frac{d}{2}.$$

If a circular schlieren stop is used with a sufficiently large particle of circular cross-section the image takes the form of a ring of radius R. If we take an element dl of such a ring, situated at the angle θ we have $dl = R d\theta$ and if δR is the width of the ring,

$$I_{sca} = 4I_0\delta Rf \int_0^\pi (1+\cos k^*y)R \, d\theta;$$

since $y = Y + R \cos \theta$, the centre of the ring being at Y, then

$$I_{sca} = 4I_0 R\delta Rf \int_0^\pi [1+\cos k^*y \cos (k^*R \cos \theta) - \sin k^*y \sin (k^*R \cos \theta)] \, d\theta,$$

or

$$I_{sca} = 4\pi R\delta RI_0 f[1+J_0(k^*R) \cos k^*y].$$

$J_0(k^*R)$ is a Bessel function of order zero, with zeros at $k^*R = 2.405$, 5.520 etc. Hence the a.c. component has zeros for diameters.

$$2R = 0.766\lambda^*, \quad 1.757\,\lambda^* \quad \text{etc.}$$

The limitations regarding very small particle sizes, which were detailed above for illumination of the whole area, also become less serious for the schlieren type of optical system. The dark-field schlieren image, when using a strip stop, consists of two slivers of illumination at its extremities. These differ from being infinitesimal only to the extent to which the diffracted light derives from regions other than the edge and to the effect on the light pattern of diffraction elsewhere in the systems.[9] However, since this marking is symmetrical about the particle and since the fringe separation corresponds to the width of the whole particle—at least for the first extinction—the approximation is a good one, provided the schlieren stop is small and the numerical aperture of the optical system is large. In the simplest case of only one imaging lens, the detailed structure of the schlieren image depends on the open aperture, the stop and the boundaries of the lens (see e.g., Speak and Walters,[10]). If this aperture were infinite in extent, a point object would be imaged as a point. When a very small schlieren stop is used—and the parallelism of laser beams makes this feasible—the uncertainty in the schlieren edge is, in practice, limited only by the lens aperture.

The dark-field schlieren system is also particularly suitable for very large particles for which the total illumination method is dominated by backward reflection from a three-dimensional body. Although here again the light can be reflected forward and extinction conditions precisely calculated for any known shape, the schlieren method can be used directly, without modification either to the optical system or to the method of data analysis—irrespective of shape, size or reflectivity of the test object.

SOME OPTICAL SYSTEMS

Several configurations suitable for particular purposes are shown in fig. 5. The method was originally intended to select particles of abnormal size (diseased cells) and this exemplifies probably the simplest application possible. Such particles can be held, e.g., on a microscope slide driven at a known velocity, or conveyed in a stream of liquid along capillary tubing. If the fringe spacing is set at a value giving zero (or minimum) a.c. amplitude for the standard size, any particle of abnormal size will signal its presence by its a.c. component. Since the particle velocity can be arranged independently in such applications, suitable filter circuits could be used for the known a.c. frequency. Under these conditions it would not even be necessary to have only one particle passing through the test space at a time, although it would be desirable not to have more than one *abnormal* particle there.

Under less controllable conditions, however, it is necessary to collect light from only one particle at a time into the photomultiplier, otherwise the sizes will " add up " in a manner depending on their separation. This requirement is similar to that, though more stringent than, in velocimetry (see above) and in a cloud of particles can be arranged most readily by making the area of the fringe field smaller than the minimum particle separation. Using a focused laser beam in a system such as that shown in fig. 5a (similar to the " velocimeter " of Rudd [11]) would be suitable for quite dense clouds.

In the case of velocimetry there would be no merit in having the separation between the two slits or two apertures adjustable. For present purposes, however, the two apertures can be mounted on a micrometer screw, or pair of callipers, which may

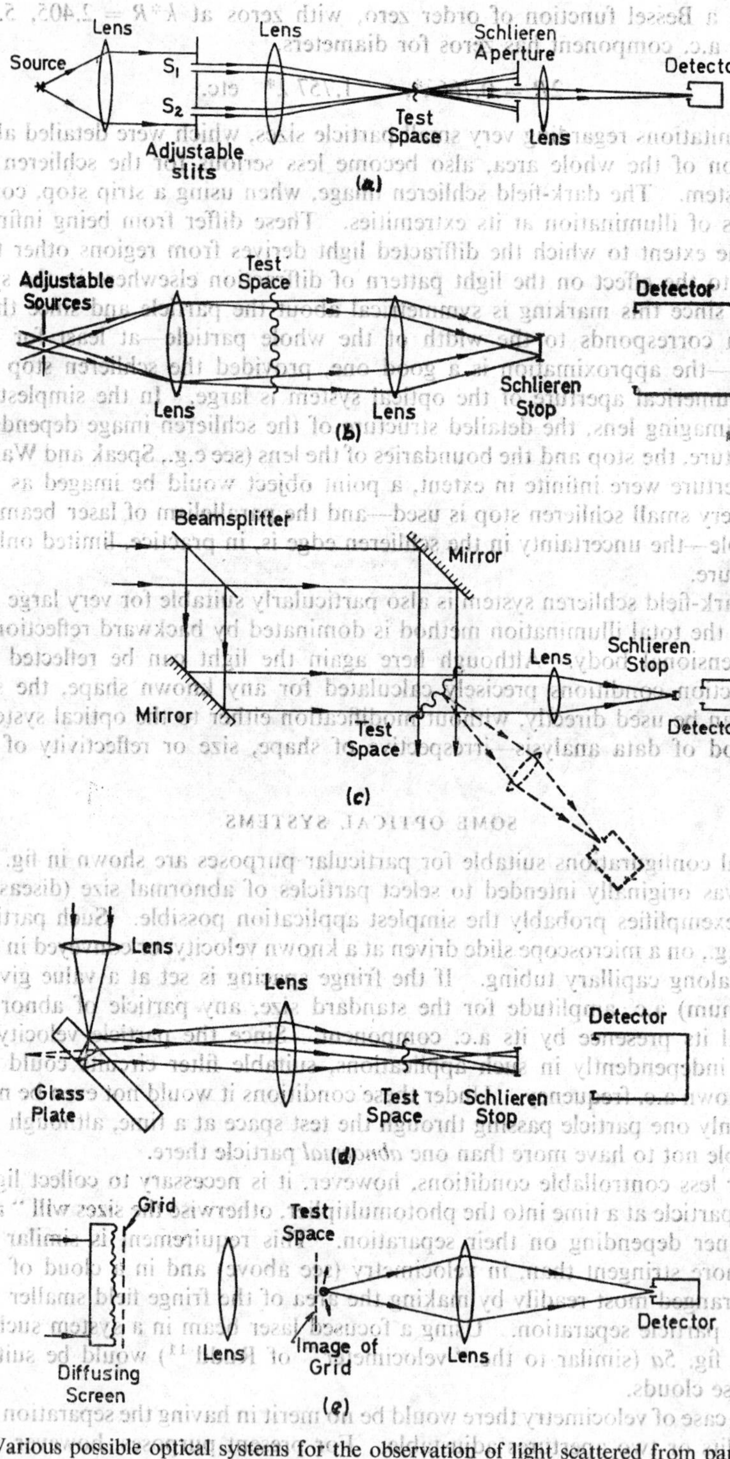

(a)

(b)

(c)

(d)

(e)

FIG. 5.—Various possible optical systems for the observation of light scattered from particles subjected to modulated illumination.

then be adjusted to the disappearance of the a.c. signal when the particle size can be expressed directly in terms of the separation so measured. The particle velocity may be deduced for each slit separation (other than that giving zero a.c. signal) during this adjustment, thereby improving the accuracy of velocimetry. The accuracy of both measurements is limited by the aperture widths which also define the depth of the sampling zone along the optic axis. This system would be well-suited to size determination in monodisperse clouds, whether or not the particles move with a uniform velocity component perpendicular to the fringes, so that the adjustment of fringe spacing can be carried out during the passage of a succession of individual particles—in which case the velocity of each particle as well as the common size can be deduced. For tenuous clouds extending over appreciable areas a system such as that shown in fig. 5b may be preferable, in order to reduce the delays which would occur between successive signals for a small test area. To increase the angle between the beams and decrease fringe spacing, conventional interferometers may be used, e.g., fig. 5c, though the limitations on minimum particle size discussed above still apply and there may be little point in reducing fringe separation to its theoretical minimum of $\lambda/2$. All the optical systems not using diffused light in fig. 5 are based on schlieren imaging, for convenience. If that is not desired, it would be advisable to move the photodetector off axis (e.g., in the position shown dotted in 5c) to avoid saturation by light which has not interacted with particles.

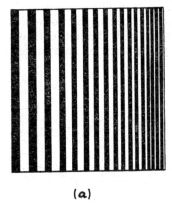

(a)

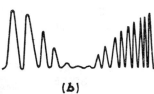

(b)

FIG. 6.—(a) Grid of variable spacing for particle sizing. (b) Signal due to a particle traversing the grid. Particle size corresponds to central grid spacing.

Many other optical systems may be useful for particular purposes. Probably the simplest method of achieving interference with laser light uses the front and rear reflections from a piece of glass (almost any optical quality, if a sufficiently small area is used).[12] Fringe spacing can then be varied by varying magnification (fig. 5d). The same method of varying spacing can be used when projecting a grid within the test region in which case neither a laser, nor indeed monochromatic light, is required (fig. 5c). As regards this system, the " Doppler theory " gives cancellation in pairs at each wavelength when the correct separation is reached.

The major difficulty which arises when particles are all of different size is the need to carry out the adjustment in fringe spacing during the passage of each particle, unless a spectrum analysis can be carried out on a large number of records. Such adjustment could be carried out mechanically only for particles travelling very slowly and being widely dispersed, so that the " null point " for one could be determined before another entered the test space. An attractive alternative is the use of a grid, or fringe system, the spacing of which is arranged to vary across the test space. Fig. 6a shows such a grid while fig. 6b shows the signal expected from a particle travelling across it at constant speed whose diameter corresponds to the centre of the range. This system can be contrived by interfering wavefronts the angle between which varies across the field, e.g., planar and spherical, or by projecting the image of an actual grid made in this form. The use for this purpose of an optical system such as that shown in fig. 5c would allow the overall grid magnification to be varied as well, so that a large range of particle sizes could be accommodated.

EXPERIMENTAL TESTS

The variation of the signal with ratio of fringe spacing to particle size should be much the same whichever optical system is used, except that those based on varying magnification also vary the overall illumination level. This, however, is a trivial point and it was considered that the simplest convenient arrangement could be used for comparison of the signals with the above theory. Preliminary work at the Applied Physics Laboratory was based on an arrangement similar to that shown in

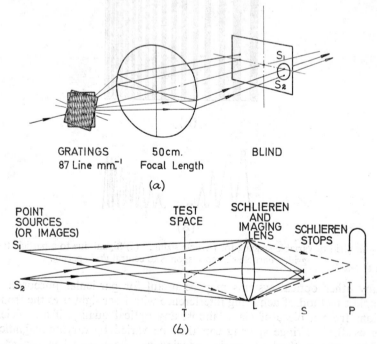

Fig. 7.—Apparatus for particle sizing. (a) Production of the two effective point sources; (b) the schlieren optics.

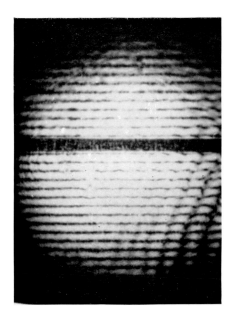

PLATE 1.—Image of wire traversing interference pattern.

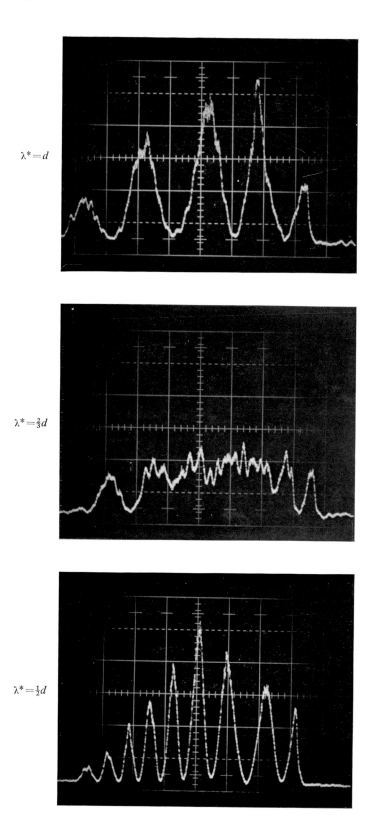

PLATE 2.—Typical photomultiplier output produced by wire traversing a variable interference pattern.

fig. 5d, largely because a shadow interferometer based on front and rear reflections at a glass slab had just been set up for fire research.[13] These experiments were cursory owing to shortage of time.

The work at Imperial College was based on a system similar to fig. 5b and is illustrated in fig. 7a. Fig. 5b is a special case of the system in fig. 7a, as there the two sources S_1 and S_2 are effectively at infinity. The narrowly confined test space of fig. 5b was not required for a test in which the object could be precisely located. In practice, the problem is one of being able to adjust the separation of S_1 and S_2 conveniently and precisely. To achieve this, a collimated laser beam passed through a pair of identical gratings having 87 lines mm^{-1} (see fig. 7b). The diffracted beams were then brought to a focus using a 50-cm focal length lens. When both gratings were accurately aligned with respect to each other, the diffracted orders coincided exactly. Rotation of one grating in its own plane rotated one set of diffracted orders about their common central maximum. A blind placed in the focal plane selected only one order from each grating, so as to produce two point sources corresponding to S_1 and S_2 in fig. 7a. The separation of the point images depended only on the relative rotation of the two gratings. The separation of the sources was therefore easily and precisely adjustable, and therefore the fringe spacing was readily varied.

TABLE 1.—FRINGE SPACINGS CORRESPONDING TO MAXIMA AND MINIMA IN THE DOPPLER BEAT FREQUENCY SIGNAL FOR A SINGLE PARTICLE SIZE

grating setting min.	max.	order no. n	$1/n$	fringe spacing
1.50		0.5	2.000	0.0730
	3.30	1.0	1.000	0.0394
5.00		1.5	0.667	0.0275
	6.80	2.0	0.500	0.0208
8.80		2.5	0.400	0.0168

The dimensions of the optical system beyond S_1 and S_2 were: $S_2T = 77.0$ cm; $TL = 26.2$ cm; $LS = 15.0$ cm; and $SP = 20$ cm (see fig. 7a). A single stop 2.5 mm wide was used to block off the direct beams. The aperture in front of the photo-multiplier was 3.0 mm long and 0.3 mm wide. The fringe spacing was continuously variable from effectively infinity down to 170 μm.

The test object was a thin moving wire the average diameter of which was measured with a micrometer as 0.0399 ± 0.0001 cm. It was attached to a fly wheel and driven through the test region by a constant speed electric motor with its axis parallel to the fringes, as is illustrated in plate 1.

Each time the wire crossed the fringe system the periodic signal picked up by the photomultiplier was displayed on a oscilloscope. Starting with an infinite fringe spacing, the oscilloscope traces were observed as the fringe spacing was decreased. A series of readings were made of the grating settings corresponding to the minimum and maximum amplitude in Doppler beat frequency traces. Three examples of the traces recorded are shown in plate 2, and the complete set of data is given in table 1. The grating settings were calibrated by measuring the associated fringe spacings with a travelling microscope.

As discussed in the previous section, we expect that for this system minima in a.c. amplitude occur when

$$\lambda^* = D/(n+\tfrac{1}{2}), \qquad n = 0, 1, 2, 3 \ldots$$

S7—7*

Similarly maxima occur whenever

$$\lambda^* = D/n, \qquad n = 1, 2, 3 \dots$$

One interesting result of the experimental test is that the minima in a.c. amplitude approach, but never quite reach, zero.   This is due to the Gaussian modulation of the fringe amplitudes across the field and becomes obvious by reference to fig. 8 which

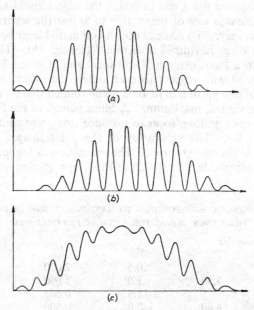

FIG. 8.—Effect of adding two unbalanced out of phase a.c. signals.   (a) signal produced by leading edge of object ; (b) signal produced by trailing edge of object ; (c) net signal from detector : the sum of (a) and (b).

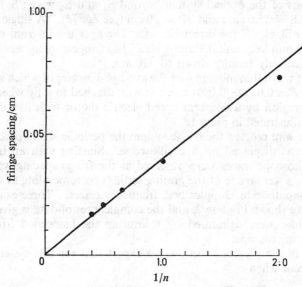

FIG. 9.—Linear least-squares fit to the points listed in table 1.

also explains the shape of the observed traces. The schlieren images of the leading and trailing edges derive from somewhat different regions and the two intensities are therefore never fully matched. Should this become a practical limitation to accuracy, it would be necessary to use a wider field of fringes, in relation to the width to be measured, or to avoid a Gaussian distribution altogether (see fig. 5c).

To illustrate the deduction of D and assess variation in individual readings, as compared with the mean, a graph of λ^* against n^{-1} was plotted. This is shown in fig. 9, where a linear least-squares fit has been made to the points. Taking all points into account, the slope gives $d = 0.0377$ cm, a 5.5 % difference from the micrometer reading. However, the error in locating the first minimum is much greater than for the other points. If this first point is omitted one obtains $d = 0.0404$ which is only 1 % different from the directly measured value.

Since the form of the records and analysis is independent of the optical system and of the nature of the test object, there seemed little point in extending the experimental tests to other configurations. It is concluded that the results conform accurately to the theroretical predictions.

[1] M. J. R. Schwar and F. J. Weinberg, *Proc. Roy. Soc. A*, 1969, **311**, 469.

[2] F. Durst and J. H. Whitelaw, *Proc. Roy. Soc. A*, 1971, **324**, 157.

[3] L. E. Drain, *J. Phys. D., Appl. Phys.*, 1972, **5**, 481.

[4] A. Erdélyi, *Higher Transcendental Functions* (McGraw-Hill, New York, 1955).

[5] G. N. Plass, *Appl. Optics*, 1966, **5**, 279.

[6] A. R. Jones, *J. Phys. D., Appl. Phys.*, 1973, **6**, 417.

[7] F. J. Weinberg, *Optics of Flames* (Butterworths, London, 1963).

[8] M. D. Fox and F. J. Weinberg, *Brit. J. Appl. Phys.*, 1960, **11**, 269.

[9] K. G. Birch, *Optica Acta*, 1968, **15**, 113.

[10] G. S. Speak and D. J. Walters, *Aero. Res. Council, Rep. Mem.*, 1954, 2859.

[11] M. J. Rudd, *J. Phys. E., Sci. Instr.*, 1968, **1**, 723.

[12] A. K. Oppenheim, P. A. Urtiew and F. J. Weinberg, *Proc. Roy. Soc. A*, 1966, **291**, 279.

[13] J. E. Creeden, R. M. Fristrom, C. Grunfelder and F. J. Weinberg, *J. Phys. D., Appl. Phys.*, 1972, **5**, 1063.

Processes, Sources and Particle Size Distributions

By J. R. Brock

Dept. of Chemical Engineering, University of Texas, Austin, Texas 78712, U.S.A.

Received 28th March, 1973

Rational control policies for particulate air pollutants ultimately must consider the particle size distribution. This point is illustrated by a simple example of the inadequacy of regulations based on limitation of total particulate mass emissions from primary sources. A general model for the evolution of the atmospheric aerosol size distribution is discussed for the particular case of an urban area. Conservation equations for particulate matter and nucleating vapour are developed. An important element in the development of the general model is knowledge of the particle size distribution associated with various primary sources of particulate matter. Such primary sources are classified according to the basic aerosol generation process of homogeneous and heterogeneous nucleation and comminution.

Aerosols from primary sources in which particle generation occurs by homogeneous nucleation are considered to be well aged aerosols, which by virtue of coagulation have reached asymptotic limit or " self preserving " distributions. As a practical matter, however, randomization will alter the asymptotic limit distributions from primary sources. Inherent complications in attempts to characterize the particle size distributions of aerosols formed by heterogeneous nucleation are discussed. Aerosols generated by comminution are known to approach asymptotic limit distributions which in certain cases have the log normal form, although randomization again will alter such asymptotic forms.

1. INTRODUCTION

The pollution of the atmosphere with aerosols is a topic of current concern. Adverse health effects have been traced to exposure of urban populations to high ambient levels of particulate matter and sulphur oxides. Reduction in visibility is an obvious consequence of an increase in the amount of atmospheric aerosol. Considerable speculation continues as to the possible role of pollutant aerosol in inadvertent modification of weather and even the global energy balance.

In many of these instances, the unfavourable effects are related not solely to the total quantity of suspended particulate matter but in a detailed manner to the aerosol size distribution. Therefore, it would appear that formulation of a rational policy for control of pollutant aerosol must consider the size distribution.

As an illustration of this point, consider a single elementary example. Controls on emissions of particulate matter from sources have been directed primarily toward reduction of total mass emissions. From a regional or international standpoint this may not be sufficient. Consider that the rate of change of total suspended particulate mass, m, owing to a primary source emission is a function of the primary source emission rate, a, and the residence time, b^{-1}, of the aerosols from that source. As we shall discuss later, these simple assumptions are not generally correct, but they will serve for the purposes of this simple illustrative example.

The functional relationship described above may be expressed in the form:

$$\frac{dm}{dt} = a - bm \qquad (1.1)$$

where b^{-1} is a function of particle size, which for a particular source category will be chosen as the residence time of the mass median diameter. For short time periods:

$$\frac{dm}{dt} \sim 0 = a - bm \qquad (1.2)$$

so that $m = a/b$ gives the total mass of atmospheric aerosol at any time owing to a particular source category. Table 1 presents some comparisons for several source categories in the U.S.A. In these examples, the largest tonnage sources of particulate emissions are not the largest contributors to the inventory of suspended particulate matter. There is, of course, no pretension that the data in table 1 are accurate, but they do serve to illustrate the point that total mass emissions may not be a reliable guide to assessment of atmospheric degradation by primary sources.

TABLE 1.—MASS OF AEROSOL IN ATMOSPHERE OWING TO INDICATED PRIMARY SOURCES

primary source (uncontrolled)	mass median diam./μm (uncontrolled) ref. (1)	inverse particle residence time/yr^{-1} ref. (2) b	source mass emission rate/ton yr^{-1}, U.S.A. ref. (1) a	mass of particulate matter of atmosphere U.S.A. a/b
1. automobile	0.4	20	4×10^5	2×10^4
2. coal-fired electric utility, pulverized	10	625	3×10^6	5×10^3
3. crushed stone, sand, gravel	20	1 250	5×10^6	4×10^3
4. petroleum FFC units	0.5	30	4.5×10^5	1.5×10^4

In general, rational control policy for particulate matter requires detailed answers to such questions as: What are the sources of aerosols in the atmosphere? What are the processes producing changes in the aerosol size distribution in the atmosphere? How are particles removed from the atmosphere? Detailed answers to these questions would imply a knowledge of the evolution of the aerosol particle size distribution in the atmosphere.

The purpose of this paper is to develop an analytical framework for the examination of some of these questions. We begin with the formulation of a model for the evolution of the atmospheric aerosol size distribution. Consequences and approximations of the model are discussed. As an important element of the general model, examination is made of the particle size distributions arising from basic aerosol generation processes and associated with primary sources of particulate matter.

2. MODEL OF THE ATMOSPHERIC AEROSOL

In this section, an analytical model for the atmospheric aerosol is discussed. While the general model is not necessarily limited, the direction of the discussion is toward the evolution of the particle size distribution in the atmospheric boundary layer of urban areas. A major element in the evolution of the particle size distribution, and the essential feature of the hydromechanical description of the atmospheric boundary layer, is the presence of turbulence. These facts make difficult a rigorous derivation of an evolution equation for the atmospheric aerosol. The nature of these difficulties in the development of aerosol dynamics in a turbulent medium has been outlined in ref. (3). In the development of this model, a first assumption is that the velocity of the suspending gas is not altered by the presence of particles. While this assumption may be valid for the ambient urban aerosol, it clearly excludes detailed consideration of aerosol dynamics in such systems as dense or hygroscopic plumes, fogs, clouds, etc. A second assumption is that aerosol particles and gaseous contaminants diffuse similarly in the presence of atmospheric turbulence. Justification for this assumption is given in ref. (3) and (4). Brownian diffusive transport of individual particles is considered to be negligible compared with turbulent diffusive transport.

With this discussion in view, the following relation is assumed to describe the evolution of the density function, $n(\mu, \mathbf{X}, t)$ for the atmospheric aerosol:

$$\frac{\partial n}{\partial t} + \mathbf{V} \cdot \mathbf{V}n = \tfrac{1}{2} \int_0^\mu b(\mu - \mu', \mu') \cdot n(\mu')n(\mu - \mu')\, d\mu' - n \int_0^\infty b(\mu', \mu)n(\mu')\, d\mu' +$$

$$\frac{\partial^2}{\partial \mu^2}[\alpha(\mu)n] - \frac{\partial}{\partial \mu}[\beta(\mu)n] + \mathbf{G}(\mu) \cdot \mathbf{V}n + \sum_p \dot{v}_p + \sum_N \dot{v}_N \qquad (2.1)$$

where $n(\mu, \mathbf{X}, t)\, d\mu$ is the number of aerosol particles haveing masses in the range μ, $d\mu$ at a point in space $\mathbf{X}$ at time t. ω is the fluid velocity. The first two terms on the right hand side of the equation represent the change in n owing to coagulation. The third and fourth terms describe the change in n owing to condensation of trace gaseous substances.

The change in n owing to gravitational settling is given by the fifth term in which $\mathbf{G}(\mu)$ is the gravitational settling velocity of a particle of mass μ. $\dot{v}_p(\mu, \mathbf{X}, t)$ is the rate of input at $\mathbf{X}$, t of particles of mass μ from primary source P, and the summation is extended over all primary sources which may be treated as point, line or area sources. Similarly $\dot{n}_{N_i}(\mu, \mathbf{X}, t)$ represents the rate of production of particles of mass μ at $\mathbf{X}$, t by homogeneous nucleation of the ith chemical species. It should be noted that heterogeneous nucleation of condensable species is accounted for by the condensation terms, three and four. It should be noted that the coagulation coefficient $b(\mu, \mu')$ and condensation coefficients $\alpha(\mu)$, $\beta(\mu)$ may be very complicated functions if refinements such as particle shape, composition and other physico-chemical properties are included.

Coupled to eqn (2.1) are conservation equations for those substance undergoing heterogeneous and homogeneous nucleation:

$$\frac{\partial S_j}{\partial t} + \mathbf{V} \cdot \mathbf{V}S_j = \sum_r \dot{s}_{jr} + \sum_p \dot{s}_{jp} - \sum_{r'} s_{jr'} - \int_0^\infty (s_j, \mu)n(\mu)\, d\mu \qquad (2.2)$$

$$\frac{\partial h_i}{\partial t} + \mathbf{V} \cdot \mathbf{V}h_i = \sum_q \dot{H}_{jq} + \sum_p \dot{H}_{jp} - \int_0^\infty \mu \dot{n}_N(\mu)\, d\mu - \sum_{q'} H_{jq'}. \qquad (2.3)$$

S_j is the mass concentration of the jth chemical species undergoing heterogeneous nucleation. $\dot{s}_{jr}$ represents the rate of production of this species by the rth chemical reaction and s_{jp} the rate of production by the Pth primary source. Similarly $s_{jr'}$ is the rate of removal of j by the rth chemical reaction. The last term on the right hand side of eqn (2.2) is the rate of removal of species j by condensation onto the existing aerosol; the function $\gamma(S_j, \mu)$ will in general be a complex function of the physico-chemical properties of the particles. The first three terms on the right hand side of eqn (2.3) are analogous respectively to those in eqn (2.2). The last term is the rate of removal of i by homogeneous nucleation as defined in eqn (2.1).

Eqn (2.1), (2.2) and (2.3) are, of course, coupled closely to the energy and momentum balance equations for the atmosphere.[3] We shall discuss this coupling shortly.

However, consider now the first two moments of n:

$$N = \int_0^\infty n(\mu)\, d\mu \qquad (2.4)$$

$$M = \int_0^\infty \mu n(\mu)\, d\mu, \qquad (2.5)$$

N being the total number of particles per unit volume and M the total mass. Through performing the indicated integrations one obtains the following moment equations from eqn (2.1):

$$\frac{\partial N}{\partial t} + \mathbf{V} \cdot \mathbf{V}N = -\tfrac{1}{2} \int_0^\infty \int_0^\infty b(\mu, \mu')n(\mu)n(\mu')\, d\mu\, d\mu' +$$

$$\int_0^\infty \mathbf{G}(\mu) \cdot \mathbf{V}n\, d\mu + \mathcal{N}_p + \dot{\mathcal{N}}_N \qquad (2.6)$$

$$\frac{\partial M}{\partial t} + \mathbf{V} \cdot \mathbf{V}M = \int_0^\infty \{\beta(\mu)n + \mu\mathbf{G}(\mu) \cdot \mathbf{V}n\}\, d\mu + \mathcal{M}_p + \dot{\mathcal{M}}_N. \qquad (2.7)$$

The details of the integration of eqn (2.1) to obtain eqn (2.6) and (2.7) are well known [3] and are therefore omitted here. $\mathcal{N}_p$, $\dot{\mathcal{N}}_N$ and $\mathcal{M}_p$, $\dot{\mathcal{M}}_N$ represent respectively total number and mass of particles contributed by both primary sources and homogeneous nucleation.

It is clear from eqn (2.6) and (2.7) that N is unaffected by condensation processes but is altered by coagulation, whereas the reverse is the case for M. Hence the two moment eqn (2.6) and (2.7) provide complementary information on these two important processes shaping the size distribution.

For a turbulent fluid, eqn (2.1), (2.2) and (2.3) are not in a useful form. By analogy with the usual procedure for turbulent dispersion of non-reactive gases we can express quantities in these equations in terms of time averaged quantities with an overbar and fluctuating components. For example:

$$\mathbf{V} = \bar{\mathbf{V}} + \mathbf{V}' \qquad S_j = \bar{S}_j + S_j'$$
$$n = \bar{n} + n' \qquad h_i = \bar{h}_i + h_i' \qquad (2.8)$$

where by definition $\bar{\mathbf{V}}' = 0$, etc.

Unfortunately, eqn (2.1), (2.2) and (2.3) are non-linear in n, S_j and h_i so that the usual procedure of introducing Prandtl's mixing length hypothesis is not sufficient.

This is a familiar problem occurring in the analysis of non-linear chemical reactions in turbulent fluids.[5] It has recently been discussed for atmospheric chemical reactions.[6] Unfortunately, there is no simple resolution. For example, if one seeks to ignore a product such as $\overline{n'^2}$ relative to $\bar{n}^2$ it is necessary that characteristic coagulation times, $1/bn$, and temporal variations in $\bar{n}$ be much greater than the Lagrangian time scale of the turbulence. In addition, the spatial variation of $\bar{n}$ must be large compared with the length scales of the turbulence. These conditions may not always be met; and if they are not, we do not have a convenient hypothesis such as Prandtl's to relate quantities such as $\overline{n'n'}$ and $\bar{n}^2$. More detailed study of these questions appears to be essential for further development of the present theory.

We proceed, then, under the restrictions indicated above, and neglect terms such as $\overline{n'n'}$ relative to $\bar{n}\bar{n}$, etc. With the introduction of Prandtl's mixing length hypothesis, eqn (2.1), (2.2) and (2.3) become:

$$\frac{\partial \bar{n}}{\partial t} + \mathbf{V} \cdot \mathbf{V}\bar{n} = \mathbf{V} \cdot \mathbf{K}\mathbf{V}\bar{n} + \frac{1}{2}\int_0^\mu b(\mu', \mu-\mu')\bar{n}(\mu') \cdot \bar{n}(\mu-\mu') \, d\mu' -$$

$$\bar{n}\int_0^\infty b(\dot{\mu}, \mu')\bar{n}(\mu') \, d\mu' + \frac{\partial^2}{\partial \mu^2}[\bar{\alpha}(\mu)\bar{n}] -$$

$$\frac{\partial}{\partial \mu}[\bar{\beta}(\mu)\bar{n}] + \mathbf{G}(\mu) \cdot \mathbf{V}\bar{n} + \sum_p \bar{v}_p + \sum_N \bar{v}_N \tag{2.9}$$

$$\frac{\partial S_j}{\partial t} + \mathbf{V} \cdot \mathbf{V}\bar{S}_j = \mathbf{V} \cdot \mathbf{K}\mathbf{V}\bar{S}_j + \sum_r \bar{s}_{jr} + \sum_p \bar{s}_{jp} - \sum_{r'} \bar{s}_{jr'} - \int_0^\infty \gamma(\bar{S}_j, \mu)\bar{n}(\mu) \, d\mu \tag{2.10}$$

$$\frac{\partial h_i}{\partial t} + \mathbf{V} \cdot \mathbf{V}\bar{h}_i = \mathbf{V} \cdot \mathbf{K}\mathbf{V}\bar{h}_i + \sum_q \bar{H}_{jq} + \sum_p \bar{H}_{jp} - \sum_{q'} \bar{H}_{jq'} - \int_0^\infty \bar{n}_N(\mu) \, d\mu \tag{2.11}$$

where $\mathbf{K}$ is the so-called eddy diffusivity.

The difficulties in the concept of eddy diffusivity applied to atmospheric dispersion are well known and extensively reviewed.[7]   We restrict our discussion here to urban particulate pollution.   In order to apply these equations in the descriptions in the description of the aerosol concentration in an urban area, it is clear that detailed knowledge of chemical reaction rates, nucleation rates, and physico-chemical alterations of the particulate matter is necessary. In addition, meterological data in the form of mean winds, atmospheric stability conditions, relative humidity, temperature, and radiative flux are essential.   The boundary and initial conditions will depend also in part on this meteorological information.

A discussion of the solution of eqn (2.9), (2.10) and (2.11) is beyond the scope of this paper.   It is possible, however, to indicate the relative importance of some of the terms in these equations which will serve to provide a framework for later investigations.   With the restriction of the discussion to pollution by aerosols of an urban area, various characteristic time scales may be introduced as scale factors in eqn (2.9), (2.10) and (2.11).

For an urban area, a characteristic residence time, t_{RES}, may be introduced as the ratio of the crosswind diameter, D, of the area to the mean wind velocity U—that is, $t_{RES} \sim D/U$.   Obviously, a problem occurs in this definition if winds are light and variable, as occurs during inversion conditions.   This point will be touched on later.

There are also characteristic diffusion times for longitudinal, t_{LONG}, and vertical, t_{VERT}, dispersion:

$$t_{LONG} \sim L^2/K_L$$

and

$$t_{VERT} \sim H^2/K_H$$

where L is the longitudinal distance perpendicular to a line in the mean wind direction, through a point of observation, H is the vertical distance above the surface. K_L and K_H are the corresponding eddy diffusivities.   For particulate systems, the characteristic particle gravitational settling time, $t_{GRAV} \sim H/V_g(\mu)$, must be considered along with t_{VERT}.

There are also characteristic times for the aerosol growth processes.   For coagulation:

$$t_{COAG} \sim \frac{1}{b(\mu, \mu')}\bar{n}(\mu)$$

where for the collision pair, $n(\mu) \geqslant n(\mu')$. For condensation:

$$t_{COND} \sim 1/\Delta C_j \bar{u}_j h(r)$$

where ΔC_j is the difference between the number density of j in the gas and just at the surface of the particle. $\bar{u}_j$ is the molecular mean speed of j. $h(r)$ is a function of particle radius, r, and Knudsen number Kn, such that for Kn $\to 0$, $h(r) \sim r$.

In addition to these characteristic times, there are times associated with the gas phase reactions, homogeneous nucleation processes, flux rates of particulate matter to boundary surfaces, etc.

If one is interested solely in the evolution of the aerosol distribution in urban areas, it is clear that only those processes with characteristic times within the period t_{RES} need be considered. The assumption here, of course, is that upwind, outside the urban area the aerosol concentration is low and plays no important role in the evolution processes occuring in the urban area.

By way of example, for an urban area with a cross wind diameter of 30 km and a mean wind speed of 2 m/s, $t_{RES} \sim 4$ h. Consequently, for $K_L \sim 8 \times 10^6$ cm²/s, primary sources located longitudinally more than approximately 3 km from the line in the direction of the mean wind speed through a reference or monitoring point need not be considered in interpreting observations at that monitoring station. In the same manner, one can conclude that coagulation between two particles both with radii greater than 0.1 μm can be neglected in eqn (2.9) inasmuch as for such coagulating pairs of particles at known urban concentrations, $t_{COAG} \gtrsim 30$ h. Also, in photo-chemical smog reactions, the induction period for formation of ozone, which appears to be one of the reactants producing particles by nucleation, is of the order of 4 h, so that for the conditions of this particular example such processes cannot be neglected in eqn (2.9).

From this, one can infer that it is not generally necessary to consider all the complication inherent in eqn (2.9), (2.10) and (2.11) in that some of the terms may be of negligible order for certain meteorological and boundary conditions.

A difficulty arises with these arguments under inversion conditions where the mean wind speed is very small and highly variable in direction. In these circum-stances, the ground surface and inversion base suggest the applicability for the urban raea of a so-called " box model " in which, unfortunately, much detail is lost. It is assumed that the urban region, closed at the top by the inversion base, corresponds to a well-mixed container. If eqn (2.9) is integrated over this defined volume, and the volume integrals are converted where applicable to surface integrals, the following result is readily obtained:

$$\frac{\partial \langle n \rangle}{\partial t} = \tfrac{1}{2} \int_0^\mu b(\mu', \mu-\mu')\langle n(\mu')\rangle\langle n(\mu-\mu')\rangle \, d\mu' - \langle n \rangle \int_0^\infty b(\mu, \mu')\langle n(\mu')\rangle \, d\mu' +$$

$$\frac{\partial^2}{\partial \mu^2}[\langle \alpha(\mu)\rangle\langle n \rangle] - \frac{\partial}{\partial \mu}[\langle \beta(\mu)\rangle\langle n \rangle] - \sigma\langle n \rangle + \sum_{p+N} \tau_i \omega_i \qquad (2.12)$$

where $\langle n \rangle$ is the volume-averaged density function. $\sigma(\mu)$ represents the inverse residence time of particles of mass μ in the volume and is a function for the conditions specified above of the mean wind, dispersion coefficients, and surface removal processes. $\tau_i f_i(\mu)$ represents the rate of input of particles from primary or homo-geneous nucleation source i with density $\omega_i(\mu)$ and characteristic time τ_i^{-1}.

This model has been applied [8] in the discussion of the evolution of the size spectrum for particle radii greater than 0.1 μm. As noted above, coagulation of pairs of particles found in this portion of the atmospheric size spectrum can be neglected over reasonably long time periods. Hence for radii greater than 0.1 μm, eqn (2.12) becomes:

$$\frac{\partial\langle n\rangle}{\partial t} = \frac{\partial^2}{\partial\mu^2}[\langle\alpha'(\mu)\langle n\rangle\rangle]-\frac{\partial}{\partial\mu}[\langle\beta'(\mu)\langle n\rangle\rangle]-\sigma n+\sum_p \tau_i\omega_i \qquad (2.13)$$

where the small nuclei below 0.1 μm may be considered as participants in the condensation process on the large particles; the new coefficients α' and β' include this consideration.

If primary source inputs are neglected, it is easy to show [8, 9] that, as a result of condensation, eqn (2.13) leads to certain characteristic forms for the particle size distribution for particles greater than 0.1 μm radius. Of course, primary sources in many urban areas may be dominant. Therefore, in such circumstances, if generalizations concerning urban particle size distributions are to be found, one must look at characteristics of the particle size distributions of typical dominant primary sources. Consideration is given to this topic in the next section.

3. PROCESSES AND SIZE DISTRIBUTIONS

The necessity for consideration of the particle size distribution of primary sources has been noted above. Primary sources, as defined by the relations developed in Section 2, include all those sources injecting particles as such directly into the atmosphere. Particles from a given primary source may be generated by the processes of nucleation, comminution, or by combinations of these processes.

Nucleation may be homogeneous or heterogeneous. The term *homogeneous nucleation* embodies all those processes in which vapour molecules interact physically or chemically to form particles; the particle growth process begins from particle sizes of molecular order and may proceed by coagulation, condensation or a combination of these. In *heterogeneous nucleation*, new particles are not formed; vapour molecules condense physically or chemically onto existing particles, and, primarily, one is dealing with a condensational growth process.

Particle generation by comminution involves successive, usually mechanical, subdivisions of liquids or solids to the fine particle state. Aerosol generation at the air-sea interface and dust rise by wind action at the air-land interface are important examples of natural primary sources of particles formed by comminution. These sources, in fact, are estimated [10] to constitute the two largest contributors of aerosol mass on a world wide basis.

With these definitions, characteristics of the particle size distribution produced by the particle generation processes of nucleation and comminution will now be examined.

HOMOGENEOUS NUCLEATION

Automobile exhaust represents perhaps one of the important examples of an anthropogenic primary source in which particles are apparently generated principally by homogeneous nucleation as defined here. The residence time of the aerosol, before injection and subsequent fairly rapid dilution in the atmosphere, in this and other important industrial combustion sources, is usually of the order $0.1 \sim 1$ s. Therefore, the particulate emissions from such sources are comparatively well-aged aerosols, for which the particle size distribution has had sufficient time to reach a " self-preserving " form by coagulation.[11] The term " self-preserving " refers to the tendency of aerosols coagulating with the same collision parameter, $b(\mu, \mu')$, to achieve similar particle size distributions after sufficient time of coagulation. Also, a simple calculation is sufficient to show that usually aerosols formed by homogeneous nucleation will, in the time period $0.1 \sim 1$ s, have an average size which is in the sub-micrometre range. If $\mathcal{M}$ is the total mass concentration of condensed material formed by nucleation, the order of the mean radius of the coagulated aerosol should be:

$$r \sim [3\,\mathcal{M}(1+bN_0t)/4\pi\rho N_0]^{\frac{1}{3}} \tag{3.1}$$

where N_0 is the initial embryo concentration and ρ is the particle density.

Eqn (3.1) becomes for $N_0\,t \gg 1$:

$$r \sim (3\mathcal{M}bt/4\pi\rho)^{\frac{1}{3}} \tag{3.2}$$

and the order of the mean radius becomes independent of N_0. As an example, for an automobile using leaded gasoline, the undiluted exhaust has a total particulate mass concentration, $\mathcal{M}$, of $\sim 10^{-7}\text{-}10^{-8}$ g/cm³. Eqn (3.2) indicates, as do measurements,[12] that most of the aerosol is certainly in the submicrometre range.

For anthropogenic primary sources of aerosol formed principally by homogeneous nucleation and in which subsequent particulate growth is by coagulation, one *might* infer that particle size distributions from all such sources should have the same functional form and should differ only in the parameters of the "self preserving" form. The inference is the same if simultaneous condensation occurs.[13]

Published studies [11] of the numerical solution of the coagulation equation in the free molecule and continuum regimes support the foregoing conclusion. However, experimental measurements of coagulating aerosols reveal that generally the aerosol is more polydisperse than predicted by the self-preserving functional form. The explanation for this behaviour is a very familiar one to statisticians.[13] The aerosol measured in the coagulation experiments does not represent a single population, but instead a mixture usually in random proportion of a heterogeneous population. In other words, the aerosol actually measured is a composite of many different aerosol populations, each with a different history. Thus, the particle distribution function realized in an experiment, $G(X)$ is:

$$G(X) = \sum_i p_i F_i(X) \tag{3.3}$$

where the p_i are random weights attached to the various members of the heterogeneous population each with distribution function $F_i(X)$.

For an infinitely composite population:

$$G(X) = \int F(X, a)\,\mathrm{d}U(a). \tag{3.4}$$

In experimental realizations of coagulation, not only systematic spatial or time variations or random experimental error serve to create a composite population but, for dilute systems, unavoidable random fluctuations also contribute.

As a result of the effect of heterogeneity of population, the aerosol formed by homogeneous nucleation from a given primary source will always be more poly-disperse than predicted by the "self-preserving" theory. Unfortunately, the extent of this increase in polydispersity for a given primary source will probably depend on the details of that source such as geometry, flow dynamics, etc. As a result, it remains to be determined whether or not for various primary sources of this type generaliza-tions are possible. Certainly the fact of the "self-preserving" form provides a useful base from which to proceed in the inquiry.

HETEROGENEOUS NUCLEATION

The dense hygroscopic plumes emitted from various industrial processes are examples of aerosols formed by heterogeneous nucleation. In these instances, water vapour has condensed on an existing hygroscopic aerosol, which may itself in turn have been generated by homogeneous nucleation or comminution.

For the simple process of condensation of a pure substance on an aerosol of some given initial density function $n_0(r) \, dr$ of particle radius, r, it is a simple matter to examine the development in time of $n(r, t)$. In this case the evolution of $n(r, t)$ is:

$$\frac{\partial n}{\partial t} + \frac{\partial}{\partial r}[f(r)n] = 0 \qquad (3.5)$$

where $f(r)$ is the growth law for a particle of radius r. For example, in the continuum region, $Kn \rightarrow 0$, neglecting the Kelvin effect, $f(r) = a/r$, where a is a constant.[3] Similarly, in the free molecule region, $f(r) = a$, a constant [3] if the Kelvin effect is neglected.

Eqn (3.5) is a first order equation for which solutions may readily be found for arbitrary initial conditions. However, perhaps the most interesting feature of the pure condensation process is the tendency of condensation to produce a less polydisperse aerosol in the continuum region, when the Kelvin effect can be neglected. In this case, it is a simple matter to show that the ratio of the standard deviation σ to the mean radius γ_1, approaches zero with increasing time:

$$\frac{\sigma}{\gamma_1} = \frac{\sigma_0}{(\gamma_{1,0} + 2at)^{\frac{1}{2}}} \qquad (3.6)$$

where the subscript $_0$ designates initial conditions.

Similarly, in the free molecule regime:

$$\frac{\sigma}{\gamma_1} = \frac{\sigma_0}{\gamma_{1,0} + a'N_0 t}, \qquad (3.7)$$

N_0 being the initial total particle concentration. This characteristic of pure condensational growth has been utilized for the production of approximately monodisperse aerosols in variations of the original Sinclair–La Mer aerosol generator.[3]

If, as in the previous examples, the concentration of condensing vapour is held fixed but the Kelvin effect is included in the term $f(r)$, it can be shown [15] that $\sigma/\gamma_1 \rightarrow 0$ as a result of condensation. However, if the quantity of condensing vapour is limited, one finds that in an initially polydisperse aerosol after condensation has proceeded, the smaller particles will begin to evaporate while the larger ones continue to grow.

Also, additional complication beyond the scope of this discussion arises in consideration of a hygroscopic aerosol which grows at humidities below the critical supersaturation of some of the particles. In such cases, $n(r)$ can become bimodal and very polydisperse.

More general condensation processes, including stochastic effects, have been examined elsewhere [9] (see also Section 2). Such processes, as well as randomization indicated in eqn (3.3) and (3.4), usually act to increase the polydispersity of an aerosol. Additional complication can be introduced by considering as well simultaneous coagulation and condensation.

When the deterministic condensational growth described by eqn (3.5) is the only process altering the aerosol size distribution, the final distribution clearly will be determined by the initial size distribution. This initial size distribution will be that owing either to homogeneous nucleation or comminution or both. When the condensation process is stochastic and/or randomization occurs, the final particle size distribution resulting from condensational growth will become asymptotically independent of the initial distribution, the equivalent of the "self-preserving" behaviour for a coagulating aerosol.

However, in general, it is much more difficult to draw conclusions concerning the nature of the particle size distribution resulting from condensation in these cases than for coagulation. Unlike the coagulation equation, the condensational growth equation is coupled to the conservation equation of the condensing vapour; the state of the suspending gas usually plays a secondary role in the coagulation of fine particles. Furthermore, the ability of particles to grow by condensation depends in detail on particle composition or surface properties; such characteristics are usually not considered to be of great importance in coagulation. Therefore, for sources in which particle generation by heterogeneous nucleation plays an important role, detailed examination of the process dynamics will be necessary to characterize the particle size distribution.

COMMINUTION

Important natural sources of aerosol particles generated by comminution have been cited at the beginning of this section. Anthropogenic sources of aerosol generated by comminution are also of common occurrence and include emissions from industrial operations such as mineral, rock, and gravel processing, sand blasting, cement manufacture, etc., as well as inadvertent emissions resulting from farming operations, etc.

The process of comminution begins with a body of macroscopic size and by successive subdivisions or splittings, liquid or solid particles capable of aerosolization are formed. It is therefore the inverse operation to homogeneous nucleation and subsequent coagulation. The evolution equation for comminution may be represented by the relation:

$$\frac{\partial n(\mu)}{\partial t} = \int_{\mu}^{\infty} c(\mu/\mu')n(\mu')\,d\mu' - c(\mu)n(\mu) \tag{3.8}$$

where $c(\mu/\mu')\,dt$ is the probability that a particle of mass μ' will split in time dt to form 1, 2, 3 ... particles of mass μ and $c(\mu)\,dt$ is the probability that in the same time a particle of mass μ undergoes splitting. The basic assumption of eqn (3.8) is that each particle splits with a probability independent of the presence of other particles. Clearly additional detail can be introduced.

It is possible to show that the splitting process approaches asymptotically a limit distribution,[16] which, for certain assumptions concerning the splitting probabilities, can be approximated by the log normal distribution. Just as the coagulation process has for certain assumptions concerning collisions an asymptotic limit distribution, so too does the process of comminution.

A common assumption in the discussion of the splitting process [16] is that the probability of splitting is proportional to some power of the mass of a particle. Clearly, if a comminution process is carried out so that a particle of, say, 1000 μm is split with unit probability, a particle of 1 μm radius will be split with a probability orders of magnitude less (10^{-9} in fact, if splitting is directly proportional to particle mass for particles of unit density). For this reason, many large sources of particles produced by comminution, such as those cited above, will produce particles in the range of larger particle sizes.

Although asymptotic limit distributions may exist for a given comminution process, randomization can be expected to be important, owing to the comparatively small number of particles per unit volume in typical comminution processes. However, very large particles are not important in the consideration of sources of air pollution, so that the distribution produced by a comminution process can be truncated at the order of 100 μm radius. Therefore, the particle size variation of interest will generally be over only one or two orders of magnitude of particle radius. As a result the range of polydispersity which might arise from randomization is restricted.

4. CONCLUSION

While the model described in Section 2 for the evolution of the atmospheric aerosol appears to be very complex, it is nevertheless suggested that, owing to the important role of the particle distribution in many of the detrimental effects of air pollution, this complexity eventually must be faced. Characterization of the primary sources of pollutant aerosol is one of the necessary first steps.

It is recognized, of course, that primary sources of particulate matter will not generally fit into the separate categories discussed here. The aim here has been to examine the basic aerosol generation processes and to inquire into the characteristics of the resultant particle size distributions. Further progress along these lines will require adequate field data, which are at present insufficient.

This work was supported in part by a research grant from the Division of Chemistry and Physics, National Environmental Research Center, E.P.A. The author also wished to thank Prof. J. Bricard of the University of Paris for many helpful discussions.

[1] *Particulate Pollutant System Study*, MRI Contract No. CPA 2269104 (EPA, 1971).
[2] N. Esmen and M. Corn, *Atmospheric Environment*, 1971, **5**, 571.
[3] G. Hidy and J. R. Brock, *The Dynamics of Aerocolloidal Systems* (Pergamon, Oxford, 1970).
[4] N. Fuchs, *The Mechanics of Aerosols* (Pergamon, Oxford, 1964).
[5] R. Bird, W. Stewart and E. Lightfoot, *Transport Phenomena* (Wiley, NY, 1960).
[6] R. Lamb, *Atmospheric Environment*, 1972, **6**, 257.
[7] F. Pasquill, *Quart. J. Roy. Met. Soc.*, 1971, **97**, 369.
[8] J. R. Brock, *Atmospheric Environment*, 1971, **5**, 833.
[9] J. R. Brock, *J. Coll. Interface Sci.*, 1972, **39**, 32.
[10] G. Hidy and J. R. Brock, *Proceedings 2nd IUAPPA Clean Air Congress* (Academic Press, New York, 1971).
[11] R. Drake in *Topics in Current Aerosol Research* (Pergamon, Oxford, 1972).
[12] R. Lee *et al*, *Atmospheric Environment*, 1971, **5**, 225.
[13] J. Pich, S. Friedlander and F. Lai, *Aerosol Sci.*, 1970, **1**, 115.
[14] M. Girault, *Calcul des Probabilities* (Dunod, Paris, 1972).
[15] J. R. Brock, to appear.
[16] A. Kolmogorov, *Akad. Nauk SSSR*, 1941, **31**, 99.

A Field Study of Radiation Fog

BY W. T. ROACH,† R. J. ADAMS,† J. A. GARLAND‡ AND P. GOLDSMITH†

Received 3rd January, 1973

A survey of the history of theoretical and practical studies of the basic physics of fog formation in the atmosphere is followed by an account of some preliminary results of field investigations into fog.

---

1. INTRODUCTION

A supersaturated atmosphere in which fog droplets may grow may be produced by cooling or by mixing of two damp (but not necessarily saturated) masses of air at different temperatures (due allowance being made for any consequential release of latent heat by condensation). However, unlike the situation in many industrial processes involving fogs and smokes, the conditions under which these processes may occur are uncontrolled and highly variable. Stewart [1, 2] has said ". . . the interactions between the different processes lead to such complexities that there has been little success in calculating the important features of the final state on a foggy night from observable initial conditions ". This situation has changed little in recent years.

A deeper understanding of the physical processes of fog formation, maintenance and dissipation is a necessary condition for assessing future prospects of improving methods of fog modification and forecasting. This paper consists of a brief summary of past investigations followed by an account of some preliminary results of the current Meteorological Office field investigations of radiation fog.

2. PAST INVESTIGATIONS

(*a*) Taylor [3] made a study of radiation fogs at Kew, and noted that clear skies, light winds and high relative humidities were conducive to fog formation, but that fog actually occurred on about half the occasions when it was expected. He observed the cooling and drying-out of the atmosphere near the ground on a clear night and realized that the initial formation of fog appeared to depend upon a balance between these two processes. As he put it " . . . if the dryness caused by the deposition of dew on the ground diffuses upwards at a greater rate than the coldness is conducted upwards, fog is less likely to form than if reverse conditions hold ".

He attributed the " conduction " to turbulent diffusion, and also suggested that " . . . it is possible that the cooling due to radiation from the fog particles after a fog has started may have the effect of making it thicker ". He discounted the effect of radiation before fog formation, a view we now know to be wrong. However, he laid the foundations for our understanding of the formation of radiation fog.

(*b*) The next practical studies were made by Stewart [1, 2] who realized the need to measure simultaneously as many as possible of the parameters likely to be significant

† Meteorological Office, Bracknell, Berks
‡ Atomic Energy Research Establishment, Harwell

in fog formation. From his observations, he drew the following main conclusions. (i) Direct cooling of the lowest km of atmosphere by radiation and by convection (turbulent diffusion) were comparable. (ii) The surface deposition of water was comparable to that lost from the air by cooling. (iii) The lowest layers of atmosphere often reached and remained at saturation for up to a few hours before fog actually formed. Before saturation was reached, however, large fluctuations in relative humidity (not reflected in temperature observations) were usually observed. (iv) Once fog formed, it usually did so within a few minutes. Subsequently, its depth tended to increase in steps. Stewart also developed Taylor's suggestion that fog droplets could produce their own contribution to radiative cooling.

(c) Many investigations of the atmosphere near the ground have been made in conditions favourable for fog formation but with other objectives in view. Monteith [4] noted that the rate of dew deposition decreased abruptly when the wind speed dropped below about 0.5 m s^{-1} at 2 m above ground. The implication is that turbulent diffusion virtually ceased, thus removing the primary mechanism for dew deposition. He also noted that " saturation (within the grass cover below about 1 cm) was always followed by the formation of fog ". This appears to conflict with Stewart's observation (iii) above, and may reflect some significance of the state of the ground in fog formation.

Rider and Robinson [5] noted that " the change of temperature in the lowest layers of air is normally the small resultant of much larger tendencies due to changes in radiative and convective fluxes acting in opposite directions ". They also noted a quasi-periodic oscillation of period of about 10 min in temperature in the lowest 0.5 m on some radiation nights, once at about the time of fog formation.

In summary, the occurrence of radiation fog depends upon a fine balance between the drying and cooling of the atmosphere near the ground. The drying-out is caused by dew deposition which generates a water-vapour gradient down which turbulent diffusion drives a flux of water vapour. The cooling is caused by a combination of radiation and turbulent diffusion. The strength of the turbulent diffusion is controlled by the wind field which is always a fluctuating quantity. These, however, are essentially qualitative conclusions which do not tell us why fog forms when it does, nor what its evolution and structure will be given initial meteorological and aerosol information, nor does it give any precise quantitative information on heat and water budgets and the role of latent heat release in these.

3. THE METEOROLOGICAL OFFICE PROJECT

This investigation is a collaborative field project between the Cloud Physics and the Boundary Layer Research Departments of the Meteorological Office and the Aerosol Group of the Health Physics Department A.E.R.E., Harwell. The first exercise was carried out at Cardington, Beds., late in 1971, when the following parameters were measured.

CLOUD PHYSICS DEPARTMENT, METEOROLOGICAL OFFICE

(i) Net radiative fluxes at 2, 9 and 37 m above ground using Funk net flux radiometers (F_2, F_9, F_{37}). (ii) Downward flux of radiation at 1 m using a Linke–Feussner (directional) radiometer (F_{LF}). (iii) Fog top detector and thermistor (for temperature profile up to 300 m) on 700 ft^3 balloon. (iv) Continuous record of temperature at surface and 2 m (T_0, T_2). (v) Continuous record of dew-point at 2 m. (vi) Spatial and size distribution of fog droplets using holography at 1 m.

BOUNDARY LAYER RESEARCH UNIT, METEOROLOGICAL OFFICE

(vii) Wind speed measurements at 2, 4, 8, 16 m (U_2, U_4, U_8, U_{16}). (viii) Wind direction measurements at 16 m. (ix) Soil flux measurements at depths of 6 and 15 cm. (x) Deposition of moisture at surface using a lysimeter (S_0). (xi) Temperature measurements at 4, 8, 16 m at 2-min intervals (T_4, T_8, T_{16}). (xii) Tethered balloon ascents at 6-h intervals giving temperature, dew-point and wind speed to 1 km.

HEALTH PHYSICS DEPARTMENT, A.E.R.E., HARWELL

(xiii) Visibility at 1m (V_1) with a transmissometer and at 5m (V_5) with a nephelometer. (xiv) Liquid water content using an impinger. (xv) A cloud condensation nucleus counter. (xvi) A cascade impactor for drop size distribution. (xvii) Air chemistry sampling equipment.

The meteorological instrumentation used to make these measurements is in general well established. Special arrangements had to be made to keep the polythene domes protecting the detector surfaces of the radiometers free from moisture. The construction and operation of the radiometers is described by Funk.[6]

The aerosol instrumentation included some relatively novel features, particularly the use of holographic techniques for obtaining 3-dimensional " snapshots " of the spatial distribution and size of fog droplets (above about 5 μm radius) within a volume of about 500 cm^3. A description of this technique has been published by Pavitt, Jackson, Adams and Bartlett.[7] Drop-size distributions down to about 1 μm were also obtained by impacting fog droplets on thin plastic foils coated with gelatin as described by Garland.[8]

The fog top detector consisted essentially of a hot-wire detector which evaporated fog droplets in an air-stream drawn over it by a pump. The resulting change of resistance in the detector element is converted to frequency change and transmitted to a ground receiver using standard electronic techniques. The instrument was mounted on a tethered balloon, which was moved up and down through the fog top.

The cloud condensation nucleus counter was developed at Harwell from a thermal diffusion cloud chamber, and maintained supersaturations of up to 1 % in an airflow of 10 cm^3 s^{-1}. Droplets formed on cloud nuclei in the chamber scatter light from a narrow collimated beam to a photomultiplier, and the resulting pulses are counted automatically by a specially designed electronic counter.

The transmissometer consisted of a collimated receiver and projector separated by about 30 m. The integrating nephelometer [9] consists essentially of a photomultiplier which detects the amount of light scattered in a small volume of the atmosphere illuminated by a flash lamp.

The chemical sampling of the atmospheric aerosol was obtained by drawing air at about 0.3 m^3 min^{-1} (but 0.01 m^3 min^{-1} for gaseous sampling) through an area of a filter paper tape. The paper tape is moved forward once per hour. Further details of the samplers and analytical techniques are described in Eggleton and Atkins.[10]

4. RESULTS

One good case study was obtained on 7 Dec. 1971, and some account of this is given here as it illustrates the wealth of information which can be obtained from a project of this type, and it has, in our view, served to bring some of the main problems into sharper focus.

(*a*) THE RADIATION FOG OF 7 DEC., 1971

A sheet of stratocumulus cloud covered the observing site until 0330 GMT, when a complete clearance of cloud occurred. Fog began to form soon after 0400, soon thickened and persisted until its rapid dispersal at 1030. Its depth never exceeded 40 m and for most of its duration was 15-25 m deep. Wind speeds within the fog were 1.0 ± 0.5 m s^{-1} until shortly before dispersal when there was a steady increase to 2-3 m s^{-1}.

The " life " of the fog appeared to consist of two major phases—an " optically thin " phase (phase I) followed by an " optically thick " phase (phase II). The main phases can be subdivided into further identifiable phases. The transition between each phase usually lasted a few minutes. Table 1 gives a survey of the development of the fog. The " optical thickness " refers to the infra-red transmission properties of the fog in a vertical direction.

TABLE 1.—HISTORY OF FOG DEVELOPMENT

phase	period	remarks	
I *a*	0400-0430	Layer of ground mist 1-2 m deep. Surface inversion begins to develop.	
I *b*	0430-0645	Visibility at 1 m fluctuates between 100 and 200 m until shortly before 0600 when it decreases to 50-100 m. Depth of fog fluctuates between 10 and 40 m. Surface inversion about 10 m deep by end of period.	optically thin fog
II *a*	0700-0845	Inversion lifts off ground and settles near 20 m, taking the fog top with it. Sunrise at 0755.	
II *b*	0900-1000	Inversion and fog top lifted a further 5-10 m.	optically thick fog
II *c*	1000-1030	Dispersal phase. Gradual thinning followed by rapid dispersal. Freshening surface winds.	

(*b*) TEMPERATURE AND DEW-POINT

Fig. 1*a* shows a temperature-time cross-section for the lowest 60 m of atmosphere based on 20-min means from (iii), (iv) and (xi) of the list of measurements. The vertical scale is linear in $\sqrt{\text{height}}$ in order to offset undue cramping of isotherms near the ground. There are three main cooling events: the first was associated with the sky clearance and onset of phase I; the second was associated with the transition from phase I to phase II when the surface inversion lifted off the ground; and the third was associated with the transition from phase II*a* to phase II*b*. The major heating event occurred during the dispersal phase (II*c*). There were also lesser, but marked heating and cooling events during the fog period, e.g., the heating in the lowest metre at the onset of phase II. The atmosphere at 2 m became saturated at about 0400 and remained saturated during the rest of the period. Balloon measurements made at 0505 suggested that the atmosphere was saturated up to at least 100 m during this period.

(c) WIND

Fig. 1*b* shows a wind speed-time cross-section for the 2-16 m layer of atmosphere, also based on 20-min means. The wind direction at 16 m is also shown. There is a significant association between wind minima and cooling events. There is also some

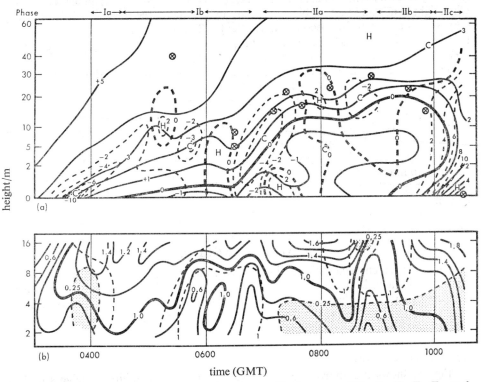

FIG. 1.—(*a*) Temperature-time cross-section based upon 20 min means of T_0, T_2, T_4, T_8, T_{16} and observations of temperature up to 60 m made at irregular intervals with a balloon-borne thermistor. The ordinate is linear in $\sqrt{\text{height}}$. Full lines are isotherms at intervals of 1°C. Dotted lines are approximate isopleths of local heating and cooling rates at intervals of 2°C/h. Observations of fog top height: H, maximum heating zone; C, maximum cooling zone. (*b*) Time cross-section of wind speed, based upon 20 min means of wind speed at 2, 4, 8, 16 m. The ordinate is linear in log (height). Full lines are isotachs at intervals of 0.2 m s⁻¹. Uniform separation of isotachs in the vertical indicate regions of log-linear wind profile. The dotted lines indicate the approximate field of gradient Richardson number between 2 and 16 m.

tendency for wind minima to be associated with wind veer. It follows that wind minima also occurred during the periods of fog development (transitions from phase I to II, and II*a* to II*b*). The shape of the wind profile does not in general conform to a log-linear shape, although there is (except for short periods) a general increase of wind with height. Wind speed averaged about 0.8 m s⁻¹ at 2 m increasing to 1.3 m s⁻¹ at 16 m.

(d) TURBULENCE

The wind and temperature structure of the atmosphere near the ground, when averaged over about an hour, is a function of, and can therefore be used to give approximate information on, the statistical properties of the turbulent field. For instance, it should be possible to infer the magnitudes of the turbulent fluxes of heat, water vapour and momentum. In the lowest 50-100 m, it is usually found (and assumed) that these fluxes are constant with height, and would not therefore change the quantity of heat, momentum and water vapour contained in a given layer. This is usually known as the " constant flux " layer. However, in the case under discussion, when light winds and very stable conditions are prevalent, the turbulent field becomes very weak and may in fact become intermittent. The profiles of wind and temperature (particularly wind) become so irregular and variable, that it is no longer possible to fit them to any existing model of low level turbulence.

Direct observations of turbulent fluxes are difficult if not impossible to make and so the exchange coefficient can only be estimated from indirect methods. In fig. 1b, isopleths of the gradient Richardson number is shown. Basically, this represents the ratio of buoyancy forces (which inhibit vertical displacements of the atmosphere) and inertial forces (which tend to overturn the air through wind shear). When this number is less than about $\frac{1}{4}$, turbulence will be generally prevalent; when it is greater than about unity, turbulence has probably ceased throughout most of the volume and is confined to intermittent patches. Also, over half the total wind change with height is confined below 2 m which is probably the depth of the " constant flux " layer on this occasion.

The order of magnitude of the exchange coefficient can be obtained using scale analysis based on Fickian diffusion law, e.g.,

$$\Delta T/\Delta t = K\Delta T/(\Delta z)^2, \tag{4.1}$$

where $\Delta T/\Delta t$ is a characteristic heating rate (with the radiative contribution removed), Δz is the characteristic vertical dimension over which ΔT is observed to occur, e.g., $\Delta T/\Delta t \approx 3°C\ h^{-1}$. A change of ΔT of 3°C is observed typically over a depth of 3-10 m which gives $K \approx 10^{-2}\ m^2\ s^{-1}$. This gives a value on which to base numerical modelling of the case.

(e) FOG STRUCTURE

Fig. 2a shows the approximate time variation of the visibility at heights of 1 m (solid line) and 5 m (dashed line) above the ground. This evidence, taken together with the fog top and the radiation observations (Fig. 1a) suggest that in phase I, the opacity of the fog decreased rapidly with height, and the top was ill-defined and variable in height. In phase II, the fog top became well-defined and identified with the radiation inversion. No obvious correlation between visibility and other meteorological parameters has been found.

The radiation observations show that radiative cooling (H_R in fig. 3) was generally small in phase I, but became large in phase II. Hence the terms " optically thin " and " optically thick ". During the latter phase, the fog top lay between the upper two radiometers, and H_R in this layer (the " upper layer ") remained high throughout the phase. In phase IIb the layer appeared to be in radiative equilibrium, ($H_R \approx 0$) suggesting that the fog above this layer had become optically opaque, thus shielding the lower layer from further cooling. The drop-size distribution (fig. 2b) shows the development of a secondary peak in droplet sizes in the radius range 5-10 μm during phase II, and is mainly responsible for the increase in liquid water concentration to about 0.2 g m^{-3} in this phase.

Both the liquid water concentration and the optical extinction coefficient can be explained in terms of the observed droplet population. The number of cloud condensation nuclei (30-100 cm^{-3}) observed at 0.8 % supersaturation was of the same order as the total number of droplets in the large droplet peak. The infra-red extinction coefficient in a vertical direction could be approximately inferred from the radiation observations. In phase IIa, this agreed roughly with that expected if the drop size distribution and liquid water concentration observed near ground level persisted throughout the depth of the fog.

The holography results are summarized in fig. 4. The co-ordinates of each identifiable drop within a volume of 10 cm³ was tabulated, and for each drop the distance of its nearest neighbour was obtained and a histogram constructed. Two of the histograms shown are taken from the fog sampled, a third from hill cloud on a mountain in Wales, and the fourth represents the results of a Monte-Carlo-type

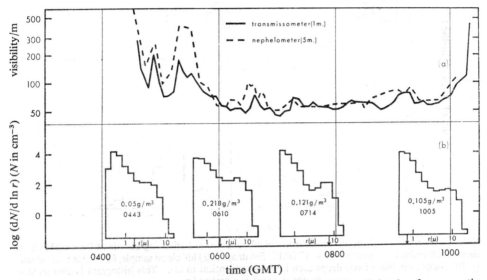

FIG. 2.—(a) Time plots of transmissometer (V_1) and nephelometer (V_5). V_1 is taken from a continuous trace. V_5 is taken from spot observations at variable intervals. (b) The histograms are drop-size distributions with the equivalent total liquid water content and time of observation written on each histogram.

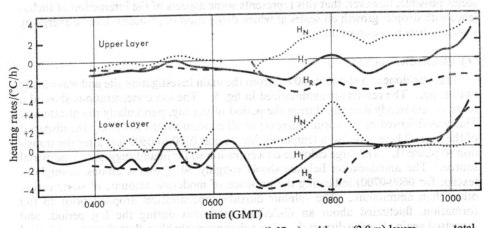

FIG. 3.—Observed heating rates averaged over upper (9-37 m) and lower (2-9 m) layers. ——— total heating rate H_T; – – –, radiative heating rate H_R; ....., non-radiative heating rate H_N.

numerical experiment which simulated the " nearest neighbour " computation shown above, except that the space co-ordinates of each droplet was chosen at random.

The difference between the random experiments and the observations is large, with discrepancies amounting to an order of magnitude for drop separation less than about 0.5 mm. In fact, on one sample of 600 drops, two droplet pairs separated by 50-100 μm was observed. The probability of this occurring at random appears to be of the

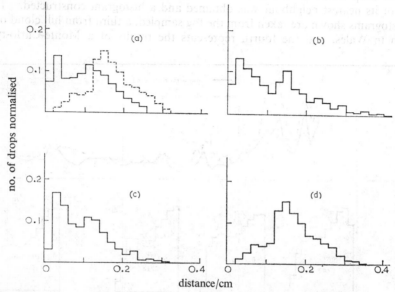

FIG. 4.—Histograms of distance to nearest neighbour : (a) radiation fog sample at 0500 GMT, 609 drops ; (b) radiation fog sample at 0647 GMT, 536 drops ; (c) hill cloud sample, 639 drops ; (d) mean of 10 random samples of 609 drops each in volume identical to (a). This histogram is also super-imposed on (a) as a dashed line.

order of 1 in 10^9. The implications of this clustering of droplets for fog investigations in particular and cloud microphysics in general cannot, at present, be assessed. It seems possible, however, that this represents some aspects of the interaction of turbulence with droplet growth on scales at which dissipation of turbulent kinetic energy by viscosity becomes important.

(f) CHEMICAL SAMPLING

This was done at a site some 800 m from the main investigation site and was mostly out of fog. The results are summarized in fig. 5. The ion concentrations showed a more or less steady decrease during the period of the fog, particularly the nitrate ion. This was followed by an abrupt increase in all concentrations following the dispersal of the fog. There was also a temporary increase at 0700 to 0800 just after the transition to phase II. The large chloride concentration so far inland suggests an industrial source. The anion–cation balance shows roughly 30 % excess anions throughout (except for 0600-0700) indicating the presence of moderate amounts of some cation other than ammonium. The sulphur dioxide concentration dropped prior to fog formation, fluctuated about an ill-defined minimum during the fog period, and increased again after fog dispersal. These changes probably reflect changes in vertical mixing which appears to be a minimum during the fog period, although it may also reflect the scavenging action of fog droplet deposition to some degree. No chemical analysis of fog water was undertaken on this exercise.

(g) HEAT AND WATER BUDGET

The net flux of radiation was measured at levels of 2, 9 and 37 m. These levels defined two layers, an upper and a lower layer. The measured radiative heating H_R and observed total heating rate H_T of these layers are shown in fig. 3. The difference

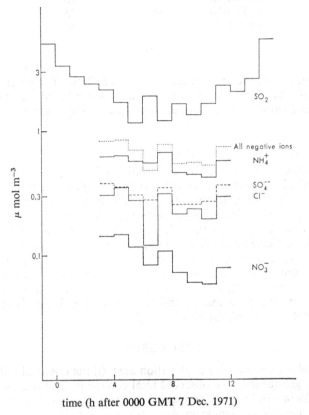

time (h after 0000 GMT 7 Dec. 1971)

FIG. 5.—Variations of concentrations in micro-equivalents/m³ of five atmospheric species with time. For SO_2, the quantity plotted is twice the concentration in microequivalents/m³.

$(H_R - H_T) = H_N$, where H_N must be attributed to convergence of eddy heat flux, or to latent heat release, or to both. The principal feature of fig. 3 is the overall tendency for the radiative cooling to be greater than the observed cooling (H_N positive)—an observation also reported by Rider and Robinson.

The cooling of the lowest 50 m or so of an initially-saturated atmosphere during the period of interest implies a removal of an amount of water vapour by condensation which can be directly estimated by using the Clausius–Clapeyron relationship and is compared with the lysimeter data in table 2 below. While the overall totals of condensed water are roughly in agreement, the totals over shorter periods are not. The liquid water content of the fog accounts for only a few per cent of the total.

The rate of water deposition on the surface is normally taken as a measure of the latent heat flux at the surface. This assumption cannot be made in fog as much of the water may be condensed as fog droplets (thus releasing its latent heat directly to the atmosphere) and then water is transferred to the ground by some mechanism other

TABLE 2.—ESTIMATES OF CONDENSED WATER

period (approx.)	condensed water/g m⁻² cooling	lysimeter
0400-0630	50	20
0630-0730	20	10
0730-0830	small	25
0830-1000	5	10
	75	65

than dew deposition—particularly in the period after 0730. The observed deposition velocity (defined here as the rate of deposition of water/liquid water concentration at 1 m) is about 2 cm s^{-1}. Gravitational settling can only account for 0.5-1 cm s^{-1} of this.

(h) QUASI-PERIODIC OSCILLATIONS

Another unexpected result was the observation of intermittent periods of marked oscillations of 10-12 min period in several of the meteorological parameters measured, notably wind speed, surface temperature and downward radiation intensity (from directional radiometer). Similar oscillations appeared occasionally in temperature at high levels, apparently when these levels were lying in the radiation inversion. The traces of these elements are shown in fig. 6. A possible interpretation of these fluctuations gives some account of the observed phase relationships. The oscillations are attributed to gravity wave propagation, and the phenomenon can be regarded as a demonstration of the varying balance between radiation and turbulence—the latter being controlled by the wind speed oscillations while the former is influenced by a sympathetic oscillation of the fog depth.

DISCUSSION

The principal results requiring explanation are : (i) the observed radiative cooling was, in general, greater than the observed total cooling in the lowest 40 m of atmosphere. (ii) Lulls in wind were accompanied by maxima in cooling, while major lulls coincided with periods of significant fog onset and development. (iii) The water condensed on cooling appears to have been mainly deposited on the ground. The water content of the fog was always a small fraction of the total water condensed out. (iv) The presence of quasi-periodic oscillations. (v) The clustering of droplets in space.

Some of these features have been reported by earlier workers. They all point to the fundamental role played by turbulence and show that the lack of a satisfactory account of the water budget remains a central problem, for on this rests an account of the heat budget and the role that microphysics plays in fog development.

The problem may be examined by considering the conventional one-dimensional equations for the heat and water budget. These are :

Heat :

$$\frac{\partial T}{\partial t} = -\frac{1}{\rho c_p}\frac{\partial F}{\partial z} + \frac{\partial}{\partial z}\left(K\frac{\partial T}{\partial z}\right) + \frac{LC}{c_p}, \tag{5.1}$$

Water vapour:

$$\frac{\partial x}{\partial t} = \frac{\partial}{\partial z}\left(K\frac{\partial x}{\partial z}\right) - C,$$ (5.2)

Liquid water:

$$\frac{\partial w}{\partial t} = \frac{\partial}{\partial z}\left(K\frac{\partial w}{\partial z}\right) + C,$$ (5.3)

Where t = time, z = vertical co-ordinate, T = temperature, ρ = air density, c_p = specific heat at constant pressure, F = net flux of radiation, K = exchange coefficient (assumed the same for heat, water vapour and momentum), L = latent heat of vaporization of water, C = rate of condensation per unit mass of air, x = humidity mixing ratio, w = liquid water mixing ratio.

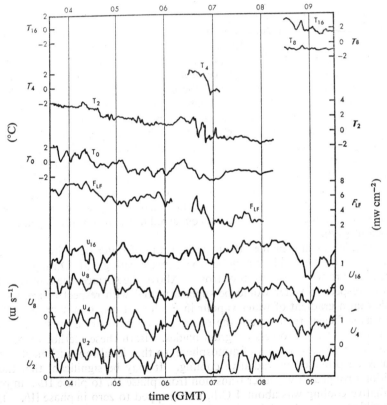

Fig. 6.—Time plots for selected periods of the following parameters: $T_0, T_2, T_4, T_8, T_{16}, F_{LF}$ based on spot readings at 1-min intervals. $U_2, U_4, U_8, U_{16}, D_{16}$ based on 2-min runs of wind.

Eqn (5.1) represents local rate of change of temperature due to radiative heating, turbulent diffusion and condensation. Eqn (5.2) and (5.3) represent local changes in the gaseous and liquid phases of water due to turbulent diffusion and condensation. Gravitational settling is ignored.

First, one may try and establish a condition whereby the atmosphere is maintained exactly at saturation with no liquid water present, and then to study deviations from this. We do this by assuming the condensation term to be zero, and eqn (5.3) also becomes identically zero. In this case, $x(= x_s$, the saturation mixing ratio) is a function of T only through the Clausius–Clapeyron relationship, hence

$$\partial x_s/\partial t = x\partial T/\partial t; \quad \partial x_s/\partial z = X\partial T/\partial z, \tag{5.4}$$

where $X = dx_s/dT$. Substituting eqn (5.4) into (5.2) and combining with (5.1) leads to

$$\mathscr{R} = K\frac{\partial T}{\partial z}\frac{\partial \ln x}{\partial z}, \tag{5.5}$$

where

$$\mathscr{R} = -\frac{1}{\rho c_p}\frac{\partial F}{\partial z};$$

represents radiative heating rate.

Eqn (5.5) can only be balanced when $\mathscr{R}$ is positive since the terms on the right-hand side are essentially positive. But $\mathscr{R}$ is observed to be negative; physically, this means that because the mixing ratio has been taken as a monotonic function of temperature, an eddy flux convergence of sensible heat is incompatible with an eddy flux divergence of water vapour. Thus, the condensation and latent heat terms have to be re-introduced, and condensation rates of the order of 1 g m^{-3} h^{-1} are needed to balance the equations for typical values of the relevant parameters. Since the liquid water content of the fog is never greater than about 0.2 g m^{-3}, this implies that the " life " of an individual droplet is of around 10 min before arriving at the surface.

While the surface inversion is on the ground, this balance can reasonably be accomplished by dew deposition, but in phase II, this seems to be no longer possible since the mechanism for dew deposition is removed. Further cooling should therefore condense water directly into the atmosphere and produce a very dense fog. There is some indirect evidence that this occurred at the top of the fog in phase IIb as discussed in §3(e).

This still leaves unexplained the increased rate of water deposition on the surface during phase II. Some ideas may be worth investigating. (i) During this phase II, surface moisture was in the form of frost. Above the surface, the atmosphere saturated with respect to water would be supersaturated with respect to ice, so that it is possible that a gradient of water vapour in the lowest metre may have been induced which was sufficient to maintain the observed deposition rate in the form of frost. (ii) Impaction of fog droplets on grass blades. Both these methods would quickly dry out the lowest few metres of atmosphere, so that local replenishment is required. This may be provided by radiative cooling. It may be significant that the rate of deposition dropped slowly after transition from phase IIa to phase IIb; in phase IIa, the radiative cooling was about 4°C/h, but dropped to zero in phase IIb. Thus, it is not possible to state what determines the total liquid water content of the fog, or why it develops when it does without considering the role of microphysics.

The balance required to keep the atmosphere within 0.1 % of 100 % relative humidity corresponds to a temperature-dew point difference not exceeding about 0.02°C—a change which will take place in about 20 s with normally observed rates of heating or cooling in the lowest few metres of the atmosphere under these conditions. This balance seems to be too fine in view of the considerable fluctuations in wind and therefore of turbulent diffusion which take place, and it seems likely that an already-present droplet population may exert the main control on the relative humidity by release or absorption of latent heat as required.

(a) ROLE OF ADVECTION

The approach both in designing the observational programme and in the discussion has been deliberately one-dimensional.   However, this is not to deny the existence of horizontal inhomogeneities which must be considered in relation to the scale on which the relevant processes operate.

It is a common observation that radiation fog forms more or less simultaneously over an area of mesoscale dimensions (say up to 100 km) implying that the vertical structure of the atmosphere is the main factor in the development of fog.

On the scale of hundreds of metres to km, on the other hand, there are always considerable spatial fluctuations of fog structure for which variations in the nature and slope of the local terrain are at least partly responsible, and will produce mesoscale circulations which are likely to control temporal fluctuations in parameters observed at a fixed point over time intervals of up to a few minutes.   In the absence of two-dimensional measurements, it becomes increasingly likely that observed changes are due to advection rather than development, the shorter the period over which the change takes place.   A useful time scale is defined by D/U, where D is the depth of the fog and U is the mean wind speed in the fog.   (In this case-study, this is about 30 s).   Providing a change takes place over a time $t \gg D/U$, then it is reasonable to ascribe it to development.

6. CONCLUSIONS

The development of fog is roughly controlled by a balance between radiation, which encourages fog, and turbulence, which appears to inhibit it, while fine control is exerted by a balance between the humidity and the droplet population.   Quantitative details of these balances must await further resolution of the details of the water balance.   One result which may prove useful in assessing future prospects of local forecasting or modification of fog is that, given a saturated atmosphere and radiative cooling, rapid development of fog is likely to occur if the wind speed drops below about 0.5 m s^{-1} at 2 m above ground.   Any conclusions which are based on one case study must be tentative, but these results do demonstrate the complexity of the competing and interacting physical processes which result in meteorological fogs.

Field Projects of this type involve a large number of participants and we gratefully acknowledge the support of all our colleagues.   This paper is published by permission of the Director General of the Meteorological Office.

[1] K. H. Stewart, Air Ministry, Met. Res. Cttee (1955), paper 912, 43 pp.
[2] K. H. Stewart, Air Ministry, Met. Res. Cttee (1957), paper 1074, 26 pp.
[3] G. I. Taylor, Quart. J. Roy. Met. Soc., 1917, 43, 241.
[4] J. L. Monteith, Quart. J. Roy. Met. Soc., 1957, 83, p. 322.
[5] N. E. Rider and G. D. Robinson, Quart. J. Roy. Met. Soc., 1951, 77, 375.
[6] J. P. Funk, Quart. J. Roy. Met. Soc., 1962, 88, 233.
[7] K. W. Pavitt, M. C. Jackson, R. J. Adams and J. T. Bartlett, J. Phys. E, 1970, 3, 971.
[8] J. A. Garland, Quart. J. Roy. Met. Soc., 1971, 97, 483.
[9] J. A. Garland and J. B. Rae, J. Phys. E, 1970, 3, 275.
[10] A. E. J. Eggleton and D. M. F. Atkins, A.E.R.E., R 6983 (1972).

Predicting the Concentration of Effluent Material within a Plume Emitted from a Tall Chimney

By D. J. Moore

Central Electricity Research Laboratories, Leatherhead, Surrey

Received 23rd November, 1972

The rates of formation of aerosols and the visual appearance of chimney plumes (including the effects of condensation of water vapour) both depend upon the dilution of the effluent gases. This dilution differs from that predicted by conventional dispersion formulae in that these latter refer to time mean concentrations, whereas what is required is the dilution at any given instant in time as the plume travels downwind.

The instantaneous dilution near the source depends on the turbulence induced by the plume's movement through the atmosphere, rather than the dispersive properties of the surrounding atmosphere at the plume level.

A theoretical/empirical model, which has been developed to predict the trajectory of hot chimney plumes, also predicts this instantaneous dilution. Dilutions calculated by this method in different conditions of wind speed and atmospheric stability for various plant emission characteristics are tabulated and compared with values obtained from field measurements.

---

1.   INTRODUCTION

If one is concerned with the concentration of material at ground level resulting from the emission from a source which is some distance away, the normal practice is to sample the material over a period of time. It is then possible, with the aid of various hypotheses about the nature of the dispersion of the material and possibly the rise of the plume material above the discharge point due to its buoyancy and initial vertical momentum, to come to a reasonably satisfactory understanding, in physical terms, of the observed concentration.

There are, however, certain aspects of plume behaviour, including the rise of the plume, the visibility of the plume and rates of chemical reactions within the plume, which depend not on the time-averaged concentrations, but on the concentration within the plume at various distances downwind at an instant in time. The time-averaged plume dimensions are the result of the meanderings of the instantaneous plume due to the large scale turbulence in the atmosphere and may bear little relation to the instantaneous dimensions. Furthermore, the dilution of any large emission of material, certainly within the first few hundred metres of its leaving the source, is almost entirely due to its motion relative to the atmosphere and the intense mixing produced by this relative motion. Thus, any information which is based on observation of the dispersion of small releases of material over extended periods of time, such as the Porton work reported by Sutton [1] is irrelevant to the problems enumerated above.

In the various attempts to explain the observed trajectories of buoyant plumes over the first kilometre or so of their path, observations of the instantaneous dimensions have been made, either from photographs [2] or from lidar [3, 4] traverses of the plume. These have, in general, shown that the plume diameter, in so far as it can be determined from the irregular shape of the plume elements, is, on a given occasion,

222

proportional to the height of rise above the source. For a plume with substantial heat emission (i.e., several MW or more) this relation appears to hold for hundreds of metres and perhaps even to over 1 km on some occasions.[2]

This sort of behaviour is consistent with the assumption that the rate of entrainment of ambient air into the plume elements is equal to the product of the surface area of plume element exposed to the ambient air, times the velocity of the plume relative to the ambient air. That is, in general, to the vertical velocity of the element. The constant of proportionality implicit in the above relationship is, in fact, a constant for a given plume element only; its value changes from element to element in a way which is not fully understood, but appears to be determined by such factors as the angle of attack of the wind at the stack top, the ratio of the wind speed to the effiux velocity and the initial buoyancy and its relation to wind forces on the emerging plume.

Despite the complexity of the problem, a number of investigators have developed models which give a very fair representation of the plume trajectories over distances out to 1 km or more. The principal differences between the models concern the idealised geometrical forms assumed for the plume elements, e.g., bent-over cones,[5-7] chains of spherical puffs [8, 9] and the expression for the relative velocity, which sometimes includes additions to the vertical velocity, with various weighting factors.[10, 11] The other source of difference is the assumptions made about the way in which the atmospheric turbulence eventually assumes the major role in the dispersion when the plume elements have become so diffuse that their physical properties (i.e., turbulence and density) are no longer distinguishable from those of the surrounding air.

A comprehensive test of a trajectory equation based on the recombining plume model has been shown [18] to give mean errors of around 10-15 % in determining plume heights over a wide range of meterological conditions, distances downwind and plant capacities. In this short paper it is not intended to explore in any depth the difference between the various plume models. They are sufficiently similar for the differences between them to be relatively small compared with the differences between concentrations calculated from their basic assumptions and concentrations calculated for an inert plume model. Here we shall show where the use of such a model, which assumes that the plume behaves as though it were no different from the surrounding atmosphere as far as dispersive properties are concerned, will lead to serious over estimates of " in-plume " concentrations.

2. THE INERT PLUME

We consider the dimensions at any instant in its time of travel of an element of the plume which contains material which has been emitted into the atmosphere without in any way changing its dispersive properties. For an emission of any size, this is clearly impossible and furthermore, if we consider a true point source with a finite emission the concentration at the source is infinite. In practice, stack emissions are usually diluted with air, or at least nitrogen, so that the material is apparently emanating from a point source some distance upstream of the actual source.

The familiar gaussian distribution of material is, in fact, due mainly to the meanderings of the plume axis over the period during which the effluent is being sampled. Most truly instantaneous traverses of the plume, e.g., by laser rangefinder, indicate a " top-hat " distribution of material, but then the traversed plumes have not been inert. Some attempts to calculate instantaneous dimensions from smoke puff photographs (e.g., by Gifford [12]) have made assumptions about the distribution of material in the plume.

If we consider that the instantaneous plume has a "top hat" distribution of material, that the axis of the time-average plumes remains within the instantaneous plume for most of a given sampling period, but points removed vertically or in the cross wind direction are out of the plume for an increasing proportion of the period as one moves away from the axis, then one could represent the instantaneous concentration by the axial concentration of the meandering time-average plume. This would give an underestimate of the instantaneous plume concentration, because the time-average axis would occasionally be out of the plume. However, for purposes of comparison with the self-diluting plume models, it will be assumed that the axial concentration in the time-average plume for sampling times of several minutes is a reasonable estimate of the average concentration within the plume elements.

Such concentrations as functions of distance from the source or time of travel through the atmosphere may be readily estimated from the data presented, e.g., by Pasquill[13] and reproduced in convenient graphical form as in "Meterology and Atomic Energy".[14]

Following Pasquill[15] we write an expression for this axial concentration:

$$C_1 = Q(x_1^{p+q})/(2\pi x^{p+q} \overline{U} \sigma_{z1} \sigma_{y1}) \qquad (2.1)$$

where C_1 is the axial concentration (units m^{-3}) at distance x/m downwind. Q is the rate of emission of the material considered (units s^{-1}). x_1 is the distance downwind at which the vertical and cross wind concentration distributions have standard deviations σ_{z1} and σ_{y1} respectively (m). $\overline{U}$ is the mean wind speed (m s^{-1}). p and q are numerical constants whose values lie between 0.5 and 1.0. If we wish to substitute time of travel, t, in place of distance x then we replace x by $\overline{U}t$ in eqn (2.1).

Eqn (2.1) may be written in the form

$$C_1 = (Q/Q_h)Q_h/(Bx^{p+q}\overline{U}) \qquad (2.2)$$

where $B = 2\pi\sigma_{z1}\sigma_{y1}/(x_1^{p+q})$ and may be regarded as a constant on any given occasion, but whose value will vary with meterological conditions. $Q_h = $ the rate of heat emission in MW.

Expressing the concentration in the form given by eqn (2.2) is convenient for comparison with the concentrations deduced for buoyant plumes which follow in section 3 below.

3. BUOYANT PLUME

For the sake of simplicity, we consider a plume of material with the same density at ambient temperature and pressure as the ambient air, emitted into an atmosphere in which the potential density (i.e., the density referred to a standard pressure) is not changing with height.

The simpler plume models then indicate that the concentration of material within a plume element is given by

$$C_2 = Q_h (Q/Q_h)/(Az^m\overline{U}) \qquad (3.1)$$

where C_2 is the concentration in a plume element which has risen a height z above the source. m is a numerical constant with a value between 2 and 3 depending on the assumed nature of the plume elements (i.e., 2 if they are conical or cylindrical, 3 if they are spherical or any other closed configuration). A may be a constant if the heat content of a plume element is assumed to remain invariant with distance from the source, or may be a function of distance if the heat content of the element is changing with distance. Its dimensions are m^{2-m}. It may be a function of the wind speed.   The various expressions for plume rise in the above assumed meterological conditions are of the form [18]

$$z = A_1 Q_h^r x^s / U \qquad (3.2)$$

if one ignores the initial momentum of the plume and assumes that the rate of entrainment is proportional to the vertical velocity.

Here r is a numerical constant equal to $\frac{1}{3}$ for the two dimensional (conical etc.) models and $\frac{1}{4}$ for the 3-dimensional (spherical etc.,) models. s is a numerical constant with values between $\frac{1}{2}$ and $\frac{3}{4}$ and A_1 is a parameter equal to $(g/\rho_e C_p \theta)^r A_2$ where g is the acceleration of gravity (m s^{-2}), C_p is the specific heat at constant pressure of the effluent (MJ kg^{-1} K^{-1}), ρ_e is the density of the ambient air (kg m^{-3}), θ is the absolute temperature of the ambient air reduced to standard pressure (K), A_2 is a parameter of dimensions (m s^{-1})$^{-(3r-1)}$m$^{(1-(r+s))}$, which represents the effect of such factors as the initial length of plume material within a plume element and the dependence of the rate of entrainment factor on the wind speed, etc.   Substituting for z in eqn (3.1) from eqn (3.2) we arrive at

$$C_2 = (Q/Q_h) Q_h^{1-mr} / (A_3 x^{ms} \overline{U}^{1-m}) \qquad (3.3)$$

where

$$A_3 = A A_1^m.$$

The buoyant plume model used above would estimate the maximum dilution due to relative motion at a given distance downwind.   If the atmosphere were stably stratified (i.e., the potential density were decreasing with height) then the plume would rise less rapidly than eqn (3.2) indicates, the difference becoming more marked as the distance from the source increased.   For practical purposes it would be sufficient to assume that the plume followed eqn (3.2) out to some distance x_T, where x_T is proportional to the stability parameter $((g/\rho_e \overline{U}^2) \, | \, (\partial \rho_e / \partial z) \, |)^{\frac{1}{2}}$ and is roughly equal to 120 $\overline{U}$ m [18] for isothermal conditions in light winds.

If one is concerned with a plume of gas with a density at ambient temperature and pressure which differs appreciably from that of air, then Q_h in eqn (3.1), (3.2) and (3.3) may be replaced by the term $(\dot{V} \Delta \rho C_p \theta)$, where $\dot{V}$ is the total volume rate of emission of the effluent (m^3 s^{-1}) (i.e., of all the gases being emitted from the stack, not just the material being considered), $\Delta \rho$ is the difference in density between the ambient air and the effluent (kg m^{-3}).

4.   COMPARISON OF INERT AND BUOYANT PLUME MODELS

The ratio of the plume concentrations calculated from the inert and buoyant plume models mentioned above may be obtained from eqn (2.2) and (3.3) and is equal to

$$C_1 / C_2 = Q_h^{mr} A_3 / (B x^{(p+q-ms)} \overline{U}^m). \qquad (4.1)$$

If we wish to use the dilution given by the buoyant plume model out to a distance x_E where the value of C_1 / C_2 is equal to 1 and the inert plume dilution beyond this distance, then x_E is given by

$$x_E = Q_h^{(mr/(p+q-ms))} (A_3/B)^{(1/(p+q-ms))} / \overline{U}^{(m/(p+q-ms))}. \qquad (4.2)$$

The equivalent time of travel to x_E, t_E, will be

$$t_E = x_E / \overline{U} = Q_h^{(mr/(p+q-ms))} (A_3/B)^{(1/(p+q-ms))} / \overline{U}^{(m(1-s)+p+q)/(p+q-ms)}. \qquad (4.3)$$

Eqn (4.2) and (4.3) are valid only if A_3 is not a function of distance from the source and/or wind speed. In some of the models, e.g., the recombining plume model, A_3 is in fact assumed to be proportional to $\overline{U}$ and inversely proportional to x. In this case

$$t_E = (A_4/B)^4 Q_h^3 \overline{U}^{-9}$$

where $A_3 = A_4 \overline{U}/x$.

Although expressions like (4.3) appear rather complicated, their interpretation is fairly straightforward. All the models indicate that the term in the denominator of the exponents is small, i.e., ms is only slightly smaller than $p+q$ (or $(1+p+q)$ in the case of the recombining plume model). The term mr is, however, a fairly large fraction and the numerator of the exponent of $\overline{U}$ is about 2. This means that t_E varies rapidly (i.e., as the third or fourth power) of Q_h and even more rapidly (i.e., as the ninth or greater power) of $1/\overline{U}$. Hence, for practical purposes, there are wide ranges of low wind speeds and high heat emissions where the buoyant plume model is valid for calculating concentrations, while the dispersion or inert plume model may be used in strong winds for most sources and in all but the lightest winds for very small sources.

Since, by the same reasoning, eqn (4.1) indicates that C_1/C_2 is a very slowly varying function of distance from the source (or time of travel), it follows that in border-line cases either model may be used over a considerable range of time or distance without serious error.

The precise values of plume concentrations for given values of $\overline{U}$ and Q_h will depend on the values chosen for A_3 or A_4 and B, and the parameters p, q, m, r and s, i.e., on the plume rise and dispersion models used.

Table 1 shows some values of the concentrations calculated from eqn (2.2) using values of $p+q$ and B consistent with plume dimensions *at several kilometres* from the sources, and from eqn (3.3) using the plume rise equation of Briggs [8] C_2(BR) and Lucas [16] C_2(LU) (see Pasquill [15]), modified to take account of distance down-wind, but not of stability or atmospheric turbulence. [18]

The plume rise model has relatively little effect on the calculated concentrations, but the dilutions in light winds are very much greater than with the inert plume model, when one is considering the large heat sources, even though the dispersion parameters used are appropriate to unstable meteorological conditions.

In very stable conditions, the buoyant plume dilutions would remain effectively constant after something like 120 $\overline{U}$ m or so of travel (i.e., 120 s in a 1 m s^{-1} wind). Even so the plumes are much more diffuse than the inert plumes; consequently serious errors could be made both in estimates of plume visibility and in chemical reaction rates in plumes if the inert models were used in these sort of conditions. Taking 1 m s^{-1} as the worst condition, concentrations at 120 m downwind would be 1652 and 1181 p.p.h.m. for the C_2(BR) and C_2(LU) models respectively. Atmospheric dilution might be considered negligible in these conditions, and the plumes would then drift downwind with little further dilution. Size of source would have comparatively little effect since eqn (3.3) shows C_2 varies as a small power of Q_h, but the concentration is directly proportional to the SO_2/MJ ratio.

5. COMPARISON WITH EXPERIMENTAL DATA

Comprehensive data on peak concentrations of SO_2 at several km from the Keystone Power Plant are available. The ratio of SO_2/MJ was about 0.8 times that assumed in table 1 and the plant was emitting heat at an average rate of 100 MW during the period of the measurement (1967–69).[20] $C_2(BR)$ and $C_2(LU)$ would be about $0.8(\frac{1}{3})^{\frac{1}{3}}$ and $0.8(\frac{1}{3})^{\frac{1}{4}}$ times the concentration at the same time of travel for the 300 MW source in table 1, i.e., 916 and 717 p.p.h.m. for 120 s travel at 1 m s^{-1}. With these emission conditions, the highest concentration observed in the plume was in fact 767 p.p.h.m. at 4.8 km downwind on 30th October, 1967. At 10 km the concentration peak was 352 p.p.h.m. Winds as light as 0.6 m s^{-1} were recorded by pilot balloon ascent on that day.

Pasquill Category F would give a concentration of 1940 p.p.h.m. and Category E about 850 p.p.h.m. at 4.8 km and 707 p.p.h.m. and 296 p.p.h.m. respectively at 10 km.

It appears, therefore, either that Category F type of dispersion is never observed from an elevated plume (or observed so seldom that several years' measurements

TABLE 1.—CONCENTRATION (p.p.h.m.) vol/vol SO$_2$ FROM A SOURCE EMITTING 0.008 m^3 (REDUCED TO S.T.P.) OF SO$_2$ PER MJ OF HEAT EMITTED

	$Q_h = 300$ MW ; $\bar{U} = 1$ m s^{-1}			
time	$C_1(US)$	$C_2(BR)*$	$C_2(LU)*$	$C_1(ST)$
250	3342	621	472	954 930
500	1181	246	198	244 850
750	643	143	119	119 740
1000	418	98	83	77 320
2000	148	39	35	25 610

		$\bar{U} = 7$ m s^{-1}	
time	C_1	$C_2(BR)$	$C_2(LU)$
250	352	324	290
500	125	129	122
750	68	75	73
1000	44	51	51
2000	16	20	21

	$Q_h = 10$ MW ; $\bar{U} = 1$ m s^{-1}			
time	$C_1(US)$	$C_2(BR)*$	$C_2(LU)*$	$C_1(ST)$
250	158	200	201	31 830
500	56	79	85	8 160
750	30	46	51	3 991
1000	20	31	36	2 577
2000				854

C_2 values are calculated from the buoyant plume model using the following numerical values :

$C_2(BR)$ corresponds to the two-dimensional bent over cone type of plume model advocated by Briggs and others :

$C_2(LU)$ corresponds to the Priestley [17] type model of Lucas [16] and the recombining plume model of Moore [8, 9]

$C_2(BR) = Q/((0.426z)^2\pi\bar{U})$, where $z = 3.1Q_h^{\frac{1}{4}}x^{\frac{3}{4}}/\bar{U}$ which with the assumed relation between SO$_2$ and heat emission gives $C_2(BR) = 146\,014Q_h^{\frac{1}{2}}\bar{U}^{-\frac{1}{2}}t^{-\frac{3}{2}}$:

$C_2(LU) = 3Qx/(16(0.313z)^3\pi\bar{U}^2)$, where $z = 2.4Q_h^{\frac{1}{4}}x^{\frac{3}{4}}/\bar{U}$ which gives $C_2(LU) = 112\,635Q_h^{\frac{1}{2}}\bar{U}^{-\frac{1}{4}}t^{-\frac{1}{4}}$ p.p.h.m.

Taking $Bx_i^{\frac{3}{4}} = 2\pi(0.08L^{\frac{1}{4}}(7/U)^{\frac{1}{4}})$,[19] C_1 was equal to $556\,921Q_h/(t^{\frac{3}{4}}\bar{U}^2L^{\frac{1}{4}})$ in unstable (US) conditions with $L = 160$ m for the large source ; and $L = 80$ m for the small source.[19] The Pasquill Category F values of σ_y and σ_z were used in stable (ST) conditions.[14]

* The values of $C_2(BR)$ and $C_2(LU)$ at 120 m downwind in a 1 m s^{-1} (i.e, after 120 s travel) would be 1652, 1181, 532 and 503 p.p.h.m. in columns 3, 4, 10 and 11 respectively. These conditions would represent the minimum dilution at greater distances in the most stable conditions.

fail to detect it) or that the extra dispersion caused by the relative motion has the effect of making the minimum observed dilution comparable with Category E at distances of around 5-10 km downwind of large sources.

Unfortunately, there do not appear to be any comprehensive " in-plume " measurements made closer to the stack, but the dimensions of the plume recorded by the various techniques described in section 1 above indicate that the concentrations predicted in table 1 by the buoyant plume models are more likely to be correct than the much higher concentrations predicted by dispersion models.

6. CONCLUSIONS

The calculations indicate that for large heat source, the dilution of buoyant plumes in light winds is much more rapid than the classical formulae would indicate. The effect is most noticeable in the early stages of the plume's travel, because the plume's motion relative to the surrounding air is then at its greatest and the dilution effected by this relative motion far exceeds the diluting effect of the turbulence in the surrounding air. In very stable conditions, most of the dilution probably occurs within a 100 m or so of the stack, because the plume rise is completed in this distance. Further dilution will proceed at a very slow rate, so that for practical purposes in-plume concentrations may be considered constant for several km after this initial rapid dilution. Even so, concentrations at all distances out to 10 km would be less than those indicated by a simple application of the Pasquill Category F curves.

In unstable conditions, the dilution produced by relative motion is also greater than that produced by atmospheric turbulence in light winds, close to the stack for large heat sources, but the atmospheric diluting mechanism will become important at a much earlier stage than it does in stable conditions.

When it is windy, both models (atmospheric dilution and buoyant plume) give roughly the same dilutions out to several km from the source.

The work was carried out at the Central Electricity Research Laboratories and the paper is published by permission of the Central Electricity Generating Board. The author is grateful to Dr. K. W. James and Mr. D. H. Lucas for helpful criticism.

[1] O. G. Sutton, *Atmospheric Turbulence*, (Methuen, London, 1949).
[2] *Tennessee Valley Authority Report, Full Scale Study of Plume Rise at Large Electric Generating Stations*, (T. V. A. Muscle Shoals, Alabama, 1968).
[3] P. M. Hamilton, *Phil. Trans. A*, 1969, **265**, 153.
[4] P. M. Hamilton, *Atmospheric Environment*, 1967, **1**, 370.
[5] C. H. Bosanquet, *J. Inst. Fuel.*, 1957, **30**, 322.
[6] R. S. Scorer, *Int. J. Air Pollution*, 1959, **1**, 198.
[7] G. A. Briggs, *Plume Rise* (U.S.A.E.C. Critical Review Series, 1969).
[8] D. J. Moore, *Int. J. Air and Water Polution*, 1966, **10**, 411.
[9] D. J. Moore, *Atmospheric Environment*, 1968, **2**, 247.
[10] D. P. Hoult, J. A. Fay and L. J. Forney, *J. Air Polution Control Assoc.*, 1969, **19**, 585.
[11] G. Ooms, *Atmospheric Environment*, 1972, **6**, 899.
[12] F. Gifford, *J. Meteorology*, 1957, **14**, 410.
[13] F. Pasquill, *Meterological Mag.*, 1961, **90**, 33.
[14] *Meteorology and Atomic Energy*, ed. D. Slade, (U.S.A.E.C., 1968).
[15] F. Pasquill, *Quart. J. Roy. Meteorological Soc.*, 1972, **97**, 369.
[16] D. H. Lucas, *Atmospheric Environment*, 1967, **1**, 421.
[17] C. H. B. Priestly, *Quart. J. Roy. Meteorological Soc.*, 1956, **82**, 165.
[18] D. J. Moore, *Atmospheric Environment*, 1974, **8**, 131.
[19] D. J. Moore, *Adv. Geophysics—Turbulent Diffusion in Atmospheric Pollution*, ed. F. N. Frenkiel and R. E. Munn (1974).
[20] *Tennessee Valley Authority Large Power Plane Effluent Study*, Vol. 1, 1967 and 1969, Vol. 2, 1968, (U.S. Dept. of Health, Education and Welfare, 1970).

Dr. A. Arrowsmith (*University of Birmingham*) said: In the experimental work on particle deposition, Williams has measured particle sizes and concentrations after sampling with a probe of 1 cm diam in the 10 cm diam. duct. At the entrance to the probe the gas/particle flow will be influenced by the flow in the duct, which will have component eddies of larger diameter than the probe. Also, assuming isokinetic sampling, the Reynolds number of the probe flow would be an order of magnitude less than that in the duct. Under such conditions, for what lengths of the probe is the flow affected by the duct flow and thereafter, it is possible that deposition may take place in the probe through mechanisms which are of a different nature or at least intensity to those which are the object of study.

Dr. Ian Williams (*Shell Res. Ltd., Chester*) (*communicated*): In reply to Arrow-smith, the measurements of interest in this experiment were the radial distribution of polydisperse droplets as a function of several parameters, including the axial position in the duct. It has been shown that particle deposition is strongly dependent upon the Reynolds number of the flow and the particle size. For the two values of Re. no. considered the corresponding values in the probe were an order of magnitude less than in the duct; this factor together with the short residence time of a droplet within the probe is effective in reducing deposition in the probe. Except near the duct wall the ratio of the fluid eddy diameter to the probe diameter is $\geqslant 1$, this probably results in near laminar flow within the probe and subsequent low droplet deposition. A correction factor was obtained experimentally to take into account deposition within the probe. Twelve sampling probes each of 1.0 cm i.d. and 0.5 cm i.d. respectively were used to sample an aerosol source of a known, constant, size distribution and concentration under similar dynamic conditions to those existing in the duct. A deposition factor was obtained as a function of droplet size, fluid Re. no., probe diameter and probe length. This factor was applied to all subsequent experimental measurements. Alternatively, it was possible to extrapolate the effect of the sampling probe to zero length and thus eliminate the effect of droplet deposition in the probe as a result.

Prof. C. S. Kiang (*Clark College, Atlanta, Ga.*), said: Is it possible to apply the experimental technique of Carabine and Moore to study the initial aerosol formation of aqueous sulphuric acid droplets (via the heteromolecular nucleation and hetero-molecular condensation)?

Dr. M. D. Carabine (*Imperial College*) said: In reply to Kiang, the angular varia-tion of scattered light intensity would not be sufficient if clusters of a few tens of molecules are being observed. We have indicated in the paper an approximate lower limit of 0.06 μm using He–Ne radiation.

Prof. M. Kerker (*Clarkson Coll. Techn., Potsdam, N.Y.*) said: Does Carabine have some experimental results to check the efficacy of his instrument? Our exper-ience with inverting light-scattering data for distributions as broad as $\sigma_0 = 0.50$ and $a_M = 0.40$ μm has been far less successful than he reported. Indeed, for this size, we find that the results become multivalued when $\sigma_0 > 0.20$. In studying the rate of growth of sulphuric acid aerosols in a humidified atmosphere,[1] we found it necessary to start with nearly 100 % H_2SO_4 in order to obtain concentrated sulphuric acid aerosols by the condensation technique.

Dr. A. Moore (*Imperial College*) said: In reply to Kerker, theoretical light scattering data were generated for 15 angles for the size distributions characterized by:

	I	II	III	IV	V	VI	VII	VIII	IX
d_M (μm)	0.1	0.1	0.3	0.4	0.4	0.6	0.8	1.0	1.0
σ_0	0.2	0.6	0.4	0.1	0.6	0.2	0.4	0.05	0.4

The inversion programme was then tested using the following input data: (a) theoretical, (b) theoretical $\pm 2\frac{1}{2}$ % random fluctuation, (c) theoretical ± 5 % random fluctuation. Three different starting points were used for each search. The results were as follows: (a) correct answers to 3 significant figures in all cases; (b) answers to within 10 % in all cases except for V and IX at one starting point only. Considerably better than 10 % accuracy was achieved in most cases; (c) Answers to within 10 % in all cases except V where there was a 25 % error in d_M and VII where all starting points gave answers $d_M = 0.55$ and $\sigma_0 = 0.52$.

Details of the procedure will be published soon together with error contour diagrams. These should show that there is one global minimum, and possibly other " shallow areas " which the present programme interprets as minima. It is hoped to rectify this by further sophistication of the programme.

Dr. M. D. Carabine (*Imperial College*) said: In reply to Kerker, we have not yet completed our experiments to check the light scattering instrument using polymer latex suspensions, of size less than 1 μm. Troublesome back reflections in simple cylindrical vessels have justified the use of the light-trap described in the paper. Moore has commented in this discussion on tests of our strategy in the angular scanning, using hypothetical particle size distributions.

Mr. J. Maddock (*Imperial College*) said: We have been using a Rapaport–Weinstock Generator to produce sulphuric acid aerosols.[2] This relies on mechanical atomization to disperse the aerosol into an air-stream and must therefore produce an aerosol of the same composition as the stock liquid, unless the carrier gas contains water vapour. We have been using nitrogen from cylinders, containing up to 15 p.p.m. water vapour. This is sufficient to dilute the droplets considerably and therefore the gas was dried by passing it through phosphorus pentoxide. Our suppliers inform us that helium from cylinders is also likely to contain water vapour. Can Kerker state whether or not, and if so, how his gas supply was dried?

Dr. G. H. Walker (*Clark College, Atlanta, Ga.*) said: Carabine and Moore have described a potentially useful instrument which can give us valuable information about growth processes in aerosols. However, there may be difficulties in this scheme at the low concentration levels which are characteristic of many aerosols (typically 10^5-10^6 particles cm^{-3}) unless suitable restrictions are imposed upon the size of the scattering volume and upon the concentration. These problems arise because the number of particles in a given volume fluctuate and these fluctuations (which decay

[1] L. Coutarel, E. Matijevic and M. Kerker, *J. Colloid Interface Sci.*, 1967, **24**, 338.
[2] E. Rapaport and S. Weinstock, *Experientia*, 1955, **11**, 363.

very slowly) can influence the measured size distribution. These effects have been studied theoretically first by Smoluchowski and later by Chandrasekhar [1] and experimentally by Schaefer and Berne [2] in optical homodyne experiments using dilute suspensions of polystyrene spheres in water.

To gain some estimate of the mean lifetimes of particle number fluctuations in an aerosol, we consider spheroids of 1 μm radius suspended in a carrier gas (nitrogen) at 25°C. Using the Einstein–Stokes equation, we find the diffusion constant to be roughly 12×10^{-8} cm^2/s. If $n(t)$ is the number of particles in a given volume at time t, then the particle number correlation function $\langle n(0)n(t)\rangle$ decays in a time τ which can be estimated by $\tau \sim L^2/24D$, where L is a typical dimension of the scattering volume. For $L \sim 1$ mm (say), $\tau \sim 3000$ s. Even for very small particles (~ 0.1 μm), $\tau \sim 300$ s. Thus, one must observe the scattering volume for relatively long times in order to average out the effects of particle number fluctuations.

Since one is interested in making measurements of time-dependent phenomena in an aerosol which is changing much more rapidly than the relaxation of density fluctuations, time averaging is not feasible. There are several ways to avoid this problem. For a given concentration, one can either increase the scattering volume or else use a flowing carrier gas system (as has been done in recent experiments where optical homodyning has been applied to aerosol measurements.[3]) Disregarding the last possibility, it is of interest to estimate the size of the volume needed so that the number fluctuations may be safely ignored while keeping in mind that one would like as small a scattering volume as possible to minimize the effects of scattering angle variation.

First, we consider a monodisperse aerosol with a number density c. The particles are statistically independent and are described by the Poisson distribution. Thus the root-mean-square number density fluctuation $\overline{\Delta n}$ is given by $\overline{\Delta n} = \sqrt{cV}$, where V is the scattering volume. We can treat the fluctuations in particle number as noise, and, if a maximum of 4 % noise is tolerable, then we must have $cV \geqslant 625$. For a typical volume defined by an unexpanded laser beam, $V \simeq 0.03$ cm^3 and $c \geqslant 2 \times 10^4$ particles cm^{-3} in order not to exceed the permissable noise level.

For a polydisperse aerosol, the situation is similar. Suppose that we try to measure the size distribution by counting the particles in a number of different radial classes and plotting the resultant histogram. In a class with a low frequency of occurrence, the effects of fluctuations can be quite significant. For example, suppose we have an aerosol with a total concentration of 10^5 particles cm^{-3} and we use ten radial classes. Then at least one of the classes must contain less than 10 % of the particles in the scattering volume and the concentration of this particular class is less than 10^4 particles cm^{-3}. Applying the method used before, we find that $V \geqslant 0.0625$ cm^3 which is substantially greater than one might ordinarily use. Obviously, increasing the number of radial classes used (or increasing the resolution) necessitates a corresponding increase in the scattering volume. One sees that fluctuations will not present a problem in most cases provided that the scattering volume is made large enough. Only in cases of low concentration and high resolution could the scattering volume become uncomfortably large.

Prof. M. Kerker (*Clarkson Coll. Techn., Potsdam, N.Y.*) said: Can Brock say anything about the forms of the size distribution of an aerosol formed in a generator which functions by cooling of a mixture of heterogeneous nuclei and vapour. With

[1] *Rev. Mod. Phys.*, 1943, **15**.
[2] *Phys. Rev. Letters*, 1972, **28**.
[3] W. Hinds and P. C. Reist, *Aerosol Sci.*, 1972, **3**.

regard to the self-preserving size distribution, my understanding is that the semantics originates in the terminology for the spectral distribution of turbulence. What are the physical assumptions relevant to aerosols which are the basis of the mathematical approximations in the self-preserving size theory? Some astrophysicists estimate that 1000 tons of interplanetary dust enter the earth's atmosphere each day. Would this be a significant factor in the global aerosol economy?

Prof. J. R. Brock (*Univ. Texas at Austin, U.S.A.*) said: In reply to Kerker, if the conditions of growth of the heterogeneous nuclei in the vapour are known precisely, it is possible in principle to determine the resultant size distribution by integration of eqn (3.5), or suitable generalizations thereof. As indicated in the paper, under unrestricted pure condensational growth, an initially polydisperse aerosol will become less polydisperse with time. Such behaviour provided the basis of the original Sinclair–La Mer aerosol generator. In any practical experimental situation, one will have imperfect knowledge of the temporal and spatial variations of the physical parameters governing condensation. This would introduce a " randomization " whose effect is generally an increase in measured polydispersity over that predicted from the calculation based on imperfect knowledge.

The term " self-preserving " size distribution has been perhaps the source of some confusion. A " self-preserving " size distribution is one found through solution of a coagulation equation using the similarity transformation as proposed originally by Friedlander and colleagues. However, an asymptotic limit distribution may exist for a particular coagulation process for which the similarity transformation, or " self-preserving " hypothesis, may not be valid. The physical assumptions pertinent to " self-preserving " size theory require extensive discussion such as that provided in ref. (11).

Various estimates tend to show that the contribution of extraterrestrial dust to the global aerosol economy is of negligible order, providing less than 0.01 % of the total mass inventory on a world-wide basis.

Dr. E. R. Buckle (*Sheffield University*) said: With regard to the paper by Brock, the coagulation process as usually modelled, leads to theoretical distributions in an aged aerosol that are independent of the initial populations of particles. In a spontaneously condensed aerosol of the kind I described, the growth of particles by vapour condensation eventually becomes so slow, even when the vapour is still appreciably supersaturated, that coagulation becomes the only mechanism of further enlargement. This will not occur while the particles remain small and volatile for under such conditions the particle sizes are governed by much faster processes of growth and decay. While these processes are continuing to dominate the growth kinetics the initial state (i.e., the state of the vapour before the spontaneous process began) is kept in sight in the sense that the aerosol is evolving towards a final state thermodynamically related to the initial state. The so-called " Kelvin effect " in aerosols, viz., the tendency for the large particles to grow at the expense of the small, arises in the need of the system to attain the final, stable, distribution by the indefinite enlargement of fewer and fewer growing centres. According to the kinetic theory this effect will slow down in a homogeneous aerosol while the particles are still very small, but because of the thermodynamic requirements, coagulation processes will not be able to disturb the size distribution while the particles remain sufficiently volatile.

Dr. R. G. Picknett (*Chem. Defence Est., Porton Down*) said: The paper by Roach, Adams, Garland and Goldsmith should prove invaluable in fog studies. One point of note was the sudden increase in depth of fog which occurred between phases II*a* and II*b*. I have always thought that sudden changes in depth were largely associated with drift, fog zones of greater or less depth being presented to the observation point as they are carried by the wind. Thus depth change should be associated with wind. Yet in the transition between phases II*a* and II*b* there was a sudden increase in depth of 5-10 m associated with a minimum in the wind. Is this attributed to the formation of fog in previously clear air, or is there some other explanation?

Dr. T. W. Roach (*Meteorological Office, Bracknell*) (*communicated*): When observations are made from one site, it is not possible to determine the relative contributions of drift and local development to an observed change in a parameter, such as fog depth. It is, however, reasonable to suppose that changes in a shallow radiation fog which occur within a period of a few minutes are more likely to be due to drift, while those changes taking place over 15 min or longer are more likely to be due to local development. The " sudden " change in fog depth referred to by Picknett in fact took about 20 min, so that we consider this to be more likely to be due to development than due to drift, particularly as the wind dropped. Our main thesis was that if the wind dropped, turbulent diffusion weakened or even ceased, thus allowing radiative cooling to predominate.

Dr. M. B. Green (*British Gas Corp., London*) said: An application of chimney dispersal models which is particularly relevant to the symposium is their use in the prediction of the size of visible plumes found by condensing effluents. The essential feature of the analysis is to use the temperature and concentration profiles obtained from the dispersal formulae to compute, via vapour pressure considerations, the local levels of saturation of the effluent/air mixture. The volume bounded by the surface corresponding to a supersaturation of unity is, to a first approximation, the region in which condensation of the products is likely to occur. Wessel and Wisse [1] have used this approach, in conjunction with the Pasquill dispersal model to develop nomograms for the prediction of the size of cooling tower plumes. In view of the statements made in this paper about the differences between instantaneous and time averaged values of plume dispersal, does Moore believe that a true estimate of the saturation region can be obtained with the classical dispersion formulae?

Dr. D. J. Moore (*Central Elect. Gen. Board, Leatherhead*) said: In reply to Green, the paper by Wessel and Wisse [2] does not take account of the effect of relative motion on plume growth or of plume rise on the plume temperature. These effects will tend, to some extent, to be self-cancelling with regard to condensation in the plume, but Wessel and Wisse's model should be regarded as a first attempt to solve this problem. It could be seriously in error in the meteorological conditions for some sources, but one would need to put numbers in the plume trajectory and rise equations to find out when this would happen.

Dr. D. J. Moore (*Central Elect. Gen. Board, Leatherhead*) said: I agree with Brock that gas washed plumes can have negative buoyancy, especially if they contain liquid water on emission and this subsequently evaporates. It is possible that such plumes could produce higher ground level concentrations of a pollutant which had been partly removed by washing than the corresponding unwashed plume emitted with

[1] *Atm. Env.*, 1971, **5**, 751.
[2] *Atm. Env.*, 1971, **5**, 743.

normal buoyancy (at around 100°C above ambient temperature). Re-heating the washed plume would overcome this problem, but might be difficult to achieve on existing plant.

Dr. R. G. Picknett (*Chem. Defence Est., Porton Down*) said : Can Moore give more information about the formulae he quotes for a plume with a density at ambient temperature and pressure which differs from that of air?

Dr. D. J. Moore (*Central Elect. Gen. Board, Leatherhead*) said: In reply to Picknett, the plume rise and dilution are really a function of the buoyancy flux $\dot{V}\rho_0'$. For plumes which have the same density at ambient temperature and pressure as air

$$\dot{V}\rho_0' = \dot{V}\rho_e\theta_0'/\theta_0 = \dot{V}\theta_0'\rho_0/\theta.$$

where θ_0' = temperature excess of effluent = $\theta_0 - \theta$, and ρ_0' = density difference between ambient air and effluent = $\rho_e - \rho_0 = \Delta\rho$. Since $Q_h = \dot{V}\theta_0'\rho_0 C_p$, it follows that $\dot{V}\rho_0'$ may be replaced by $Q_h/C_p\theta$ for plumes of hot air. The general expression for plume rise would therefore be one using the term $\dot{V}\rho_0'C_p\theta$ rather than Q_h, and this expression would apply to an emission of any density. (The term $C_p\theta$ occurs because of the presence of a similar term in the denominator of the parameter A_1).

AUTHOR INDEX*

* The references in heavy type indicate papers submitted for discussion.

235